Inventions and Discoveries
by
People of Color

Prehistoric to Today

By

Kelvin K. Gilchrist Ed. D

Inventions and Discoveries

by

People of Color

Prehistoric to Today

Compiled by: Kelvin K. Gilchrist Ed. D

Printed in the United States of America on acid free paper

1. Ancient History   2. Technology   3. Egypt History   4. African History
5. History 6. Title 7. Chronology

Illinois | Washington D.C. | Michigan

Stallion Books Publishers is committed to a sustainable future for our business, our readers, and our planet. This book is made from paper certified by the Forest Stewardship Council.

Stallion Books Publishers
P O Box 681
Flossmoor, Illinois 60422
Stallionbookspublishers.com

Illustrations on Pages:
1, 2, 6, 8, 9, 13, 15, 17, 18, 20, 23, 25, 26, 27, 29, 31, 37, 45, 46, 52,
56, 64, 77, 93, 103, 108, 115, 116, 116,122, 125, 126

ISBN: 978-0-9914068-0-7

Manufactured in the United States of America

9 8 7 6 5 4 3 2 1

Library of Congress Cataloging-in-Publication Data

Control Number   2015905240

Kelvin K. Gilchrist, Ed. D

Inventions and Discoveries by People of Color Prehistoric to Today / Kelvin K. Gilchrist Ed.D.

Includes Indexes
Ancient History - Technology - Title - Chronology

ISBN: 9780991406807 (Hardcover)

Washington D.C.	Illinois	Michigan
P.O. Box 1071	P.O. Box 681	P.O. Box 474
Washington, D.C. 20013-1071	Flossmoor, Illinois 60422	Paw Paw, Michigan 49079

"Charles Darwin was the first scientist to publish a modern
theory of evolution in his book, *Origin of Species,* in 1859. In his book,
Descent of Man, published in 1871, Darwin concluded
that Africa was the home of man. History
has proven him correct."

Ben-Jochannan Yosef

The historical lineage of technology encompasses a multicultural arc of peoples, patterns of events, and time periods. The purpose of this book is to provide information on a selection of significant inventions, innovations, and discoveries offered to the world by people of color. The items selected range from prehistoric to today and cover basic discoveries as well as practical inventions and innovations.

This book does not attempt to write a new history of technology. The historical writers have produced some superb works. Rather, this book offers a contribution to the new rewriting of the history of technology that follows an emerging trend.

Until recent years, a certain arrogance within the academic community advanced the prevailing belief that technology was born with the western advent of modern industry, and that such constructs as the pyramids, complex mathematical equations and automated machines either did not count or were non-existent in the ancient world order. Often the impression presented was that early inventors of color somehow stumbled around in ignorance throughout history.

The earliest written historical records that describe what we today relate to as nations, date to somewhere around 3800 BCE. Time before this is referred to as the 'pre-historic era.' However, if our mission is to investigate humankind's technological achievements, examining the current 'historical' record of civilization is not enough. The story of technology takes us into the era of prehistory.

For the period before the use of written records, scholars have devised a relative chronology, one based entirely on archaeological evidence. In Africa, prehistoric chronology is largely based on analysis of the layers of debris from successive settlements in one place which have formed a record of data over a long period of time. At the end of the nineteenth century, Sir Flinders Petrie developed a relative historical chronology based not on stratography, but on a comparative study of pottery, bones and rock carvings found in a number of burial grounds of the predynasty period. Petrie studied the association of various types of artifacts in grave-groups and deduced fifty-one consecutive stages of development. Importantly, his sequence dating invention made possible the reconstruction of the past from the remains of ancient cultures.

Any account of the early development of technology was bound to be questionable. The largest single source of information lied in the vast body of excavation reports written by archaeologists over the past centuries. For a long time, numerous myths concealed the true history of Africa, Asia and other non-European continents from the world at large. African societies in particular, were looked upon as societies that had no history. In spite of important research done by such pioneers as Maurice Delafosse, and Arturo Labriola, a great many historians could not rid themselves of certain preconceptions, and the lack of written sources and documents made it impossible to engage in any scientific study of such societies.

Over the last two decades, while conducting the research for this book, I have had the opportunity to visit over twenty African countries, Asia, Europe, and the Middle East and talk with hundreds of museum curators, librarians, historians and academic scholars. Yet in many academic centers, the classical histories I consulted were negative in their evaluation of the contributions of people of color. Two examples suffice to show the extent of prejudice in the standard historiography:

Compared to the Greeks, wrote Morris Kline, "The mathematics of the Egyptians and Babylonians is the scrawling of children just learning how to write, as opposed to great literature."

David E. Smith, whose *History of Mathematics* became a model for many later historians, said of Egyptian mathematics: "So little was accomplished in this area from 1000 BCE to 300 BCE…the East has always been the East and the West has always been the West."

One may ask the question, why have the contributions of people of color so often been incorrectly attributed to others or been downplayed in historical records. W.E.B. Dubois stated that the reasons are rooted in economics and politics.

New narratives of ancient history are emerging however, thanks in large part to modern generations of anthropologists, archeologists, and historians. Since mid-twentieth century, they have been assiduously reconstructing the history of antiquity over a 4000-year period using modern analytical techniques on artifacts found at archeological sites around the globe. Their research have produced a treasure trove of publications and articles focusing on contributions by all cultures to human civilization, including this compilation.

For example, the lineage of medical technology dates back to formidable surgical firsts by the ancient Egyptians in preserving royalty for the hereafter, the ancient Babylonians, and 6th century BCE surgeon and medical device maker Susruta. The addition of "natural technology - first noted by Darwin - that is, the formation of plants and animals organs into manufactured devices, brings Africa back to the forefront of ancient human history and industrial contributions. Whether a blade-flake from Paleolithic Ghana or a prehistoric shovel shaped from Central African antlers, tool making is one of humans' first endeavors, marking our ability to adapt to our environment. Tools, however seemingly primitive, are technology.

Vico put it precisely; "what distinguishes human history from natural history is that the first is made by us while the second is not. Technology reveals the active relationship between man and nature, a direct process of his experience, consequently of the social relationships of his life and so of the spiritual phenomena that arise from them".

For this author, one of the most exciting trends is the scholarship that reconnects ancient Egypt and therefore ancient Egyptians, to neighboring Nile Valley societies and to the rest of Africa.

According to Tony Browder, "The emergence of civilization in ancient Egypt was nothing more than the outgrowth of the culture that developed (from the South) along the Nile Valley. It is in the Nile Valley where one can find the greatest primary evidence of the earliest beginnings of agriculture, architecture, engineering, language, writing, philosophy, science and religion."

Egyptians in early writings are listed as Black inventors. This concept coincides with the consensus that Egyptians and central Africans are kindred tribes of ancient stock. The evidence is far too overwhelming to list here but to touch upon a few facts:

The greatest concentration of African artifacts and skeletal remains has been uncovered in southern Egypt, by the way of the Sudan, indicating the direction from which the first Egyptians originated. Central African methods of constructing stone houses were the same throughout indigenous African nations including northwest into Egypt.

Further, the symbols, customs and gods adopted by the Egyptian civilization were originally Ethiopian: The moon god, man-headed god, sphinx, sacred reptile, ankh, circumcision and a host of other religious rites were first practiced in central Africa.

Ancient Greeks in their writings called the Egyptians *Aiguptos*, which means black. Ancient Egyptians called themselves KMT, which means Black Nation.

Numerous eyewitness accounts from ancient scholars, specifically Diodorus, Diogenes, Jospheus, Eusebius, Augustine, and Polybius, describe the Egyptians as burnt of skin and broad nosed. Herodotus, the Greek Father of History, called them "black, thick lipped and curly haired." There are no records of any ancient documents describing the Egyptians as white, red, or yellow people.

Probably the most convincing evidence unveiling the Egyptians as an indigenous African people comes from the Egyptians themselves who have, time after time, written in ancient scripts that they originated from the bottom of the mountains of the moon. i.e., Kilimanjaro, Kenya.

It might well be asked why should so great an effort be made to reconstitute the history of technology. The answer, simply, is that without a factual historical representation of the history of the world as a whole remains obscure. Furthermore, the methodology used for this history will make an invaluable scientific contribution to historiography in general, especially as far as the interdisciplinary approach is concerned.

A more accurate world history shows that people of color, including early Europeans, from their original home in Africa to migrations across Asia and the Americas, were first to employ scientific inquiry and technologies to survive a host of harsh planetary conditions; harness and conserve food, water and energy resources; and ultimately, create clusters of advanced civilizations. If international scientists are right in their predictions, the 21st century will pose unprecedented challenges to humanity. The author's hope is that this compilation, in shining a more representative light back into antiquity, will help us all, particularly today's people of color, find the path forward. After all, from discovery to invention, it's what we humans do.

Primarily, however, detailing this history is a duty of concerned scholars and, for people of color themselves, it is a right. History must serve not only as a mirror in which we recognize our own reflections, but also as a driving force that will propel us on the road to sound scholarship.

The aim of this book is to be a starting point for those interested in technological history and who wish to pursue more in-depth research into technological facts.

The main body of the book is organized alphabetically by the name of the invention or discovery. Each entry is given a brief description of the topic, its earliest origin, and general date that the invention, innovation and event occurred. In addition, each topic is assigned a broad category, such as 'Astronomy' or 'Medicine.'

At the end of the book, there are four indexes that refer to the name of the invention. The first index lists the topics alphabetically for quick referencing. The second index lists the topics by origin. The third index lists the topics by broad subjects The forth index lists by dates.

Each entry contains the name of an additional book or reference source that might be of interest to readers who want more in-depth information on the references. In many cases the titles provide additional historical information including general development and how the invention or discovery was used. There were at times many disagreements among even reputable reference sources about such basic details as dates and names.

Every attempt was made to use the more common reference materials for their ease of location in local libraries or data bases. Some of the data was housed in private libraries and educational institutions around the world. All items included in this book were required to have at least three credible sources before being considered.

I am indebted to a variety of museums, organizations, religious centers, and numerous individuals for their help in researching this book.

Special thanks are extended to Lovelle Johnson, Jason Hobbs, Teresa McGuire, Esq., Dr. Derise Tolliver, and Bonetia Triplet for their exacting editorial work.

My many thanks must also go to many librarians researchers, scholars, and database workers at locations around the world. I owe many thanks to special organizations for their tireless help with this project over the years. I must acknowledge the following by name for their special assistance such as Sammi at Cairo Museum, African Heritage Research Library, American University in Cairo, The New Alexander Library, Susan at the University of Pretoria, National Library, Netta at The Mamma Haidan Library, Esse at the National Archives of Nigeria, National Museum of Namibia Library, Special assistant Boyles at Northwestern University Center for African Studies, National, Balme Library in Ghana, South African History Museum, National Archaeological Museum of Athens, San Diego Museum of Man, Museum of Anthropology of University of Kansas, Enugu Branch, Researchers at Beijing Ancient Observatory (China), Mr. Price at Dusable Museum, Atlanta-Fulton Public Library, South Side Community Art Center (Illinois), Boston Fine Arts Museum, Virginia Technical Institute and University, Chicago State University, University of Illinois, Smithsonian, University of Michigan, Hardanger National Museum, Oslo Norway, Berry at the National Palace of Sweden archives, and a host of other institutions and individuals.

My extra-special thanks to artist Jan Spivey Gilchrist, who undertook the herculean task of providing many of the new illustrations. Dr. Gilchrist has been immensely helpful in the face of massive demands we imposed on her to draw (redraw) so many difficult reconstructions and interpretations of ancient gadgets. Without her help, the book as you see it would not have been possible.

I remain grateful to my doctorate advisor, Dr. Charles Pinder, whose course on 'The History of Inventions and Innovations' bound me into my additional studies and subsequently this book.

Apart from the specific and practical help of these people and institutions, I have to acknowledge other debts which made this research project possible – my wife, Jan Spivey Gilchrist, son, William, daughter, Ronke, grandchildren, Raena and Jarrett.

And to my father, William Lee Gilchrist, and mother Katie Sue Gilchrist. As a young man, I spent many hours at the family's place of business discussing the significance of past and emerging technologies and their impact on mankind. This experience has been the driving force for me to share my father's views of the world.

A

Abacus
Mathematics
Origin: Egypt   Date: 4000 BCE

It appears that there were very early versions of crude counting systems which varied greatly from region to region. The abacus was the first man-made device constructed to keep accurate count of quantities. A simple yet elegant instrument for keeping tally, the ancient abacus operated manually moving counters or beads strung on wire. The device was known to the Greek historian Herodotus, whose records mentioned its use around 4000 BCE, in Egypt. Other types of abacus have been found in China during a later period.

Additional reading: Ashurst, F. G. (1982). *Founders of modern mathematics.* London: Fredrick Muller.

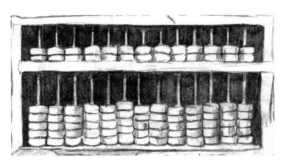

Fig. 1
Abacus of Ancient Egypt.

Abrasive
Material
Origin: India   Date: 25,000 BCE

Abrasives are substances that are used to rub material from softer substances. Dating as far back as 25,000 BCE, sand was used to polish and/or smooth down weapons made of stone. Other forms of abrasive materials used in ancient times were garnet, pumice, and emery. By the Middle Ages, grinding wheels made of quartz and flint fragments were also used.

Additional reading: Keay, J. (2000). *India: A history.* New York: Atlantic Monthly Press.

Acacia Tree
Medicine
Origin: Egypt   Date: 2000 BCE

A tomb painting at Behi Hasah, dating back to 2000 BCE, depicts an acacia tree. Medical personnel of the period made a chemical contraceptive by grinding together acacia spikes, honey, and dates. Modern scientists now know that the Acacia spike contains lactic acid, a chemical that kills sperm.

Additional reading: Bricklin, M. (1983). *The practical encyclopedia of natural healing.* Emmaus: Rodale Press.

Accordion
Music
Origin: China   Date: 3000 BCE

Prior to the accordion many crude devices were used to produce various melodic sounds. The accordion is a musical instrument that has evolved from a number of predecessors. One, called a sheng, was invented by the Chinese and was played in the court of Queen Nyyu Wa about 3000 BCE. Another form appeared in central Africa about 2000 BCE.

Additional reading: Stanley, S. (1980). *New grove dictionary of music and musicians;* vol. 20, New York: Macmillan Pub.

Accounting
Mathematics
Origin: Babylon   Date: 3600 BCE

Historical records show that the Babylonians initiated using clay tablets to record and account for the payment of wages in Babylon around 3600 BCE. In ancient Egypt, several record-keeping systems developed for specific transactions dating as far back as 4000 BCE. More complete accounting systems evolved later in response to expanding commercial needs.

Additional reading: Oppenheim, A. (1979). *Ancient Mesopotamia: Portrait of a dead civilization,* Rev. ed. Chicago: University of Chicago Press

Acupuncture
Medicine
Origin: China   Date: 2600 BCE

Acupuncture is a medical practice developed by the Chinese in 2600 BCE. Based on the philosophy of balance between the forces of yin and yang, the traditional theory holds that the life source corresponding to an organ of the human body circulates along fourteen cutaneous meridians (kings). All pathology can be explained by a disturbance of energy flux and can be healed by acting on one of several points located on these meridians. Acupuncture treatments usually involve piercing the skin with delicate pins.

Additional reading: Roberts, J. (2003). *The complete history of China.* London: Sutton Pub.

Addax   Domestic
Origin: Africa   Date: 4500 BCE

The addax has its origins in northern Africa and was domesticated as far back as 4500 BCE. A species of boviform or ox-like antelope, the addax was both a source of food for the ancients and a beast of burden. The average height of the addax ranged from three to four feet tall. Very large numbers of addax remains indicate that this animal was very common to the period.

Additional reading: Adams, W. (1977). *Nubia: Corridor to Africa.* London: Allen Lane.

Adhesive   Chemistry
Origin: Egypt   Date: 3300 BCE

The foothill country from Palestine to Iran was the homeland of the seed-bearing grasses that were the forerunners of wheat and barley. The first domesticated plants were used to produce food and many household substances. Family field workers of the period also used plants to make a sticky substance to attach leaves and other materials together.

Additional reading: Hitching, F., (1978). *The atlas of world mysteries.* New York: HarperCollins.

Adze   Device
Origin: Africa   Date: Prehistoric

The early inhabitants of Africa were the earliest known to make and use the adze. This tool was used for smoothing wooden objects. Carpenters and farmers later adopted the adze in their respective trades. The head was shaped like an axe with the cutting edge at a right angle to the line of the handle.

Additional reading: Davidson, B. (1969). *The African genius.* Boston: Little, Brown.

Aepyornis   Domestic
Origin: Africa   Date: Prehistoric

The Aepyornis was a flightless bird about the size of an ostrich that lived during the Pleistocene Epoch. Sometimes called the 'elephant bird,' its fossilized eggshells were as large as footballs with a holding capacity of two gallons. These huge prehistoric eggs were particularly coveted among nomadic tribes as a portable source of food, which enabled them to travel great distances to and from different locations.

Additional reading: Bovill, E. W. (1933). *Caravans of the Old Sahara:* London: Oxford Press.

Agriculture   Production
Origin: Turkey   Date: 9000 BCE

The domestication of plants and animals first began about 9000 BCE in the foothill country fringing the open valleys and deserts of the Middle East. These ancient foothills were homeland to the seed-bearing grasses that were the forerunners of wheat and barley. The rich soil and mild climate created an environment of biblical proportions conductive for cultivating crops. Hence the region appears to be the origin of the world's first gardens, where nomads reaped and sowed consumable crops.

Additional reading: Hyams, E., (1971). *A history of gardens and gardening.* London: Dent Press.

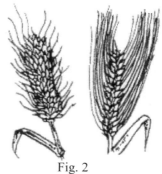

Fig. 2
Agriculture
The earliest farmed crops were
harvested over 9,000 years ago

Air Compressor   Mechanical
Origin: Egypt   Date: 1500 BCE

The earliest means of compressing air was achieved with a foot-operated blow sack made from animal skin. The process was devised by the Egyptians around 1500 BCE, when they first implemented the blow sack to increase air flow in furnaces to melt materials such as gold and silver. For many centuries afterward, manual power continued to drive the process.

Additional reading: Barber, F. (1900). *The mechanical triumphs of ancient Egyptians.* London: Trubner and Co.

Additional reading: Bell, E. (1945). *The development of mathematics.* 2nd ed. New York: McGraw Hill.

Air Transport — Transportation
Origin: Iraq   Date: 2100 BCE

Around 2100 BCE, the Sumerians observed that a pigeon or dove would return to its nest, regardless of the distance and for however long it was separated from its home. By the 2000 BCE, Egyptians deployed pigeons to deliver military communications. Many local communities also trained pigeons as warning signals against natural disaster as well as human threats such as pillage or war.

Additional reading: James, P. and Thorpe, N. (1994). *Ancient inventions.* New York: Ballantine Books.

Alarm   see   Earthquake Alarm.

Alcohol   see   Distillation or Beer.

Algebra — Mathematics
Origin: Egypt   Date: 1700 BCE

An ancient papyrus written by Egyptian priest Ahmes suggests that he was familiar with problems in algebra. He used symbols to stand for unknown numbers and for our plus/minus signs. Around 600 BCE, the Greek astronomer Thales studied with Egyptian priests and later taught his avid student, the Greek scholar Pythagoras, who introduced algebra to the West.

Additional reading: Aaboe, A. (1964). *Episodes from the early history of mathematics.* New York: Singer Pub.

Algebra 2 — Mathematics
Origin: Egypt   Date: 900 BCE

During the ninth century BCE, Abu Kamil developed the mathematics form called Algebra 2. Kamil, sometimes also known as Al-Hasib, was credited for creating Advanced Algebra. His work included equal roots and coefficients of equations. This Egyptian mathematics soon spread to other regions of the world where many modifications have occurred over the centuries.

Algorithm — Mathematics
Origin: Babylon   Date: 1800 BCE

The effectiveness of the Babylonians computational skills did not result from their system of numeration alone. Mesopotamian mathematicians were also proficient in developing algorithmic procedures, among which was a square-root process often ascribed to later societies. The origin of algorithmic problem-solving is sometimes is attributed to the Greek scholars or to Heron of Alexandria; occasionally one finds it called Newton's algorithm. However, this Babylonian procedure is as simple as it is elegant and is still used in modern mathematics functions.

Additional reading: Cajori, F. (1894). *A history of mathematics.* London, Macmillan & Co.

Almond Tree — Domestic
Origin: Israel   Date: 3000 BCE

The seeds from the almond tree were used as far back as 3000 BCE, for domestic and health purposes in Israel. Some of the derivative products included almond oil, butter, and mill. The almond seed was also genetically altered to produce an almond peach, a hybrid between the almond and peach; almond rock snow; and the almond tree bark. In addition, extract from the almond was formulated to yield a coloring used to cover graying hair on certain parts of the body.

Additional reading: Gleason, K. (1987). Garden excavations at the Herodian winter palace in Jericho; *Bulletin of the Anglo-Israel Society 7.*

Alpaca — Domestic
Origin: Peru   Date: 5000 BCE

The earliest evidence of the domestication of the alpaca comes from archeological digs in northern Peru. The skeleton remains of the earliest domesticated alpaca were reconstructed and carbon tested, dating the site as early as 5000 BCE. It remains unclear if these animals were raised for food and/or as beasts of burden.

Additional reading: Spencer, L. (1913). *The myths of Mexico and Peru.* London: George Harrap pub.

Alphabet   Communication
Origin: Syria   Date: 2000 BCE

The earliest recorded alphabets were developed in Ugarit (Syria), created by stripping down Mesopotamian cuneiform characters to only thirty signs, each sign representing a different sound. Elsewhere in the Middle East, scribes were developing alphabets that used symbols easier to write on papyrus than the wedge-shaped letter of cuneiform script. Considered the first uniform alphabet, the Ugaritic system of letters was developed some time after 2000 BCE, in the area of Syria and Palestine.

Additional reading: Diringer, D. (1948). *The alphabet: A key to the history of mankind.* London: Hutchinson's Scientific and Technical Pub.

Alquerque (Checkers)   Entertainment
Origin: Egypt   Date: 1200 BCE

The earliest predecessor of checkers, Alquerque, was found in the Egyptian temple of Karna, built in 1200 BCE. The game of strategy was played in tournament form in which members from different houses competed. The Egyptian game was introduced into Spain by the Arabs, who called it El'quirkat.

Additional reading: Beal, G. (1975). *Playing-cards and their story.* New York: Arco Pub. Co.

Amber   Minerals
Origin: Africa   Date: Prehistoric

The earliest use of amber has been identified from artifacts from the Jebel Cave excavated by A. P. Okaladnikov. Dating from the early Neolithic period, the finds include handcrafted jewelry styled into a myriad of different articles made from seashells, stone, amber and wood.

Additional reading: Perlin, J. (1991). *The role of wood in the development of civilization.* New York: Norton Pub.

Amulet   Jewelry
Origin: Africa   Date: Prehistoric

An amulet is a small object that protected the warrior from disease and warded off evil influences. The earliest amulets, which have been found in prehistoric graves, were made of shells, beads, and white quartz stones. Stone axes flint and arrow-heads were also made into amulets.

Additional reading: Binford, L. (1981). *Bones: Ancient man and modern myths.* New York: Academic Press.

Anchor   Navigation
Origin: China   Date: 3000 BCE

The first recorded anchors were made of stones or sacks containing sand or pebbles. They were used by Chinese sailors during the third millennium BCE, and later by the Greeks and Egyptians. Some weighing as much as 1500 pounds, these crude anchors were simply thrown overboard. Around 600 BCE mooring evolved with the manufacture of the angle-palm grapnel, a small anchor with several flukes for more secure grasping.

Additional reading: Roberts, J. (2003). *The complete history of China.* London: Sutton Pub.

Anesthetic   see   Mandrake Plant.

Animal Domestication   Agriculture
Origin: Africa   Date: 10,000 BCE

By 10,000 BCE, the domestication of cattle and goats in western Africa had taken a large step forward. These animals now supplied settlers with milk, butter, cheese, and meat. Prior to this development, people hunted and gathered food, with the insecurities attendant to searching for sustenance. Herding provided a much more secure food supply and soon became part of everyday life. Such animal husbandry allowed the settlers to form villages and larger communities.

Additional reading: MacDonald, K. and MacDonald, R. (1999). *The origin and development of domesticated animals in arid West Africa.* London: University College Press.

Antibiotics   Medicine
Origin: Nubia   Date: 3200 BCE

The Nile River Valley has long been the source of many of the world's great wonders. After the annual flooding subsided, the mud of the Nile, once dried by the sun, yielded a rare chemical that served as a pain reliever. The ancient Nubians used this mud as an ingredient in a number of other medical preparations. Recently, the mud has been found to contain natural antibiotics.

Additional reading: Bishop, W. (1960). *The early history of surgery.* London: Robert Hale Pub.

Anti-hypertensive see Reserpine.

Antimony
Chemistry
Origin: China   Date: 4000 BCE

Antimony, atomic number 51, is a blue-white metal, brittle in its pure form. First found in China in the form of sulfide stibnite, it was frequently used in alloys with lead, tin, or copper. It also existed as a black powder. Its sulfide form was known to the ancients as a cosmetic material.

Additional reading: Chang, Kwang-chih (1976). *Early Chinese civilization.* Cambridge: Harvard University Press.

Anvil
Tool
Origin: Egypt   Date: 1360 BCE

The early metal workers fashioned iron tools with crude anvils. These ancient tools were built on the hardened rock quarries around massive tombs. The early anvils were simple metal slabs supported by solid foundations. The builders of the tomb of Makeda, Queen of Sheba, used crude anvils to sharpen and make their construction tools.

Additional reading: Barber, F. (1900). *The mechanical triumphs of ancient Egyptians.* London: Trubner and Co.

Apricot Tree
Domestic
Origin: Israel   Date: 3600 BCE

The foremost recordings of apricot trees were found on tablets in a tomb in the Middle Eastern area. The tablets, dating back to 3600 BCE, depicted trees in a garden being described as apricot trees. The fruit seeds were located in the hard pit or stone of the fruit, and are allied to the plum, but oval-shaped and orange in color. The juice was made into bitter tasting ale.

Additional reading: Allen, H. (1961). *A history of wine; great vintage wines from the Homeric age to the present day.* New York: Horizon Press.

Aqueduct
Construction
Origin: Jordan   Date: 1000 BCE

The earliest known reference to the use of aqueducts was identified in a clay tablet circa 1000 BCE, depicting Mesho, building two aqueducts to supply water to the ancient city of Karcho. Actual construction of aqueducts used for supplying cities with water dates back to 700 BCE, when Sennacherib (Assyria) built a stone canal that crossed a wide valley and was waterproofed with a glue-like substance that increased the efficiency.

Additional reading: Butzer, K.W (1976). *The early hydraulics civilization in Egypt: A study in cultural ecology.* Chicago: University of Chicago Press.

Arch
Architecture
Origin: Egypt   Date: 3000 BCE

The oldest example of the arch was constructed around 3000 BCE, erected over a tomb which was uncovered in Helouan, Egypt near present day Cairo. The arch was made using flat uncooked clay bricks, which rested on the walls, with the rows of bricks arranged radially and the circular arch interstices filled in with mortar and strengthened with pieces of pottery. This same technique was also used in Mesopotamia.

Additional reading: Breasted, J. (1906). *Ancient records of Egypt, vols. 1-5;* Chicago: University of Chicago Press.

Architecture
Civil
Origin: Egypt   Date: 2800 BCE

The Egyptian Imhotep was the first architect credited with designing and building the oldest known structure made entirely of stone, the Saqarah Pyramid. The pyramid was built for Pharaoh Djoser around 2800 BCE. Imhotep enjoyed great prestige, designing as many as fifty architectural projects. Imhotep's drawings were very detailed and showed different elevations of the structure.

Additional reading: Rice, M. (2003). *Egypt's making: The origin of ancient Egypt, 5000-2000 B.C.* 2nd ed. New York: Roulledge Pub.

Arithmetic   Mathematics
Origin: Babylon   Date: 4300 BCE

Clay tablets used by ancient Babylonians revealed that they were skilled in arithmetic as early as 4300 years ago. By 1600 BCE, the Egyptians were also familiar with many concepts of arithmetic, according to a document written by Egyptian priest Ahmes. The Egyptians devoted a great deal of time to the computation of fractions and used symbols equivalent to our "plus" and "minus" signs. Around 600 BCE, the Greek astronomer Thales, having studied with Egyptian priests, introduced arithmetic to Europe.

Additional reading: Al-Kashi, J. (1956). *The key to arithmetic, treatise on the circle.* Moscow, Russia: Noskva, Gos.

Armillary Ring   Astronomy
Origin: China   Date: 52 BCE

The Chinese astronomer, Ken Shou- Ch'ang, built the stellar observation device called an armillary ring, consisting of a metal circle that represented the equator. The first Armillary Ring designs were crude and didn't work well by 52 BCE.

Additional reading: Ling W., & Needham, J. (1955). *Homer's methods in Chinese mathematics.* T'oung Pao Leidon, vol. 43.

Army   Military
Origin: Sumer   Date: 2500 BCE

The Sumerians enlisted the earliest known standing army. They developed and utilized basic military formations as early as 2500 BCE, many of which are studied and implemented in modern warfare. Sumerian soldiers wore leather armor and fought with a wide array of cured metal and wooden weapons.

Additional reading: Kramer S. , (1956) *From the table of Sumer, twenty five firsts in man's recorded history,* Indian Hills, Colo. Falcon's Wing Press.

Aromatic Plants   Domestic
Origin: Egypt   Date: 1500 BCE

Aromatic plants were first used by the Egyptian Queen Hatshepsut as early as 1500 BCE. These plants had a fragrant smell, and when coupled with the warm,

slightly pungent scent of spices, yielded a spicy sweet fragrance. Later, the aromatic plants were mixed with other substances to alter or mask odors.

Additional reading: Ohrbach, B. (1986). *Scented room Cherchez's book of dried flowers.* New York: Clarkson N. Potter.

Arrow   see   **Bow.**

Arsenic   Chemistry
Origin: Egypt   Date: 370 BCE

Commonly existing as a steel-gray metal, arsenic, atomic number 33, is found in a reddish form as arsenic sulfide. The Egyptians observed arsenic sulfide as early as 370 BCE. It was isolated by the Greek scholar Aristotle around 350 BCE. The chemical symbol for arsenic is AS.

Additional reading: Kenrick, J. (1850). *Ancient Egypt under the pharaohs. Vols. 1-2.* London: B. Fellowes.

Art   Communication
Origin: Africa   Date: 44,000 BCE

The oldest art found exists in Africa, dating back to 44,000 BCE. Humans painted rock slabs in the Orange River Valley of Namibia. Much of the art was used to communicate with others, but many art images were drawn for enjoyment and the recording of history.

Additional reading: Africanus, L. (1896). *The history and description of Africa, 3 vols.* Ed. London: Brown, Kakluyt Society.

Fig. 3
Art
Early images date back to prehistoric times. This was a common form of communication

Arthritis Treatment — Medicine
Origin: Egypt Date: 1600 BCE

The Egyptians were the first to make many medical procedures including arthritis treatments. Egyptian medical remedies and procedures are documented in papyrus manuscripts, especially those discovered in modern times by Edwin Smith and George Ebers in 1872. The papyrus included medical treatment for arthritis, hookworm infection, common colds, and surgery for head injuries.

Additional reading: Sigerist, H., (1967). *Primitive and archaic medicine.* London: Oxford University Press.

Artificial Spawning — Agriculture
Origin: China Date: 1600 BCE

The Chinese were the first to breed fish, building artificial spawning grounds placed in streambeds. These were wicker screens onto which the fish deposited their eggs. After the eggs were fertilized, the breeders collected them in buckets and vendors sold them to the general population, who seeded their ponds and with them.

Additional reading: Roberts, J., (2003). *The complete history of China.* United Kingdom: Sutton Pub.

Asphalt — Transportation
Origin: Mesopotamia Date: 1000 BCE

Before man knew how to build roads, rainwater caused a great deal of mush and mud. One solution was paving, but because the process was costly and took a long time, it was reserved for the main population centers. In the Middle East, beginning with Mesopotamia in the first millennium BCE, wherever there were oil-bearing rocks, bitumen or asphalt was used in the construction of an impermeable road covering.

Additional reading: Oppenheim, A. (1979). *Ancient Mesopotamia: Portrait of a dead civilization,* Rev. ed. Chicago: University of Chicago Press.

Aspirin — Medicine
Origin: Africa Date: Antiquity

The Bantu people of Africa used plants that contained salicylic acid for the treatment of a host of illnesses, primarily headaches. The remedy was also used in parts of Western and Southern Africa. Today, this chemical is mixed with other substances to produce aspirin.

Additional reading: Hewat, M. & Miller, T. (1970). *Bantu folklore.* Westport: Negro Universities Press.

Ass — Domestic
Origin: Egypt Date: 2500 BCE

A cross breed of a wild horse-like animal, the ass was being harnessed as a beast of burden as early as 2500 BCE. Over a period of time, the ass was transformed in appearance. The dark stripe was a distinct mark seen on the tombs at Soggara in Egypt, in an image that bore the shoulder markings of the right-hand ass.

Additional reading: Hill, P. (1917). *Prehistoric times,* New York: Harper & Row.

Astro Survey — Astronomy
Origin: Egypt Date: 1492 BCE

The Egyptians were the earliest to plot the heavens as clock and calendar. This process was depicted in drawings shown surveying the positions of heavenly bodies. Queen Nefertari's scientists developed an instrument consisting of a plum-like object and a forked stick. They used this device to find an accurate North-South line and to time the exact moments of a star crossing the meridian. In this way, they were able to map the position in the sky.

Additional reading: Pappademos, J. (1983). *An outline of Africa's role in the history of physics, in: Blacks in science;* New Brunswick N.J.: Transaction Books.

Astrolabe — Astronomy
Origin: Mesopotamia Date: 100 BCE

An ancient astronomical instrument, the astrolabe, was designed to predict the positions of the sun and stars. The earliest type was devised by the Mesopotamians around 100 BCE. the astrolabe tool was advanced as a teaching tool for scientists of the period. The instrument had a grid of lines that helped define positions of astronomical objects. The grid rotated to represent the movement of the stars across the sky. The armillary metal grid defines the moving sky in three dimensions. The flat two-sided astrolabe represents the sky in two dimensions, adding the position of a few key stars.

Additional reading: Webster, R., Macalister, P. and Etting F. (1974). *The astrolabe: Some notes on its history, construction and use,* Lake. Bluff, Illinois: Paul Macalister & Associates.

Astronomy   Astronomy
Origin: Mesopotamia   Date: 2000 BCE

Rudimentary astronomical observations were made in the great empires of Mesopotamia, Egypt, and China. The most accurate of these from Mesopotamia, concerned motions of the planets. As early as 2000 BCE, observers noted that Venus returned to the same position five times in eight years. About 1000 BCE, the Mesopotamians became comparatively accurate in their findings, and from 700 BCE, they were systematically recorded. It then became possible to calculate the correct average values of the main periodic phenomena of the heavens, such as the periods of the planetary revolutions, and make accurate astronomical predictions as a result.

Additional reading: Neugebauer, O. (1962). *The exact sciences in antiquity.* New York: Dover Pub.

Aulos   Musical
Origin: Mesopotamia   Date: 2000 BCE

Mesopotamian wind instruments included the flute, aulos, and the end-blown. The aulos, a twin-piped, double-reed instrument, is a predecessor of the oboe and the trumpet. A silver aulos was found in a tomb at Ur and is on display at the University of Philadelphia. The aulos had a significant important place in everyday society, because it was one of several musical instruments thought to be used in the after life.

Additional reading: Duchesne, G. (1976). *Music in ancient Mesopotamia and Egypt.* World Archaeology.

Auroch   see   Cow.

Automation   Control System
Origin: Africa   Date: 6000 BCE

For centuries inventors devised various machines and gadgets that were self-acting. In central Africa, many types of man-made automatic trapping mechanisms were employed to capture food. Much of the early automation was used in food gathering or war between opposing tribes.

Additional reading: Albright, W. (1940). *From the stone age to Christianity.* Baltimore: John Hopkins Press.

Figure 4: Automation
These prehistoric automatic devices were
used for hunting large animals.

Autopsy   Medicine
Origin: China   Date: 205 BCE

Autopsies were recorded as early as 205 BCE. The book, *Emperor's Cannon of Internal Medicine* recorded the length of human skeletons and blood vessels, as well as the position, shape, size, and weights of internal organs. These early autopsy records were maintained for public review by students of medicine.

Additional reading: Hsu, Cho-Yun. (1965). *Ancient China in transition, 722-222 B.C.* Stanford Cal: Stanford University Press.

Avocado   Domestic
Origin: Nubia   Date: 2200 BCE

The people of Nubia were raising the avocado as far back as 2200 BCE. The trees produced a large fruit-like pear called an alligator pear. The seeds from the avocado tree were used primarily for food. The avocado was spread throughout Africa and Asia by traders and merchants.

Additional reading: Hemphill, J. (1976). *Herbs: Their cultivation and usage.* New York: Simon and Schuster.

Awl   Mechanical
Origin: Africa   Date: Prehistoric

The earliest known awl-like tool was discovered in a dry sand bed of central Africa. It was a small tool, having a slender cylindrical, tapering shape with a pointed blade that had holes, pierces, and prickers. The first awl was made from a treated animal skin.

Additional reading: Ochoa, G., (1995). *The timeline book of science.* New York: Stongsong Press.

Ax   Mechanical
Origin: Africa   Date: 250,000 BCE

The first shaped stone axes had no handles. They were roughly triangular with one sharp edge and the other two smoothed for a more comfortable grip. This type of axe was a natural development from simple stone knives. They have been found in the remains of ancient settlements in Africa, Europe, and Asia.

Additional reading: Brooks, L. (1971). *Great civilizations of ancient Africa.* New York: Four Winds Press.

Fig 5
Ax head
This is a sample of early crafted ax heads

B

Bag Press   Mechanical
Origin: Nubia   Date: 2000 BCE

The earliest grape bag press recovered in Nubia dates back to 2000 BCE. Many archeologists support the idea that numerous bag-like presses were made hundreds of years before in central Africa and the technique migrated to Nubia around 2000 BCE. Grapes were put into a tall leather bag stretched between two posts. Bar handles were placed at both ends of the bag and twisted, squeezing out the juice of the grapes.

Additional reading: Adams, W., (1977). *Nubia, corridor to Africa.* Princeton, N.J: Princeton University Press.

Bakery   Mechanical
Origin: Egypt   Date: 5000 BCE

Illustrations of bread and wheat processing appear on Egyptian tomb walls dating back to 3200 BCE. Bakery goods were a food staple of ancient Egyptians. The bakery was central to their community life. Grains and wheat were major crops cultivated during the period.

Additional reading: Rice, M. (2003). *Egypt's making: The origin of ancient Egypt, 5000-2000 B.C.,* 2nd ed. New York: Roulledge Pub.

Balance   Mechanical
Origin: Egypt   Date: 5000 BCE

The earliest balances consisted of a beam pivoted at its center with pans at either end for holding standard weights and the material to be weighed. The simplest balance developed by Egyptians around 5000 BCE, were quite accurate. The Romans invented the "knife edge" fulcrum on which the beam balanced, increasing its accuracy. In laboratories, the balance was usually enclosed in a glass box, eliminating dirt and air currents. Both single and double pan models existed.

Additional reading: Erman, A. (1971). *Life in ancient Egypt.* New York: Dover Pub.

Ball   Domestic
Origin: Egypt   Date: 2000 BCE

Balls were some of the earliest children's toys. The first records of ball games come from paintings on the walls of Egyptian tombs dating back to 2000 BCE. The balls were made from animal skins and stones. In tombs and burial areas in Egypt, toy like balls, dolls and marbles have been recovered. It appears that all classes had access to such toys.

Additional reading: Martell, H. (1995). *The kingfisher book of the ancient world: From the ice age to the fall of Rome.* New York: Kingfisher Pub.

Ball Bearing — Mechanical
Origin: Mesopotamia   Date: 2000 BCE

The Mesopotamians devised a system for transporting heavy objects around 2000 BCE. The use of ball bearings comes from the same concept; using balls to reduce the friction between two moving objects at the point of contact. It appears that the ball bearings were used in the construction of large structures.

Additional reading: Pannell, J. (1964). *An illustrated history of civil engineering.* London: Thomas and Hudson.

Ballooning (Hot Air) — Transportation
Origin: China   Date: 12 BCE

The Chinese developed the hot air balloon more than two thousand years ago. The earliest version was made from eggshells filled with dry plant stems. When the plants were set on fire, the air in the shells heated, causing them to rise and fly away. The Mongolians learned of balloons from their new Chinese subjects around 200 CE.

Additional reading: Morrison, T., (1987). *The mystery of the Naza lines.* Woodridge: Nonesuch Expeditions Ltd.

Bamboo — Domestic
Origin: Africa   Date: 6000 BCE

The bamboo tree has been used for thousands of years as tools as well as for food. The hollow structure of the wooden bamboo cane has been depicted in early cave drawings dating as far back as 6000 BCE The bamboo tree was also used for deep underwater exploration.

Additional reading: Singer, C. (1978). *A history of technology.* Oxford: Clarendon Press.

Banana — Domestic
Origin: Africa   Date: Antiquity

The banana was one of the first plants that humans consumed; the earliest known human consumption of banana dates back to 30,000 BCE in the western region of Africa. Many historical archaeologists believe that this plant in particular was planted and harvested much earlier.

Additional reading: Schoenburn, D. L. (1993). Cattle herds and banana garden: The historical geography of the western Great Lakes regions. *African Archaeological Review II*, p 39-72.

Bandage see Dressing and Bandages.

Bank — Financial
Origin: Iraq   Date: 2000 BCE

The first banks began as early as the second millennium BCE, by the sacred women of Babylonian temples. The more conventional commercial banking system also originated in Babylon and advanced significantly there, along with commerce, by the end of the seventh century BCE. Lending arrangements written on clay tablets were straightforward contracts, specifying the loan amount and terms for repayment.

Additional reading: Roux, G. (1966). *Ancient Iraq.* New York: Penguin.

Barley — Agriculture
Origin: Iraq   Date: 4500 BCE

Barley was first cultivated in the Near and Middle East in early Neolithic times. The earliest record of planting and cultivation of barley was found at Jarmo in Iraq and in storage pits of Egypt's Fayum Oasis, dating from 4500 BCE.

Additional reading: Rosengarten F., (1973). *The book of spices.* New York: Jove, Publisher.

Basalt — Chemistry
Origin: Tanzania   Date: 1500 BCE

Basalt is black, heavy, compact rock, often imbedded with tiny glittering particles. This material was used as a pavement material and in the Third Dynasty step-pyramid at Saqqara. Records show that workers of the period repaired the crude road system often used by the royal family with basaltic rock.

Additional reading: Chittick, N. (1975). *An early salt-working site on the Tanzananian coast.* London: Azania 10, 151-153.

Basil
Origin: Africa   Domestic   Date: 10,000 BCE

The earliest mention of skinning and tanning dates back to Africa over 10,000 years ago. The nomads of the region raised and skinned animals including sheep for their skin and fur. The sheep's skin was processed, which we call tanning today, and used in religious ceremonies. Several centuries later the tanned skins were used for body covering or armor during military campaigns.

Additional reading: Binford, L. R. (1981). *Bones: Ancient man and modern myths.* New York: Academic Press.

Basketry
Origin: Iraq   Mechanical   Date: 8000 BCE

Early Neolithic peoples living in a shanidar cave in northern Iraq were making baskets around 8000 BCE. Most of the baskets were used for gathering food. Native Americans in what is now Utah in North America were making baskets and woven bags around 7000 BCE. Archeologists have recovered fragmentary baskets at these and other ancient villages and have found impressions of matting on clay slab.

Additional reading: Baldwin, G. C., (1973). *Inventors and inventions of the ancient world.* New York: Four Winds Pub.

Bathtub
Origin: Babylon   Domestic   Date: 1800 BCE

According to early drawings dating back to 1800 BCE, wealthy Babylonians used private bathtubs with in-ground drainage systems designed in stone and wood. Many of the early tubs were used in religious ceremonies.

Additional reading: Derry, T. and Williams, T. (1960). *A short history of technology.* Oxford: Clarendon Press.

Batter
Origin: Egypt   Civil Engineering   Date: 3400 BCE

As early as 3400 BCE, early Egyptian architects experimented with different ways to build large structures. The batter was first employed by the Egyptians and Babylonians, who built the walls of pyramids or ziggurat sloped inwards so the top would be narrower than the bottom. Throughout history the batter has been modified and was often used in construction of many kinds of structures.

Additional reading: Palmer, G. (1968). *Archaeology a-z, a simplified guide and dictionary.* New York: Frederick Warne Pub.

Battering Ram
Origin: Nigeria   Military   Date: 5000 BCE

The battering ram in its earliest form dates back to 5000 BCE. Used by the Nigerians in their military campaigns, this ancient weapon, as depicted in early drawings, was a military device employed for battering down walls or gates under siege. The ram consisted of a beam of wood with a mass of iron at one end occasionally in the form of a hood.

Additional reading: Connash, G., (1981). *Three thousand years in Africa: Man and his environment in the lake Chad region of Nigeria.* Cambridge: Cambridge University Press.

Battery
Origin: Iraq   Chemistry   Date: 1600 BCE

Included in the collection of the Iraq Museum, a plain small clay jar has been touted as the most amazing find in the archaeology of science. This apparent battery cell is estimated to be more than 2200 years old and the jar appears to be very similar to the casting of a modern day electric battery.

Additional reading: Winton, W., (1962). *Baghdad batteries B.C.* London:

Bean
Origin: Africa   Domestic   Date: 8000 BCE

In the southern region of Africa, prehistoric farmers harvested plants from the zygophyllum family, which bore fresh leaves and flower buds that yielded pear-shaped seeds. Later the shrub was re-named capers or bean capers. Seeds were planted seasonally and used for an array of domestic uses. The Egyptians classified the plant seeds as lotus.

Additional reading: Wheelwright, E. (1974). *Medicinal plants and their history.* New York: Dover Publisher.

Bearing (Roller)   Device
Origin: Africa   Date: 1000 BCE

Around 1000 BCE, roller bearings made from wood and bronze were installed on the wheels of carts in what is now South Africa. These bearings were oval and not round as the later bearings developed in China. The oval shaped bearings were instrumental in the platform design of military carts. The early shapes made it less likely to break down during military campaign.

Additional reading: Davidson, B. (1959). *The lost cities of Africa.* Boston: Little, Brown and Company.

Bee Keeping   Domestic
Origin: Egypt   Date: 3200 BCE

Early archeologist records indicate that the Egyptians were the first known culture to domestically keep bees and harvest the byproduct now known as honey. The bee's honey was used by royalty to sweeten the bitter drinks. The bee keeping process spread to other areas by travelers throughout the region.

Additional reading: Crane, E. (1983). *The archaeology of beekeeping.* London: Duckworth Pub.

Beer (Alcohol)   Domestic
Origin: Sumer   Date: 3500 BCE

The earliest account chronicling beer brewing credits the Sumerians around 3500 BCE. The beer types of alcohol varied from region to region. During this same period, wine was developed. Both wine and beer were used by the culture as social and medical substances.

Additional Reading: Ronan, C. (1982). *Science: Its history and development among the world's cultures.* New York: Facts on File.

Beeswax (Glue)   Chemistry
Origin: Egypt   Date: 4500 BCE

As far back as 4500 BCE, beeswax was used in Egypt for painting as well as for coating. Beeswax was not used as an adhesive in the ordinary sense, but for painting materials on small and large surfaces. Beeswax was also used in other applications, such as the mummification process, shipbuilding, making magical figures, casting, and covering surfaces.

Additional reading: History of bees in Egypt. (1923). *Journal of Egyptian Archaeology,* London.

Beet   Agriculture
Origin: Mesopotamia   Date: 6600 BCE

Domestication and agricultural production of the beet began in Mesopotamia about 6600 BCE. The beet was used in medical treatment of wounds and infections. Its succulent root was also foraged for food. Other types of beets were cultivated in other varieties both as an esculent and as an ornamental foliage plant.

Additional reading: Oppenheim, A. (1979). *Ancient Mesopotamia: Portrait of a dead civilization,* Rev. ed. Chicago: University of Chicago Press.

Bell   Mechanical
Origin: Africa   Date: Prehistoric

According to the archaeological scholar Nathaniel Spears, the earliest bell was used by spiritual elders to drive away and protect against evil forces and to increase the power of benevolent forces. Spears believed that when lightning flashed and peals of thunder crashed, humans became awake for the first time because of the overwhelming power of sound and fire. At that very moment, in a desire to fight back with some equally frightening sound, humans in African prehistory may well have seized a club and hit a rock. In doing so, the first humans created the first bell.

Additional reading: Spear, N. (1978). *A treasury of archaeological bells.* New York: Hasting House Pub.

Bellow   Mechanical
Origin: Egypt   Date: 2000 BCE

It is now well established that to create and maintain a fire with white heat intensity, it is necessary to first create a draft. Prior to the development of the bellows, attempts to accomplish this were not very effective. Around 2000 BCE, the bellows were invented in Egypt, and metal forging took a leap forward. An inscription on a Mesopotamian clay table calls for skins of two large goats to make bellows for a bronze foundry.

Additional reading: Baldwin, G. (1973). *Inventors and inventions of the ancient world.* New York: Four Winds Press.

Belt Drive   Mechanical
Origin: China   Date: 15 BCE

In 15 BCE, *Yang Hsiung's Dictionary of Local Expressions* revealed that the Chinese referenced an invention known as the belt drive device used by local craftsmen of the period, which would not be known in Europe until 1430 CE. The belt was made of rope like materials and was weaved into a belt shape. This form of belt was quite efficient for the period.

Additional reading: Usher, A. (1954). *A history of mechanical inventions,* 2nd ed. Cambridge: Harvard University Press.

Benzoic Aldehyde   see   **Almond Tree.**

Berm   Civil Engineering
Origin: Nubia   Date: 2600 BCE

The Nubians and Egyptians were the first to address the problem of flooding by the development and construction of berms and, later, a city-wide drainage system. Engineers as early as 2600 BCE, fabricated a berm which was the first, flat space shelf or border separating a mound from a ditch. These berms allowed for an easier flow and control of water.

Additional reading: Palmer, G., (1968). *Archaeology a-z, a simplified guide and dictionary.* New York: Frederick Warne.

Birth Control   see   **Acacia Tree.**

Bit   see   **Wood Drill.**

Bit   see   **Horse Bit.**

Bitumen   Minerals
Origin: Palestine   Date: 4000 BCE

Bitumen is a naturally-occurring mineral pitch found the world over, but ancient Palestinians and Babylonians applied the hydrocarbon's first practical applications. Dating back to 4000 BCE, bitumen was mixed with other materials and/or used as mortar cement or for bonding. Early builders of the period noted the special characteristics of bitumen, which when heated gave the popular substance greater pliability and elasticity.

Additional reading: DeBono, E. (1974). *Eureka!: How and when the greatest inventions were made: An illustrated history of inventions from the wheel to the computer.* London: Thames & Hudson.

Blade   Military
Origin: Africa   Date: Prehistoric

The earliest known blade-shaded devices made by humans were found in Central Africa around the area that is Kenya. The blade was carved from an unknown animal bone and was used primarily for hunting and defense. Many of these stone-like blades had similar shapes and forms, leading to the inference that the blades were shaped for a specific purpose.

Additional reading: Hodges, H. (1970). *Technology of the ancient world.* New York: Knopf Pub.

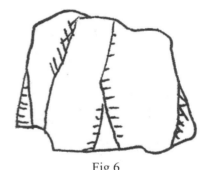
Fig 6
Stone Blade

Blade Flake   Tool
Origin: Ghana   Date: 1,500,000 BCE

During the Paleolithic period, the African continent experienced a small explosion in the production of a wide range of new specialized tools and weapons applying novel production techniques. The birth of blade flakes weapons and tools spread from West Africa during the second half of the last glacial period. New methods were developed for working flint and stone, such as the production of narrow blades and punch like tools.

Additional reading: Semenov, S., (1964). *Prehistoric technology; an experimental study of the oldest tools and artifacts from traces of manufacture and wear.* New York: Barnes and Noble.

Blast Furnace   Mechanical
Origin: China   Date: 2000 BCE

The use of a blast of air to facilitate the melting of iron ore was known as far back as 2000 BCE, in China. At first the heat blasts were produced by hand-operated bellows. Later, short chimneys were built in order to achieve a better blast. Furnaces of this sort have been found in Sumerian and Chinese ruins dating back to 1400 BCE.

Additional reading: Roberts, J., (2003). *The complete history of China*. London: Sutton Pub.

Blow Gun   Military
Origin: Indonesia   Date: 1500 BCE

The earliest recovered blowgun and dart set dates back to 1500 BCE. The blowgun, from the Malay Peninsula, was made with an inner tube of bamboo and an outer shell of bamboo stutter tube, having an overall length ranging from three- to nine- feet. The blowgun was used for hunting and warfare.

Additional reading: Gove, P., (2002). *Webster's third new international dictionary of the English language*. Springfield: Merriam-Webster.

Blow Pipe   Domestic
Origin: Africa   Date: Prehistoric

The earliest recovered blowpipe dates back to over 10,000 years ago. It was made of wood, which was turned into a stone-like hardness. The pipe was a tube through which a flow of air is blown on a flame to keep fires going. The early blowpipes were too heavy to be moved, and often had to be abandoned when migrating.

Additional reading: Hill, P. (1917). *Prehistoric times*. New York: Harper & Row.

Bludgeon   Military
Origin: Africa   Date: Prehistoric

The bludgeon was a short, stout stick, also called a club. The bludgeon, according to pictorial and written descriptions, has gone through a number of materials and construction modifications. The exact date of its development is unknown; however, it is assumed that it dates back to the Neolithic period. Several cave drawings in what is now South Africa show individuals using the bludgeon in battles and hunting expeditions.

Additional reading: Cole, S. (1963). *The prehistory of East Africa*. New York: Macmillan.

Boar   see   **Pig.**

Boat   Transportation
Origin: Africa   Date: Prehistoric

Archeologists believe that the first prehistoric water transport was by fallen trees. Simple boats made from hollowed-out logs, also known as dugout canoes, were carved in West Africa and other regions circa 16,000 BCE. China conveyed people and materials on flat rafts built from bamboo beginning around 4000 B.C. In 8000 BCE small boats appeared in Mesopotamia as far back as the sampan, a boat made from bamboo and planks.

Additional reading: Gibson, C. (1948). *The story of the ship*. New York: Henry Schuman Pub.

Body Armor   Military
Origin: Africa   Date: 10,000 BCE

Many early drawings have depicted warriors covered with plant and animal like coverings while engaged in armed conflict. The earliest body armor used during battle was found in a cave in central Africa. This crude reinforced animal-like skin was used to shield the body from flying objects. The body armor dates back to 10,000 BCE, and was used for multiple purposes.

Additional reading: Denbow, J., (1986). A new look at the later prehistory of the Kalahari. *Journal of African History*. London: Vol. 27, No. 1, pp 3-28.

Bola   Military
Origin: Africa   Date: 6200 BCE

Early hunting tools such as the spear, blade, and hatchet date back as far as 6200 BCE, in the southern regions of Africa. Bolas were sometimes used to entrap large animals, though primarily used to trap small animals. Period cave sketches show women making bolas out of bamboo and/or vines. The bolas were a series of vine-like cords tied together at one end and weighted.

Additional reading: Diop C. (1974). *The African origin of civilization myth or reality.* Westport: Lawrence Hill and Co.

Bookkeeping   see   Accounting.

Boomerang   Military
Origin: Africa   Date: 3000 BCE

The non-returning boomerang proved a most useful hunting tool. Up to four feet in length and weighing one and one half pounds, it was much larger than the returnee and could kill a large animal from a distance of 600 feet if thrown from an elevated position.

Additional reading: James, P. and Thorpe, N. (1994). *Ancient inventions.* New York: Ballantine Books.

Borer   Tool
Origin: Africa   Date: Prehistoric

Numerous tools have been recovered from archeological sites across Central Africa. One of these early tools was a borer, a simple flint instrument, chipped on one side only, used by people of the lower Paleolithic Age. Similar types of flint tools have been found throughout Asia dating toaround 3400 BC.

Additional reading: Stewart, J. (1960). *An archaeological guide and glossary.* London: Phoenix House.

Boring Machine   see   Drill.

Boron   Chemistry
Origin: Babylonia   Date: 4000 BCE

Boron, atomic number 5, was first unearthed in Babylonia as a yellowish-brown crystalline solid or as an amorphous greenish-brown powder. It is now used in the manufacture of certain semiconductor products and also as a means of increasing the strength of metals and alloys. Prehistoric Babylonians identified the chemical around 4000 BCE. Its chemical symbol is B.

Additional reading: Considine, D. and Considine, G. (1983). *Van Nostrand's scientific encyclopedia,* 6th edition, New York: Reinhold, Co.

Botany   Horticulture
Origin: Syria   Date: 400 BCE

An early scientist named Theophrastus established a classification chart for inquiring into plants. He cited the work of the Assyrian horticulturists as dating back to 400 BCE. Part of a relief from the royal park at Nineveh revealed vines and flowers in set arrangements.

Additional reading: Robert, J. (1997). *The Pengiun history of the world.* New York: Penguin Books.

Bottle (Glass)   Chemistry
Origin: Egypt   Date: 1500 BCE

Although decorative glass first appeared around 3000 BCE, it was not until 1500 BCE that glass workers learned to make vessels. They dipped a sand-filled cloth bag into a vat of melted glass, which then coated the bag and conformed to its shape. The sand was removed and the bag disintegrated, leaving a glass bottle.

Additional reading: Binford, L. (1981). *Bones: Ancient man and modern myths.* New York: Academic Press.

Bow   Military
Origin: Sudan   Date: 8000 BCE

Drawings of archers found in the Saharan tombs in what is now considered Sudan suggest that the origins of the bow and arrow in the region can be placed around 8000 BCE. Stone points discovered in Parpallo, Spain around the same time period appear to be the tips from arrows.

Additional reading: Dorsey, G. (1931). *The story of civilization: Man's own show: Civilization* New York: Halcyon House.

Fig 7
Bow
The above image appeared on a cave wall in Northern Africa

Bow Drill
Mechanical
Origin: Africa   Date: 3200 BCE

The earliest known bow drill was first seen on cave drawings in West Africa dating back to 3200 BCE. Wanderers of the lower plains used this crude device, comprised of a smooth cylindrical stick rounded at one end with a flint point. The nomadic tribes deployed the bow drill as a defense against wild animals and also for hunting.

Additional reading: Clark, J. (1950). *The stone age cultures of northern Rhodesia.* Claremont: South African Archaeological Society.

Bowl
Domestic
Origin: Africa   Date: Prehistoric

The first bowl was developed in Africa some 100,000 years ago and was formed naturally from shells or animal bones. Later, the rock or clay was used to shape bowls that would contain water, food, and other substances. The earliest recovered handmade bowl, housed in the British Museum of Natural History, was excavated in Egypt and dated circa 3100 BCE.

Additional reading: Stewart, J. (1960). *An archaeological guide and glossary.* London: Phoenix House.

Bowling
Sport
Origin: Egypt   Date: 3200 BCE

Nine pins and a ball of stone were found in the tomb of an Egyptian child who lived around 3200 BCE. The bowling alley was covered by three arches through which the ball had to pass. The structure and style of bowling is unclear because no written record has been discovered to date describing how the early bowling game was played.

Additional reading: Hill, P. (1917). *Prehistoric times.* New York: Harper & Row.

Bow-ring
Military
Origin: Nubia   Date: 690 BCE

Nubian archers, recognized for their expertise with the bow and arrow during the sixth century, used thumb rings known as bow-rings to help them pull their bowstring tight. During hunting archers deployed the bow-ring especially to target swift moving animals. Over the years, the bow-ring shape changed and later versions of the weapon appeared in Europe as a hand strip used by archers during battle.

Additional reading: Davidson, B. (1969). *The African genius.* Boston: Little, Brown.

Boxing
Sport
Origin: Africa   Date: 4000 BCE

Boxing, as an organized sport of fist fighting, originated in Central Africa about 4000 BCE, as part of ceremonial activities. A decorative fresco in Iraq, dated around the same period, revealed boxers with their fists wrapped in pieces of leather. In ancient Greece, where boxing was called pancrace, the gloves were lined with pieces of iron and often the contest was fought to the death.

Additional reading: Adams, W. (1977). *Nubia, corridor to Africa.* Princeton, N.J: Princeton University Press.

Brahmi Numeral
Mathematics
Origin: India   Date: 300 BCE

Around 300 BCE, an unknown Indian mathematician developed a numbering system called Brahmi Numerals, which is a decimal system. This numbering system of numeration is unique because it is used without a place-value notation, which does not use zero, and has its own symbols for the tens, including 100 and 1000. Place valued notations had already been developed by the Nubians. The Brahmi numerals system was a faster way of processing values.

Additional reading: Struik, D.(1987). *A concise history of mathematics.* 4th ed., New York: Dover Publication.

Brain Surgery   see   Surgery.

Branding
Communication
Origin: Egypt   Date: 1500 BCE

In a practice dating back to 1500 BCE, during the reign of Hatshepsut, the Egyptian scholar was among the social groups that marked other humans and their domesticated animals with branding irons for identification. Many of the ruling families had their servants and animals branded with their family emblem. A farmer's family symbol was often applied by hot iron to identify livestock such as horses, cattle, ibex, and others.

Additional reading: Schmandt, B. (1992). *Before writing,* Texas: University of Texas Press.

Brass   Metallurgy
Origin: China   Date: 1000 BCE

An alloy blended from copper and zinc, brass was in manufacture as long ago as 1000 BCE, by people in China in a process that heated copper with charcoal and powdered zinc ore. The Persians were known to have used it around 500 BCE. Brasses are classified according to the amount of zinc they contain. Different properties, such as tensile strength, corrosion resistance, or decorative appearance, are obtained by controlling the type and quality of constituents added.

Additional reading: Clarke, D. (1994). *The new illustrated science and invention encyclopedia: How it works.* New York: Stuttman

Brazier   Domestic
Origin: Nubia   Date: Antiquity

Many tombs of the ancient world contained a brazier, a small container used by the servants to make and maintain fires for the household and considered a necessary device for the after life. The brazier was also used in battles to make fireballs that were hurled from catapults. The earliest brazier recovered was in Nubia made of carved bone, while succeeding versions were forged from stone and iron.

Additional reading: Hill, P. (1917). *Prehistoric times.* New York: Harper & Row.

Bread   Agriculture
Origin: Egypt   Date: 5000 BCE

Unleavened yeast was clearly a dietary feature of Neolithic peoples. However, the earliest evidence of leavened bread dates from the beginning of the Bronze Age. Research on fossilized pieces of bread found in Egyptian lakeside dwellings reveal that they had been prepared by combining slightly crushed wheat with water, then spreading the mixture on a hot stone,

piled over with hot ashes. About the same time, 7000 years ago, Nubian neighbors added flourish to bread by pulling the flour dough into the shape of little rolls.

Additional reading: Rice, M. (2003). *Egypt's making: The origin of ancient Egypt, 5000-2000 B.C.* 2nd ed. New York: Roulledge Pub.

Brewing Beer   Agriculture
Origin: Egypt   Date: 2017 BCE

It is recorded that in 2017 BCE, the Egyptians introduced a beer made of malted rye, which was first brewed in the town of Pelusium. By 60 BCE, large quantities of Egyptian beer were drunk in Alexandria, its preparation detailed in the Papyrus written by Anastasi IV. Brewing beer and other drink substances appear to be one of the first commercial ventures of the time period.

Additional reading: Neuburger, O. (1930). *The technical arts and sciences of the ancients.* New York: The Macmillan Co.

Brick   Material
Origin: Mesopotamia   Date: 2500 BCE

The mass production of bricks and their use as a building material has existed for thousands of years. The earliest examples of clay bricks were found on sites in Mesopotamia built around 2500 BCE.

Additional reading: Hill, D. (1997). *A history of engineering.* London: Routledge Pub.

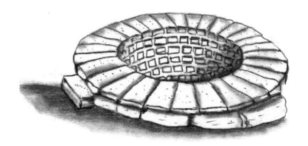

Fig 8 Brick
Used in early times

Bridge   Civil
Origin: Babylonia   Date: 600 BCE

The earliest bridges were built of timber, leaving no recorded trace for centuries. Around 600 BCE,

Nabopolassar of Babylonia built a stone bridge that rested on brick piers across the Euphrates. Other bridges like the Trajan's bridge over the Danube, built around 99 CE, had one curricular arch with a span of 65 feet.

Additional reading: Roberts, V. and Trent, I., (1991). *Bibliotheca mechanica.* New York: Hill J.A.

Bridge Floating
Origin: Persia   Mechanical   Date: 400 BCE

According to military records dating back to 480 BCE, Xerxes I, King of Persia, developed a floating bridge using a double line of hundreds of boats tethered together with flax. Nearly a mile long in length, the fabled bridge enabled the Persian army to cross the Hellesport strait in seven days and successfully capture Athens. This type of bridge structure became common in many regions.

Additional reading: Hodges, H. (1970). *Technology in the ancient world.* New York: Knopf Pub.

Brocade
Origin: Mesopotamia   Textile   Date: 2900 BCE

The earliest known brocade was woven in Mesopotamia as early as 2900 BCE. The recovered remnants of brocade fabrics were designed with a pattern of raised or flocked figures set in gold or silver and thought to be worn by the royal families. Later patterns included many kinds of materials wrought or flowered with a raised design.

Additional reading: Openheim, A. (1979). *Ancient Mesopotamia: Portrait of a dead civilization,* rev. ed. Chicago: University of Chicago Press.

Bronze
Origin: Egypt   Materials   Date: 3700 BCE

The oldest known use of bronze was a rod found in the Egyptian pyramid at Meidum around 370 BCE. The second advance in the field of materials came around 3000 BCE, with the first production of bronze in Syria. Bronze is made from copper with an addition of approximately ten percent tin. While no one knows just how that mixture first originated, one suggestion is that an ore was smelted in which there were elements both of copper and tin. Another, and perhaps a more

likely suggestion, is that the early smiths of Syria and eastern Turkey, where some of the first mining was done, experimented. Bronze was the world's main metal for two thousand years, lending its name to an era, the Bronze Age.

Additional reading: Binford, L., (1981). *Bones: Ancient man and modern myths.* New York: Academic Press.

Brush
Origin: Egypt   Mechanical   Date: 1700 BCE

The brush was in common use in ancient Egypt dating back to 1700 BCE. Made primarily of vegetable fiber, the brushes were constructed from bundles of coarse hay, and by binding the twigs together at the top with rope, string or palm leaves. The fan-shaped brushes of split reeds were used both for such household chores as sweeping and fanning the cooking charcoal.

Additional reading: Baldwin, G. (1973). *Inventors and inventions of the ancient world.* New York: Four Winds Press.

Fig 9
Early Egyptian Brush

Bubale
Origin: Kenya   Domestic   Date: 6000 BCE

An ox-like antelope, the bubal first roamed in what is now known as Kenya in Africa. The Nubians, Egyptians, and Syrians also domesticated the bubal and used it as a beast of burden. In certain parts of the African continent, the bubal was raised for food. The bubal appeared to remain a local animal. There are no known records of this animal being found in other areas of the world.

Additional reading: Iliffe, J. (1995). *Africans: The history of a continent.* Cambridge: University Press.

Bubble   Chemistry
Origin: Africa   Date: 10,000 BCE

The earliest records of bubble carvings were found in the southern region of Africa in a stone, depicting what seemed to be a fishing exercise. The image shows several members of the group blowing through bamboo-like tubes, creating a flow of air bubbles. The blowing of air through bamboo caused the fish to rise to the surface for easier catching.

Additional reading: McGrath, K. and Travers, B. (2001). *The Gale encyclopedia of science*, Detroit: Gale Group.

Bucket   Device
Origin: Mesopotamia   Date: 2600 BCE

The Mesopotamians were the first to design and construct what are now considered buckets. These wooden utensils, initially used to draw water out of the wells, were soon employed to also quench fires in local villages as early as 2600 BCE. The early buckets were usually made of leather or wood.

Additional Reading: Noel H. (1969). *Historical archaeology.* New York: Knopf Pub.

Buffalo   Domestic
Origin: China   Date: 7000 BCE

After large people migrations from Africa had settled areas of Asia and Europe, the process of cultivating plants and domesticating animals began. Records show that between 7,000 and 6,000 BCE, the water buffalo was domesticated in China and East Asia. Water buffalo were raised as labor animals but also served as food for many.

Additional reading: Moule, A.(1937) *Boats towed by a swimming buffalo in China.* T'oung Pao, 2nd ser., XXXIII, p. 94 .

Burin   Tool
Origin: America   Date: Prehistoric

The earliest flint beak-shaped burin from Mezin was found in the Alaskan region of North America by V. T. Luanson in 1954. The burin, with a shaft-like handle, was used to manufacture many other tools. The burin allowed the artisan to strike off a single flake vertically with one blow. The sharp blade-edge was then removed, eliminating the need to use more laborious blunting by hard force.

Additional reading: Stewart, J. (1960). *An archaeological guide and glossary.* London: Phoenix House.

Burner   see   Incense Burner.

C

Cabbage   Agriculture
Origin: Egypt   Date: 3500 BCE

As early as the era of Dira Abu'n Nega of Egypt, cabbage was grown as a common staple to Egyptians' daily diet. It also appears that cabbage juices were used to polish and restore metal brightness. Cabbage was domesticated from wild plants around 3500 BCE. There is some evidence that the Egyptians also used the juice of cabbage for some medicinal purposes.

Additional reading: Kowalchik C. and Hylton W., (1998). *Rodale's illustrated encyclopedia of herbs.* Pennsylvania: Rodale Press.

Cabinet   Domestic
Origin: Nubia   Date: 2700 BCE

Several original cabinets recovered from the Nubian tombs were chiseled out of stone. One of the stone chests was found to house and protect the royal jewels. Another stone cabinet stored the royal papers of the pharaoh's scribers. Such early cabinets were small with quite elaborate designs on both the inside and outside. Many of the cabinets contained obscure built-in compartments that provided additional security.

Additional Reading: Noel H. (1969). *Historical archaeology.* New York: Knopf Pub.

Calcite   Materials
Origin: Nigera   Date: Prehistoric

Serrated flint saws containing traces of calcite materials have been found in central Africa and were dated back to the early Neolithic period. The calcite appears to have existed in many of the earliest man-made tools, such as the ax head. Flint tools have been found made of calcite, formed and processed into such artifacts as fish hooks, beads, and pendants in the basin of the central plains of Africa.

Additional reading: Connah, G., (1981). *Three thousand years in Africa: Man and his environment in the lake Chad region of Nigeria.* Cambridge: Cambridge University Press.

Calculator   see   **Abacus.**

Calendar   Astronomy
Origin: Egypt   Date: 4228 BCE

The Egyptians had instituted a 365-day calendar as early as 4228 BCE. The calendar aided agriculture by helping them to predict the date of the annual flooding of the Nile. This early calendar was designed around the earth's cycles, representing seasons, religious dates, as well as star cycles.

Additional reading: Lockyer, J. (1964). *The dawn of astronomy: A study of the temple worship and mythology of the ancient Egyptian.* Cambridge Mass.: M.I.T. Press.

Caliper Rule   Measurement
Origin: China   Date: 3000 BCE

The caliper rule, which dates to 3000 BCE, was used in China to measure the diameter of an object. The wooden rule served as the prototype for the bronze upgrade. Ancient Chinese improved the caliper rules efficiency and many new design tools and devices were developed with greater capabilities.

Additional reading: Roberts, J., (2003). *The complete history of China.* London: Sutton Pub.

Camel   Domestic
Origin: Egypt   Date: 3200 BCE

The camel, a large ruminant quadruped distinguished by its humped back, long neck, and cushioned feet, was domesticated as early as 3200 BCE. It became a much-traded property in Egypt, Western Asia, and Northern Africa. In the arid regions of the world, the camel was the chief beast of burden.

Additional reading: Dorsey, G. (1931). *The story of civilization: Man's own show.* New York: Halcyon House.

Canal   Civil
Origin: Syria   Date: 900 BCE

The problem of water control has plagued man for thousands of years. The Egyptians and Assyrians built canals for irrigation purposes as early as 900 BCE. In 700 BCE, King Sennacherib of Assyria built a canal fifty miles long, and added the technological leap of a sluice gate that opened mechanically. The canal was lined with stones, making it waterproof.

Additional reading: Payne, R. (1959). *The canal builders.* New York: Macmillan Co.

Candle   Illuminating
Origin: Egypt   Date: 400 BCE

As a rudimentary source of light, cone-shaped candles were included in the decorations of the Egyptian tombs built around 300 BCE. Egyptian culture is also credited as the first to introduce the wicked candle, as well as candle-holders made of clay. During the Middle Ages, candles were made by dipping the wicks into molds containing animal or vegetable fat.

Additional reading: Dorsey, G. (1931). *The story of civilization, man's own show.* New York: Halcyon House.

Canoe   Transportation
Origin: Africa   Date: 8000 BCE

Archaeologists discovered the remains of a dugout canoe in Africa believed to date to 50,000 BCE. Such boats, consisting of a light wooden frame covered with animal skins, were typical of this region, allowing the inhabitants to travel great distances. It wasn't until 8000 BCE that canoes were constructed and assembled from more than one piece of wood.

Additional reading: Breunig, P. (1996). The 8000-Year-old dugout canoe from dufuna (NE Nigeria). Harare: University of Zimbabwe,

Fig 10
Canoe

Canopic Jar — Domestic
Origin: Egypt   Date: 3500 BCE

The Egyptians were the first to perfect the process of mummification. Teams of embalming priests mummified bodies in workshops where all the special tools and equipment were kept. Canopic jars were used to protect different organs: Inset for the liver, Ha'py for the lungs, Duamutef for the stomach, Oebehsenuf for the intestines; this time-tested process has proved to be the best way to preserve human remains for long periods of time.

Additional readings: Hart, G. (1990). *Ancient Egypt*. New York: Alfred Knopf Pub.

Capacity (Unit) see Foot Measurement.

Carbon — Chemistry
Origin: America   Date: 1200 BCE

Carbon, atomic number 6, can take the form of diamond, graphite, and amorphous carbon. As early as 1200 BCE, Native American documents refer to carbon in its diamond form. Diamond and graphite are widely distributed as naturally occurring deposits, while amorphous carbon takes the form of coal, timber, petroleum, and other natural materials.

Additional reading: Williams, T. (1987). *The history of invention*. New York: Facts on File.

Cardan — Mechanical
Origin: China   Date: 1500 BCE

Invented by Fang Feng in the second century BCE, the cardan was indirectly referred to in the seduction scene of the Ode to Pretty Ladies written by the Chinese author, Ssuma Hiangju (Sima Xiangru). The cardan dates to 1500 BCE, consisting of a set of interlocking circles linked to one another by pivots with converging geometric points.

Additional reading: Holmyarp, A. (1954). *History of technology and invention. Vol. 3*. London: Oxford University Press.

Carpet — Textile
Origin: Mesopotamia   Date: 2700 BCE

The early name for a mat covering was karpete and later changed to carpet. Mesopotamian weavers were the first to develop a carpet material made from wool. The first carpets were used to cover tables, chairs, and beds. A different textured fabric, carpet was woven in a pattern of different colors was designed to spread on floors for standing and kneeling.

Additional reading: Gille, B. (1986). *The history of technique. Vol. 2*. New York: Research Science Pub.

Caterpillar see Silk worm.

Cartography — Astronomy
Origin: Mesopotamia   Date: 3000 BCE

Cartography was, and continues to be, one of the most complex areas of inventiveness, where innovation has, more often than not, been cumulative and cross-cultural. At its prehistoric advent, mapmaking evolved as knowledge expanded to incorporate topographical, geographical, and geodesic information. Cartography consists of the mathematical method of writing down a spherical or hemispherical formula, representing an advanced level of surface. Maps date back to the third millennium BCE.

Additional reading: Harley, J., and Woodward, D. (1987). *The history of cartography*. Chicago. University of Chicago.

Cartouche — Domestic
Origin: Egypt   Date: 2700 BCE

The cartouche was an elongated, oval frame drawn around the names of the pharaohs in Egyptian hieroglyphs, perhaps to signify the all-embracing royal rule. Dr. Thomas Young discovered the meaning of cartouches when he studied a copy of the Rosetta Stone in 1812. Skilled craftsmen of this time period designed the cartouches, and passed the trade from generation to generation where improvements were made.

Additional reading: Palmer, G. (1968) *Archaeology a-z, a simplified guide and dictionary*. London: Frederick Warne.

Cast — Domestic
Origin: Nubia   Date: 4000 BCE

The cast was developed in the Nubian region as early as 4000 BCE. The solid material filled a mold after the original object that occupied the cavity had been removed and these cast allowed easier reproduction. This form of fossil was commonly found in porous rocks such as sandstone.

Additional reading: Lepsius, R., (1852). *Discoveries in Egypt, Ethiopia and the peninsula of Sinia.* London: Hakluyt Society.

Casket see Shawibit.

Cast Iron Materials
Origin: China Date: 300 BCE

Around 300 BCE, the Chinese invented the process for casting iron to make containers. The early castings were use for military purposes, allowing weapons and food to be quickly moved to the battlefront.

Additional reading: Holmyarp, A. (1954). *History of technology and invention. Vol. 3.* London: Oxford University Press.

Castor Oil Medicine
Origin: Egypt Date: 1500 BCE

As early as 2500 BCE, the Egyptians used castor oil for its medicinal benefits, such as a massaging agent on the aging bodies of the wealthy. The taste of castor oil was associated with its effectiveness. The chemical composition has changed little over the centuries.

Additional reading: Sonnedecker, G., Kremers, E. and Urdang, G. (1976). *Kremers and Urdang's history of pharmacy.* Philadelphia: Lippincott.

Cat Domestic
Origin: Egypt Date: 4000 BCE

Most all of the historical records cite Egypt as the earliest location for domestic cats. Large cats such as lions, panthers and leopards were used for entertainment and warfare in other parts of the world. The smaller cats were bred for domestic purposes, and held a sacred place in Egyptian society. A well-known carnivorous quadruped, the cat was sought out to destroy mice and other undesirable small rodents that feasted from the royal granaries.

Additional reading: Davis, S. (1987). *The archaeology of animals.* London: Batsford.

Catalog see Star Catalog.

Catapult Mechanical
Origin: Africa Date: 4000 BCE

The catapult, a device for hurling objects, was used in warfare as early as 4000 BCE, as depicted on cave drawings in western Africa. These very crude yet fearsome weapons were also deployed by the Roman armies who improved the design so that the device could throw an object a distance of 500 yards.

Additional reading: Adams, W. (1977). *Nubia, corridor to Africa.* Princeton, N.J: Princeton University Press.

Cattle Domestic
Origin: Mesopotamia Date: 2600 BCE

Mesopotamia, with its vast arid areas, was thought to be the first country to breed cattle as early as 2600 BCE. The roaming nomadic people traveled great distances with their cattle, camels, and other domesticated animals. Many scholars believe that the cow was crossbred with other wild animals such as oxen and buffaloes to improve characteristics needed by the herders.

Additional reading: Stewart, J. 1960). *An archaeological guide and glossary.* London: Phoenix House.

Celestial Observation Astronomy
Origin: Babylon Date: 1800 BCE

Early accounts show that the Babylonian astronomers were members of the first civilization to start and complete a record of celestial observations. The celestial record includes a set of timelines of astronomical events. The charts also included a star catalog that guided sea-goers and royal travelers.

Additional Reading: (1979) *Ancient records of Assyria and Babylon, vol. I. historical Records of Assyria from the earliest times to Sargon,* Chicago: University of Chicago Press.

Cement see Mortar.

Central Heating Systems
Origin: Turkey Date: 1250 BCE

Around 1250 BCE, King of Arzawa built ducts beneath the floors of his palace in southwestern

Anatolia (Turkey), suggesting that the palace had central heating. Early records reveal that the central heating systems didn't work well. This caused many home owners to keep other human servants around to heat their home.

Additional reading: Forbes, R.J. (1967) *Man the maker: A history of technology and engineering,* New York: Forbes publishing.

Ceramic   Materials
Origin: Iran   Date: 4000 BCE

According to carbon testing, the earliest ceramic material dates back to 4000 BCE and was found in Iran. Ceramics include not only the ancient types of pottery or the artistic types of past centuries, but also ancient discovered materials known for their ability to withstand high temperatures.

Additional reading: Parker, S. (1989). *McGraw-Hill concise encyclopedia of science and technology.* New York: McGraw-Hill Pub.

Cereal   Agriculture
Origin: Mesopotamia   Date: 2900 BCE

Many archeologists believe that some form of cereal existed throughout the prehistoric world. The Mesopotamians were the first to organize planting to cultivate and to process cereal for human consumption. The main cereal plants were wheat, rye, barley, oats, millet, rice and maize.

Additional reading: Gwynne, M. (1975). *The origin and spread of some domestics foods plants in Eastern Africa.* New York: African Publishing Company.

Chain Drive   Mechanical
Origin: Turkey   Date: 260 BCE

Around 260 BCE, Philon of Byzantium designed a chain drive for use in repeat loading of a catapult device for building and/or war. This crude adoption to a war machine spread quickly to other parts of the world. This led to the use of hand woven springs in catapults and experiments with the expansion of air by heat.

Additional reading: Bunch, B. and Hellemans, A. (1993). *The timetables of technology: A chronology of the most important people and events in the history of technology.* New York: Simon & Schuster.

Chariot (For Fighting)   Transportation
Origin: Egypt   Date: 1350 BCE

King Tutankhamen of Egypt was the first ruler to lead an army using an animal drawn chariot. He charged into battle against the Nubians about 1350 BCE. The Egyptian chariots were engineered for fast striking power, using a framework of very light wood and side panels of canvas or leather. The wheels were wide set to allow quick turns. Human-drawn chariots were used in Africa and China, for domestic purposes as far back as 4550 BCE.

Additional reading: Barber, F. (1900) *The mechanical triumphs of ancient Egyptians,* London: Trubner and Co.

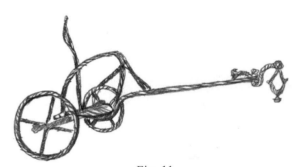

Fig. 11
Chariot
This is an example of an early chariot
constructed for open field battles

Charting   Astronomy
Origin: Babylon   Date: 1250 BCE

In 1250 BCE, the Babylonians are credited with the development of instruments that determined the southern position of a star or planet. This charting process was shared throughout the astronomical community. It appears that the Chinese, several hundred years later developed a similar charting instrument.

Additional reading: Sedgwick, W. and Tler, H. (1917). *A short history of science.* New York: The Macmillan Co.

Charting   Navigating
Origin: Polynesia   Date: 3700 BCE

The Polynesians developed charts that detailed sailing the Pacific Ocean as early as 3700 BCE. The shippers used extremely accurate stick charts, an unprecedented system of mapping ocean swells. The navigator observed the relationship between the main waves driven by the trail winds and the secondary waves reflected from an island in order to find their destination.

Additional reading: Murry, S.; Little, W.; Fowler, H.; Coulson, J.; and Onions, C. (1937). *Oxford universal English dictionary on historical principle,* London: From the original English dictionary.

Charting   see   Music Charting.

Chase   Tools
Origin: Egypt   Date: 69 BCE

Queen Cleopatra VII of Egypt is credited with the development of the chasing process in 69 BCE. This embossing process was used to form and decorate metal into elaborate shapes and designs by punching or raising the metal surface as well as its reverse side with a set of specially designed tools. Much of the jewelry adorned during this time period was created by this exacting technique.

Additional reading: Petrie, W. (1924). *A history of Egypt. Vols. 1-6.* London: Bracken Pub.

Checker   see   Alquerque.

Cheese   Agriculture
Origin: Egypt   Date: 4200 BCE

The Egyptians were the earliest known to use the by-products from cows and camels living in their region to make a crude form of sour cheese. The early cheese was fed to the sick as an ancient cure for some common sicknesses. Cheese was not yet a common food product because of the lengthy time required to process it.

Additional reading: Zaki, A. and Iskader, Z. (1942). *Ancient Egypt cheese.* ASAE. XLI.

Chemical Textbook   Science
Origin: Syria   Date: 700 BCE

Mineral compounds found in Syria were mentioned as drugs in the medical papyri. The Mesopotamian chemical texts have been dated to the seventh century BCE. One cuneiform tablet, dating to seventeenth

century BCE, described the making of a lead glaze colored with copper.

Additional reading: Gelis-Didot, P. (1843). *Voyage in Egypt and Syria.* London.

Chert   Chemistry
Origin: Africa   Date: Prehistoric

The earliest identification of chert came from Southern region of Africa. The exact date is unknown but the chert mineral was used in Paleolithic times for tool making. Chert, a form of quartz, similar to flint, is usually found in limestone. The ancient process used to extract chert from limestone is currently used today.

Additional reading: Palmer, G. (1968). *Archaeology a-z, a simplified guide and dictionary.* New York: Frederick Warne Pub.

Chicken   Domestic
Origin: Mesopotamia   Date: 2900 BCE

The earliest records showing the use of fowl came from writings found in tombs of Mesopotamian kings dating back to 2900 BCE. Originally known as cicen, the chicken was a source of fresh meat and primarily eaten by the wealthy. The domesticated chicken migrated southward and soon became a common food source for the masses.

Additional reading: Maspero, G. (1901). *The dawn of civilization: Egypt and Chaldea.* Society for Promoting Christian Knowledge.

Chimney   Mechanical
Origin: Babylonia   Date: 3100 BCE

The earliest chimney structures were discovered in the region now known as Northern Babylon. The chimney was part of a kiln, marking the first time that pottery firing was done in an enclosed structure. The chimney-like structures spread throughout the area.

Additional reading: Binford, L., (1981). *Bones: Ancient man and modern myths.* New York: Academic Press.

Chisel   Tool
Origin: Africa   Date: 6000 BCE

The chisel was made by knocking a flake off one side of the end of a blade in such a way that it left a narrow, sharp cutting edge at a right angle to the broad section of the blade. This gave the cutting edge support and helped to keep it from breaking under pressure. The advantage of this tool was that it can be repeatedly repointed simply by removing another single layer of material.

Additional reading: Semenov, S., (1964). *Prehistoric Technology; an experimental study of the oldest tools and artifacts from traces of manufacture and wear*. New York: Barnes and Noble.

Fig. 12
Chisel
The man made chisels above were made stone

Chord   see   Trigonometric Table.

Chrome Coating   Metallurgical
Origin: Egypt   Date: 1470 BCE

Egyptians first mastered the process of chrome coating during the reign of Tuthmosis. The royal and well-to-do Egyptians prior to this process were buried in rare non-coated containers. Some archeologists have found evidence that some non-wealthy Egyptians also used vaults reinforced by the chrome coating process to bury their dead. Polychromed glass vessels were commonly used in burial ceremonies. The chrome coating was thought to seal and secure the containers contents.

Additional reading: Barber, F. (1900). *The mechanical triumphs of ancient Egyptians*. London: Trubner and Co.

Cipherization (Math)   Mathematics
Origin: Egypt   Date: 5000 BCE

The first cipherization of numbers occurred in Egypt about 5000 BCE, during which time hieroglyphic numerals used special symbols for the powers of ten. The cipherization process first developed was quite complex and was refined over the years. Its records show that Europe developed a slightly different cipherization process around 1700 BCE.

Additional reading: Ashurst, F. (1982). *Founders of modern mathematics*. London: Fredrick Muller.

Circle   Mathematics
Origin: Egypt   Date: 1700 BCE

Before the invention of the written word, African astronomers drew pictorial descriptions detailing time and unique events. The Egyptian Rhind papyrus written in 1700 BCE, gave the earliest written mathematical description of the circle and its surface. Some biblical scholars believe that the symbol of the circle occurred in Ethiopia as far back as 2500 BCE. It is unclear if the earlier circle was used for arithmetic as was the place value circle of the Egyptians.

Additional reading: Newman, J. (1956). *The world of mathematics*. New York: Simon and Schuster.

Circuit   see   Electronic Circuit.

Circumference   Mathematics
Origin: Egypt   Date: 3000 BCE

About 3000 BCE, Egyptians developed the formula for finding the surface area of the sphere and the length of the circumference. Egyptian mathematical planes were as accurate as those of modern engineers. In fact, many of the contemporary basic mathematical formulas are based on Egyptian mathematics.

Additional reading: Scott, J. (1969). A *history of mathematics,* London: Taylor and Francies.

City   Systems
Origin: Iraq   Date: 8000 BCE

As early as 8000 BCE, cities were developed in Iraq and other sites including Jericho and Palestine in the Near East. These large living areas were made possible by the planting of seasonal crops and irrigation systems. These formative cities ranged from crudely constructed huts to cave colonies.

Additional reading: Childe, V. (1957). *Civilization, cities and town*s. London.

Citrus Fruit   Agriculture
Origin: Indochina   Date: 6500 BCE

Citrus fruit was first domesticated in Indochina as far back as 6500 BCE. The most common citrus fruits were lemons, limes and oranges. The citrus fruits soon became a major food source for the population. Some fruits appear in the Americas 1500 years later.

Additional reading: Key, J. (1976). *Chinese herbs.* Rutland, VT: Charles E. Tultle.

Classifying sign   see   Determinative.

Clay   Material
Origin: Africa   Date: Prehistoric

Clay has been used in some form since the dawn of human existence starting in Africa. Molded and then hardened by the sun, clay was used to make pots, bricks and coverings for wattle and daub huts. The Chinese developed a very durable water vessel by heating clay to redness. Clay pots, inscribed tablets, and cylinders have provided archaeologists with valuable information regarding the ways of life of ancient peoples.

Additional reading: Travers, B. (1996). *The Gale encyclopedia of science.* New York: Gale Research.

Clay Plaster   Construction
Origin: Egypt   Date: Antiquity

The use of clay plaster dates back to the dawn of time. The quality of the plaster varied considerably from one region to another, and ranged from coarse to very fine clay plaster mixtures. Over time the makers of clay plaster were able to add additional substances that changed the strengths and uses.

Additional reading: Newton; F. (1923). Excavation at El Amarnah. London: *The Journal of Egyptian Archaeology.*

Clay Token   see   Token.

Clepsydra   Horology
Origin: Egypt   Date: 1500 BCE

The clepsydra or water clock existed in Egypt in the fifteenth century BCE, and is likely among the world's oldest time- measuring devices. The working principle behind the clepsydra is the regulated flow of speed of liquid, usually an oil- or water-based substance. Water

gradually flows through a reed hung in a hold near the base. The passage of time is measured by the descent of the water past the hour marks. As the night was always divided into twelve parts irrespective of the season, the hours shown by the clock varied in length throughout the year.

Additional reading: Burlingame, R. (1938). *March of the iron men: A social history of union through invention.* New York: C. Scribner's Sons, Ltd.

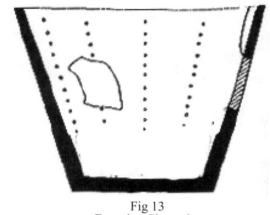
Fig 13
Egyptian Clepsydra

Cloak   see   Kell.

Clock (Mechanical)   Horology
Origin: China   Date: 3000 BCE

While clocks were made in China as early as 3000 BCE, mechanical clocks were not in popular use until the 1300s. Operated by weights or springs, they were not very precise or reliable. This prototype mechanical clock initiated a new wave of innovative devices that used springs and levers.

Additional reading: Roberts, J., (2003). *The complete history of China.* London: Sutton Pub.

Cloth (Wrap)   Textile
Origin: Africa   Date: 6500 BCE

Weaving is the interlocking of longitudinal threads called warp and transverse elements crossing at right angles called weft. An early form of weaving was made from stiff bark and found in Africa. Depictions of looms have appeared in Mesopotamia and Egypt as early as 6500 BCE..

Additional reading: Huffman, T. (1971). *Cloth from the iron age in Rhodesia.* South Africa: Arnoldia Press.

Fig 14
Cloth Making

Clothing   see   **Leather.**

Clovis Point   Domestic
Origin: America   Date: Prehistoric

The Clovis point was a heavy, tapered spearhead or dart-thrower, named after the site in New Mexico where the artifacts were found. Clovis points were made between 10,000 BCE and 9000 BCE and were constructed from mammoth bone.

Additional reading: Palmer, G. (1968). *Archaeology a-z, a simplified guide and dictionary.* New York: Frederick Warne Pub.

Club   see   **Bludgeon.**

Coal   Chemistry
Origin: Congo   Date: 4500 BCE

The first recorded use of a coal-like substance was depicted on cave walls in central Africa. Dating back to 4500 BCE, the drawing showed nomads in the process of food preparation. This process of fire development spread rapidly to other continents and appeared later in many of the images. The coal-like substance eventually became too difficult to mine and was later replaced in many areas with wood and other, more accessible, rapid burning substances.

Additional reading: Adams, W. (1977). *Nubia, corridor to Africa.* Princeton, N.J.: University Press.

Coal Mining   Mining
Origin: China   Date: 2000 BCE

Evidence suggests that coal was used in the Congo around 4500 BCE. Organized mining of coal began in China around 2000 BCE. By 1300 BCE, historical scholars concur that the mining process was very crude and dangerous. Many lives were lost and the mining work became the common labor of servants.

Additional reading: Ries, E. (1930). *Mother wit.* New York: The Century Co.

Coating   see   **Chrome Coating.**

Coconut   Agriculture
Origin: India   Date: Antiquity

The tropical palm tree, cacaos nucifera, produced what is currently called the coconut. The coconut tree grew wild in India and was grown and cultivated for human consumption. The native region of the cacaos palm tree was the tropical shorelines of the West Indian basin around 1400 BCE. The Portuguese introduced the palm tree to Europeans around 300 BCE. The name refers to the face-like appearance at the base of the shell with its three holes.

Additional reading: Keller, M., (1978). *Mysterious herbs and roots: Ancient secrets for Beauite health, magic prevention and youth.* Culver City, Cal. Peace Press.

Code (Ciphers)   Communication
Origin: Syria   Date: 1200 BCE

As early as the Bronze Age, scribes were trained in the art of deciphering scrambled or coded texts. A clay tablet from Ugarit in Syria, dated 1200 BCE, gives a simple student's exercise, the object of which was to find the answer to a four-letter code or word.

Additional reading: MacGregor, S. (1926). *The Kabbalah unveiled,* London: Routledge and Kegan Paul.

Code of Hammurabi   see   **Medical Ethics.**

Codex — Communication
Origin: Egypt   Date: 715 BCE

Codex, a manuscript arranged in leaves and sewn together at one side, appeared like the pages of a modern book. One codex, made in 715 BCE, was found at Luxor and is considered to be the oldest of the form. The codex roll was in general use until the fourth century CE.

Additional reading: Gordon, C., (1974). *Riddles in history.* New York: Crown Pub.

Coffee — Agriculture
Origin: Ethiopia   Date: 600 BCE

Coffee was grown and harvested in Ethiopia as early as 600 BCE. The early coffee bean was eaten for food; later it was used as a brew and consumed by Ethiopian men. A common drink among the wealthy, coffee soon spread to other parts of the world and was processed by various methods.

Additional reading: Redman, C. (1978). *Near East.* San Francisco: Freeman Pub.

Coin Money — Economics
Origin: Asia Minor   Date: 700 BCE

The first coins were produced by affixing an official stamp on the face of ingots. The practice began in the middle of the seventh century BCE, in Asia Minor during the reign of the Lydian King Ardys. At that time, coin currency consisted of small ingots made of a gold-and-silver alloy called electrum. The value of the coins varied by region.

Additional reading: Hobson, B., Obojsk, R. (1984). *Illustrated encyclopedia of world coins.* Garden City, N.Y.: Doubleday.

Coin-Operated Machine — Mechanical
Origin: Egypt   Date: 20 BCE

Egyptian engineer Heron designed the first slot machine, which was used in Egyptian temples. By dropping a coin into a machine, visitors received a certain amount of water from the tap for a ritual wash before worshipping. These coins were used to maintain the buildings and grounds.

Additional reading: James, P. and Thorpe, N. (1994). *Ancient inventions.* New York: Ballantine Books.

Coinage (Standard) — Economics
Origin: Asia Minor   Date: 650 BCE

The earliest records show that around 650 BCE, the Lydians of Asia Minor introduced and mass-produced the first standard coinage. These coins were used as a standard for trade throughout the region and were used in weights and measurements.

Additional reading: Kane, J. (1981). *Famous first facts: A record of first happenings, discoveries, and inventions in American history.* New York: H.W. Wilson.

Collar Harness — Transportation
Origin: China   Date: 110 BCE

The Chinese developed the collar harness for oxen and horses around 110 BCE. The early harnesses were made from bone and animal skin. The Chinese collar harness was designed in two components and was able to flex with the movement of the animal. The collar harness was not used in the West until the Middle Ages.

Additional reading: Fitzgerald, C. (1961). *China: A Short cultural history.* New York: Praeger.

Colter — Agriculture
Origin: Egypt   Date: 1 BCE

The Egyptians introduced the colter in 1 BCE. The colter is a harness-like device used for working animals. They affixed a sharp blade to a pole in front of the plowshare that enabled them to break up the heavy, damp soil found in the lower basin of Egypt. The colter increased the food production in many local villages.

Additional reading: Curwen, E. and Hatt, G. (1953). *Plough and pasture: The early history of farming, pt. 1: Prehistoric farming of Europe and the Near East.* New York: H. Schuman Pub.

Comb (Hair) — Domestic
Origin: Palestine   Date: 1200 BCE

A comb was found in a Nubian tomb that dates back to 1200 BCE. It is believed that the comb belonged to some royal family member. It was carved out of ivory and had large comb teeth. The construction made it easy to use in many different textures of hair.

Additional reading: Hill, P. (1917). *Prehistoric times.* New York: Harper & Row.

Fig 15
Ancient comb

Combine
Origin: China

Mechanical
Date: 110 BCE

Around 110 BCE, the Chinese invented a device that harvested grain by using a rotating fan to separate the grain from the chaff. The crude combine device was powered by human labor. The invention spread quickly throughout the rest of the world. Many variations were developed through the years.

Additional reading: Roberts, J. (2003). *The complete history of China.* London: Sutton Pub.

Comet
Origin: China

Astronomy
Date: 2296 BCE

Around 2296 BCE, a Chinese scientist observed a comet, and became the first to record and track such sightings. The Chinese scientist developed astronomy charts that were able to track such sightings over hundreds of years apart. Some researchers have sourced these initial astro charts as the start of structured academic study of the skies.

Additional reading: Cotterell, Y. & Cotterell, A. (1975). *The early civilization of China.* New York: Putnam Pub.

Comic Strip
Origin: Egypt

Entertainment
Date: 1500 BCE

The first comic strip was found in the *Book of the Dead,* constituting the first example of a figurative story whose successive scenes were ordered in superimposed scripts with the text. This story was written for enjoyment. The recovered comic strip was a series of joyful stories about children playing.

Additional reading: Montet, P. (1958). *Everyday life in Egypt.* New York. Edward Arnold Press.

Common Cold
Origin: Egypt

Medicine
Date: 1600 BCE

The Egyptians were the first to make many medical, mathematical, astronomical, and scientific discoveries. Egyptian medical remedies and procedures are well documented in papyrus manuscripts, especially those discovered in modern times by Edwin Smith and George Ebers in 1872. The papyrus included medical treatment for arthritis, hookworm infection, common colds, and surgery for head injuries.

Additional Reading: McGrew, R. and McGrew, M. (1985). *Encyclopedia of medical history.* New York: McGraw-Hill Pub.

Compass
Origin: China

Astronomy
Date: 270 BCE

The Duke of Chou in China built an early south-pointing carriage or magnetic compass, using a different gear to keep part of the carriage pointing in the same direction as the carriage turned. By 270 BCE, the compass for finding directions was in use in China. Earlier applications of magnetic lodestones were more magical and used for amusement.

Additional reading: Carlson, J. (1975). Loadstone compass: Chinese or Olmec primacy. *Science 189.*

Concave Mirror
Origin: Egypt

Engineering
Date: 280 BCE

Around 280 BCE, Sostratus of Cnidus built a 300-foot lighthouse for Pharos near Alexandria in Egypt. Projecting light from the earliest known concave mirrors made the light source visible for great distances. The lighthouse became one of the seven wonders of the ancient world.

Additional reading: Gjertsen, D. (1984). *The classics of science: A study of twelve enduring scientific works.* New York: Lillan Barber Press.

Concrete — Material
Origin: Egypt   Date: 2700 BCE

Prior to concrete, stone was positioned into place by carving, layering and interlocking to create strength. With the innovation and discovery of concrete a more complex stone design began to emerge. Concrete is typically a mixture of sand and small stones bound together by cement, usually hydraulic cement.

Additional reading: Parker, S. (1989). *McGraw-Hill concise encyclopedia of science and technology.* New York: McGraw-Hill Pub.

Conic Section — Mathematics
Origin: Egypt   Date: Antiquity

The ancient structures of Egypt are examples of conic sectioning. This mathematical sectioning has been studied and used in very different ways over the centuries and is a good example of how geometry evolved from antiquity to present day. Apollonius of Perga wrote the various ways of shaping a cone in his treaties. He also developed a process for forming ellipses and other shapes.

Additional reading: Coolidge, J. (1945). *History of the conic sections and quadric surfaces.* Oxford: Clarendon.

Contraceptive — Medical
Origin: Egypt   Date: 2000 BCE

Around 2000 BCE, contraceptives were introduced in Egypt as a means to control population. The wealthy were the first to use these contraceptives, followed by the general population.

Additional reading: Himes, N. (1936). *Medical history of contraception.* London: Allen and Unwin.

Cookbook — Domestic
Origin: Iraq   Date: 1700 BCE

The earliest known cookbooks were from Iraq, dating from 1700 BCE, the time of the great lawgiver, King Hammurabi. These tablets contained a large number of recipes of meat stews with ingredients that included boiled meat with garlic, onion, and fat, soured milk, and blood.

Additional reading: James, P. and Thorpe, N. (1994). *Ancient inventions.* New York: Ballantine Books.

Copper — Chemistry
Origin: Egypt   Date: 4000 BCE

Copper, a soft, yellow-red metal with an atomic number of 29 and chemical symbol Cu, has been mined for more than 6,000 years. Its earliest use may have been in Egypt as early as 4000 BCE. It ranks second only to iron in the amount of raw metal used annually and is widely distributed in many parts of the world.

Additional reading: Bisson, M. (1976). *The prehistoric coppermines of Zambia.* California: Univ. of California.

Copper Mining — Mining
Origin: Egypt   Date: 4000 BCE

Copper was in use as early as 4000 BCE. The Bronze Age had begun in Egypt where pure copper was being alloyed with lime to make bronze. Small plows, tools, and decorative objects were made with copper. The mining of copper grew into small communities where the most all the workers were copper miners.

Additional reading: Phimister, I. (1974). Ancient mining near great Zimbabwe. *Journal of the South African Institute of Mining and Metallurgy* 74, 233-7.

Coracle   see   **Boats.**

Cord   see   **Geometry.**

Core Tool — Mechanical
Origin: Africa   Date: Prehistoric

The earliest core tool was found in a cave in central Africa dating back to the prehistoric period. To make a core tool, ancient toolmakers struck or flaked a piece of flint with another rock or instrument and kept the shaped chunk or core stone for use as a cutting edge. The hand-axe, spade, and core tool were some of the earliest tools used.

Additional reading: Stewart, J. (1960). *An archaeological guide and glossary.* London: Phoenix House.

Coriander   Agriculture
Origin: Mesopotamia   Date: 3000 BCE

Coriander was native to North Africa. An annual plant, it had a series of compound leaves and global fruit. Coriander was one of the first plants to be used as food flavoring. The coriander plant was also used as a healing material.

Additional reading: MacMichael H. (1922). *A history of the Arabs in the Sudan.* Vols. 1-2 Cambridge: Cambridge University Press.

Corn   **see**   **Maize.**

Cosmetics   Chemistry
Origin: Egypt   Date: 1300 BCE

The history of cosmetics probably spans the length of human existence, starting with use in ritualistic practices and body adornment in Africa. However, ancient Egyptians are the undisputed originators of cosmetic beautification, as the iconic busts and statuary images of Queen Nefertari and royal wife Nefertiti attest. By 1300 BCE, both Egyptian royalty and the general populace engaged in such enhancements as applying paint sticks of galena (kohl) or malachite tint around the eyes. In addition to mineral sources, sticks of paint were also of fatty composition, extracted from wool and/or olive oil. Paint was kept in pots of fired clay and glass vessels. Cosmetics of the consistency of pastry were stored in dicotyledonous leaves. The Egyptians were the first to use eye shadowing, face cream, ointments and henna.

Additional readings: Hart, G. (1990). *Ancient Egypt.* New York: Alfred Knopf Pub.

Fig 16
Early cosmetic

Cosmetic Surgery   Medicine
Origin: India   Date: 900 BCE

The earliest known plastic surgery was recorded in India around 900 BCE. It was a custom in Hindu society to have the ears of their children pierced, as it was thought to ward off malignant spirits as well as looking attractive. Trained physicians made a hole in the earlobe and plugged it with cotton lint. If no infection resulted, the child returned to surgery every three days, so that increasingly larger plugs of lint and then circles of wood or lead weights could be added to stretch the skin.

Additional reading: Bishop, W. (1960). *The early history of surgery.* Robert, Hale.

Cotton   Agriculture
Origin: America   Date: 3300 BCE

Cotton was grown in America around 3300 BCE. The process of harvesting cotton was developed during this time period, and many regions of the Americas from south to north grew different strands of the plant over the years.

Additional reading: Clarke, D. and Glynn, I. (1981). (Ed.) *Patterns of the past: Studies in honor of David Clarke.* London: University Press.

Couching   Medical
Origin: Babylonia   Date: 1800 BCE

The Babylonians performed eye surgery as described in the legal codes of King Hammurabi. The couching process improved the eyesight of patients in most cases and restored sight of the crystalline lens if clouded by a cataract. A needle was inserted at the edge of the cornea and behind the iris. The lens was then pushed down and out of the way to assist in the couching.

Additional reading: James, P. and Thorpe, N. (1994). *Ancient inventions.* New York: Ballantine Books.

Counting Board   **see**   **Abacus.**

Cow   Agriculture
Origin: Egypt   Date: 5200 BCE

The first inhabitants to settle in the region known as the Fertile Crescent migrated from Africa. This area stretched in an arc shape, from the northern end of the Persian Gulf, to the Valley of the Nile River in Egypt. As early as 4200 BCE, farmers of this region domestically bred cows for food and its milk. Many other wild animals were also domesticated including oxen, sheep, and chickens.

Additional reading: Reid, A. and Meredith, J. (1993). *Houses, pots and more cows*. New York: Nyame Akuma Press.

Crane
Construction
Origin: Egypt   Date: 4000 BCE

Construction involving single stone pieces and masonry of enormous size was a common practice among Egyptian builders around 4000 BCE. The Egyptians perfected the crane by using a pair of beams angled into a V-shaped design with a pulley suspended at the top. Guide ropes held the crane in place.

Additional reading: Barber, F. (1900). *The mechanical triumphs of ancient Egyptians*. London: Trubner and Co.

Crane
Domestic
Origin: Congo   Date: Antiquity

The crane originally was a crossbreed of several now extinct birds first found in what is now known as the Congo. The crane was first hunted for food and later domesticated as pets. A large grallatorial bird of the family gruidae, these birds were abundant in marshy areas of Africa, Asia, and Europe. Early breeds of cranes are now extinct, but some closely related species are still found in certain parts of the world.

Additional reading: Connah, G. (1987). *African civilizations*. Cambride: Cambridge University Press.

Crank Handle
Mechanical
Origin: China   Date: 100 BCE

Invented in 100 BCE by the Chinese, the crank handle was designed to be interchangeable and worked on a series of mechanical tools. The crank handle played an important role in the development and modifications of newly designed tools and devices over the centuries.

Additional Reading: Fitzgerald, C. (1961). *China: A short cultural history*. New York: Praeger.

Crank-Rod System
Mechanical
Origin: China   Date: 530 BCE

The crank-rod connecting system was known in China from the fifth century BCE, during the Chou Dynasty. In 530 BCE, a Chinese engineer was the first to put together the crank and the connecting rod for the exploitation of energy. The earlier system was quite large and underwent many modifications.

Additional reading: Cotterell, Y. (1975) *The early civilization of Chin*a. New York: Putnam.

Cream   see   Dairy.

Cresceatic   see   Triangle.

Crop Rotation
Agriculture
Origin: Egypt   Date: 3600 BCE

The Egyptian Book of the Dead described a crop rotation process used as early as 3600 BCE. The rotation of annual crops such as rye, corn, and coriander was used to preserve the soil and increase crop yield. The crop rotation usually occurred every two years where the black crops such as beans, peas, and beets were planted in accordance with certain moons. Green crops such as corn, cabbage, and coriander were substituted in a cycle, increasing the crop yield. This method is still used throughout the modern world.

Additional reading: Travers, B. (1996). *The Gale encyclopedia of science*. New York: Gale Group Pub.

Crucible
Mechanical
Origin: Egypt   Date: 2000 BCE

The Egyptians were the first to master the foundry process using the crucible. The crucible was made from hardened stone and late tempered metal that withstood high degrees of heat. Many large door-type structures were developed by skilled craftsmen of the period using the crucible. Several sketches of artifacts located in the Cairo Museum in Egypt show the use of crucibles.

Additional reading: Lucas, A. and Harris, J. (1962). *Ancient Egyptian materials and industries*. London: E Arnold Pub.

Crystalline
Origin: China   Material   Date: Prehistoric

Early grinding and shaping of bone and other materials was evident in the early Stone Age period. One of the earliest Neolithic tools with ground blades was made of crystalline stone. Fragments of this stone have been found in Bak-Soh in Southern China and Hostuet in Northern Africa.

Additional reading: Watson, B. (1969). *Records of the historian: Chapters from the Shih chi of Ssu-ma Ch'ien.* New York: Columbia University Press.

Cube
Origin: Sumer   Mathematics   Date: 1700 BCE

Sumer is credited as the source of many mathematical discoveries dating back as far as 1700 BCE. Records show that the Sumerians were first in pioneering many of the accepted mathematical functions currently used: squares, square roots, cube, cube roots, and calculations for Pi.

Additional readings: Kramer, E. (1970). *The nature and growth of modern mathematics.* New York: Hawthorn.

Cube Root
Origin: Sumer   Mathematics   Date: 1700 BCE

The cube root mathmatical function was first used by Sumerian mathmaticians dating back to 1700 BCE. According to records were first in pioneering many of the accepted mathematical functions currently used: squares, square roots, cube, cube roots, and calculations for Pi. The Sumerians calculated the complex mathematical formula detailing the cube roots.

Additional readings: Dauben, J., (1985). *The history of mathematics from antiquity to the present.* London: Garland.

Cubic Equation
Origin: Babylon   Mathematics   Date: 2200 BCE

The Babylonian reduction of a quadratic form to the normal form through the substitution y=ax shows the extraordinary degree of flexibility in Mesopotamian algebra. This facility, coupled with the place value idea in computation, accounts in large measure for the superiority of the Babylonians in mathematics. There is no record in Egypt of the solution of a cubic equation, but among the Babylonians there are many instances of this. Pure cubes were solved by direct reference to tables of cubes and cube roots.

Additional reading: Boyer, C. (2000). *A history of mathematics.* New York: John Wiley.

Cubit
Origin: Sumer   Mathematics   Date: 2500 BCE

This procedure was a measurement of length; the cubit was based on the length of the forearm. The earliest known use of the cubit was recovered in Sumer. During the period the mathematician also developed a set of procedures for the cubit process.

Additional readings: Binford, L. (1981). *Ancient man and modern myths.* New York: Academic Press.

Cucumber
Origin: Syria   Agriculture   Date: 6000 BCE

The cucumber apparently grew in the wild in central and southern Asia. The earliest record of the cultivation of the cucumber dates back to 6000 BCE by the Syrians. A creeping plant, the cucumber was a native of Southern Asia and was commonly eaten as a side dish and often pickled seasonally.

Additional reading: Kowalchik C. and Hylton W., (1998). *Rodale's illustrated encyclopedia of herbs.* Pennsylvania: Rodale Press.

Cuneiform (Scroll)
Origin: Mesopotamia   Communication   Date: 2700 BCE

Scientists discovered a cuneiform tablet from Mesopotamia dating around 2700 BCE. With the growth of cities in the region, the administrators found it necessary to keep records. Stored in dry cellars, many of these tablets have survived more than several thousand years. The practice of sketching ideograms evolved to a method in which each figure was built up by impressing a reed of triangular section into the surface of the clay.

Additional reading: Marshack, A., (1972). *The roots of civilization.* London: Weidenfield and Nicolson.

Curing
Domestication

Origin: Africa   Date: Prehistoric

The curing of fresh meat dates back to the Paleolithic era. The process of curing meat was most likely first discovered by accident on the coastal regions of East Africa, then spread throughout coastal Africa. The rich salt basins preserved fresh meat kills and allowed nomads the opportunity to develop and maintain camp-sites longer.

Additional reading: Africanus, L. (1896). *The history and description of Afric*a. 3 Vols. ed. London: Brown, Kakluyt Society.

Cursus
Civil

Origin: Mesopotamia   Date: Prehistoric

The cursus was a long narrow enclosure bounded by a ditch and bank. The longest cursus in Western Africa was six miles long. It is not known what a cursus was used for, though it is possible that it was a processional way for marching or funeral sites.

Additional reading: Cotterell, A. (1988) *The encyclopedia of ancient civilization.* New York: Penguin Books.

Cutting Edge
Tool

Origin: Africa   Date: Prehistoric

Man originally found sharp pointed objects and later fashioned other materials in a host of different shapes depending on the need. The axe, fishing hook, club, and spear each had different cutting edges. It is believed that the earliest cutting edge was created by a sharp stroke of two objects. As time passed, the edges were developed from such materials as stone blade flakes and later metal.

Additional reading: Semenov, S. (1964). *Prehistoric technology; an experimental study of the oldest tools and artifacts from traces of manufacture and wear.* New York: Barnes and Noble.

Cycle   see   Sarnoic Cycle.

Cylinder   see   Piston.

D

Dagger
Military

Origin: Africa   Date: Prehistoric

Dating back to 150,000 years ago, the short flint stone dagger had a pointed edge and was probably used for hunting. Eventually it was extended in length and used for thrashing and stabbing other humans as well as animals. The wooden spear first appeared in the region around the same period. An early model is currently housed in the British Museum of History.

Additional reading: Faul, H. & Faul, C. (1983). *It began with a stone.* New York: John Wiley and Sons.

Dairy
Agriculture

Origin: Babylon   Date: 3200 BCE

The first inhabitants to settle in the region known as the Fertile Crescent migrated from Africa. This area stretched in an arc shape from the northern end of the Persian Gulf to the Valley of the Nile River in Egypt. Farmers of this region were the earliest known to domestically process and store milk from animals. In most cases the early dairies were small rooms. During the latter part of the sixth century, the Egyptians used dairy facilities as a market place to process and sell milk, cream, and other dairy related products.

Additional reading: Gille, B. (1986). *History of technique.* New York: Gordon and Breach Science Pub.

Dais
Construction

Origin: Nubia   Date: 750 BCE

After the conquest of Egypt in 724 BCE, King Kushite Piye, also known as Pinakhy, declared himself Pharoah of all Egypt and Nubia. He appeared in public on a deys, or dais, elevated above an assembled group of people.

Additional reading: Kenrick, J. (1850). *Ancient Egypt under the pharaohs*: Vols. 1-2. London: B. Fellowes.

Dam
Civil

Origin: Egypt   Date: 2500 BCE

Records show that a dam, a massive wall-like structure, was built around 2500 BCE. It measured about 84 meters (276 feet) long, 110 meters (361 feet) wide, and 12 meters (39 feet) high. Built at Wadi Gerrawe (El Kofaro) in Egypt, the dam's apparent purpose was to catch the water from the occasional flooding of the Wadi during the winter rains. The water was then used for irrigation.

Additional reading: Smith, N. (1971). *A history of dams.* London: Davies Pub.

Dart   see   **Blow Gun.**

Date Palm   Agriculture
Origin: Nubia   Date: 6000 BCE

Pre-historical data shows that some forms of farming wild plants for food took place in different parts of the world. As early as 6000 BCE, the farmers of Nubia cultivated the date plant. Fruit from the date palm grew in large clusters with a single hard seed and proved to be an important food in both North Africa and Western Asia.

Additional reading: (1983), *Medicine from the earth: A guide to healing plants.* San Francisco: Harper and Row.

Days of the Week   Information
Origin: Babylonia   Date: 300 BCE

The Babylonian calendar was used in the Near East by the third century BCE. The Romans exchanged the names of the Babylonian planetary gods for Roman equivalents. Modern European names for the days of the week were derived via the Latin and Anglo-Saxon languages, from the Babylonian gods.

Additional reading: De Camp, L. (1993). *The ancient engineers.* New York. Barnes and Noble.

Dead Sea Scroll   Communication
Origin: Palestine   Date: 2000 BCE

Written over 2000 years ago, the *Dead Sea Scrolls* were the earliest handwritten copies of the *Bible,* including the books of *Isaiah, Deuteronomy,* the *Psalms* and the *Apocrypha.* Also included were hymns and other religious works. The scrolls were found in 1947 near the northwest corner of the Dead Sea in Palestine.

The leather and copper scrolls had been wrapped in linen and packed in jars. A thousand years older than other known Biblical sources, the scrolls throw light on the life and times the early Christians. They are now housed in a specially built museum in Jerusalem.

Additional reading: Cook, S. (1930). *The religion of ancient Palestine in the light of archaeology:* London: Oxford University Press.

Decimal System   Mathematics
Origin: China   Date: 1400 BCE

In the fourteenth century BCE, Chinese mathematicians carried out calculations using rods on a squared board to create a decimal system. The number 10 was represented simply by a single rod followed by an empty square. This empty square sufficed to represent zero and the one was a known number.

Additional reading: Burton, D. (1985). *The history of mathematics.* Boston: Allyn and Bacon.

Deductive Geometry   Mathematics
Origin: Babylon   Date: Antiquity

The mathematician Thales was credited with the development of the mathematical process known as deductive geometry. The Theorem of Thales state that a right angle inscribed in a semicircle is a right angle. Most mathematics historians and scholars believe that during Thales' travels, he studied under Babylonian scholars of the period and offered this important mathematics principle to the world.

Additional reading: Coolidge, J., (1963). *A history of geometrical methods.* New York: Dover.

Deep Well Drill   Tools
Origin: China   Date: 2000 BCE

Around 2000 BCE, the Chinese invented methods for drilling deep wells to obtain fresh water and natural gases. It was recorded that a typical well could reach 1460 meters in depth. This ancient well drilling process is still used in some parts of the world today.

Additional reading: Fitzgerald, C. (1961). *China: A short cultural history.* New York: Praeger.

Dentistry   Medical
Origin: Egypt   Date: 2600 BCE

A primitive and crude form of caring for ones teeth dates back to prehistoric times. The earliest dental process was confirmed in Egyptian mummies that have been found with dentures that were made of gold or silver ligaments. Artificial teeth of ivory, silver, or gold crowns were held in place by these ligaments. The dental crowns, designed to strengthen loose teeth, were supported by surrounding healthy teeth. The first known dentist to have false teeth was Neferities, who lived around 2600 BCE.

Additional reading: Robinson, C. (1984). *Ancient Egypt, a first book*. New York: Franklin Watts Press.

Desalination   Chemistry
Origin: Egypt   Date: 350 BCE

The process of removing salt from sea water in order to make it drinkable was used in Egypt around 350 BCE. This early process used open sun and a series of collector bowls. Later the Arabs used the desalination process to make flavorings and perfumes by distilling plant juices. Many parts of the world use this ancient process of desalination today.

Additional reading: Travers, B. (1996). *The Gale encyclopedia of science*. New York: Gale Research Pub.

Determinative   Communication
Origin: Mesopotamia   Date: 760 BCE

The Mesopotamian is credited with the development of the determinative process that was also called "classifying signs." In cuneiform, these are signs placed rather regularly before or after a word to indicate the class of objects to which the word belongs.

Additional reading: Bottero, J. (1987). *Mesopotamia: Writing, reasoning, and the gods*. Chicago: University of Chicago Press.

Diagnosis   see   **Medical Diagnosis.**

Diameter   Mathematics
Origin: Egypt   Date: 240 BCE

As far back as 240 BCE, Eratosthenes of Cyrene, Librarian at Alexandria, Egypt, correctly calculated the diameter of the earth as about 8,000 miles and the circumference as about 25,000 miles. These early calculations have proved to be accurate through modern times.

Additional Reading: Bonola, R., (1955). *Non-Euclid geometry*. New York: Dover.

Diamond   see   **Carbon.**

Dictionary   Communication
Origin: China   Date: 1100 BCE

The Chinese scholar Pa-out-she developed a dictionary of 40,000 characters and included many Zodiac signs, alphabets, and counting systems. Over a period of time many new words and symbols were added to this and other dictionaries. Widely used by scholars of the period, it dates back to 1100 BCE.

Additional reading: Cotterell, Y. & Cotterell, A. (1975). *The early civilization of China*. New York: Putnam Pub.

Dictionary (Medical)   Medicine
Origin: Mesopotamia   Date: 1300 BCE

The earliest recorded medical dictionary was found at Nippur, by archeologists. A stone cuneiform table, describing treatment for various ailments, was the earliest dictionary of medicine, dating between 1300–1252 BCE. Historical records show that this medical dictionary had listed over five hundred medical terms and procedures.

Additional reading: Oppenheim, A. (1979). *Ancient Mesopotamia: Portrait of a dead civilization,* Rev. ed. Chicago: University Chicago Press.

Digging Stick   Tool
Origin: Africa   Date: Prehistoric

The oldest agricultural farming instrument was probably the digging stick, made of wood, bone and antlers. This single device was a useful and life sustaining instrument of the period. This stick was later developed into a plough-like machine and led to many other new inventions. There are numerous cave drawings in central African hills of what appears to be a human using what appears to be plow-like earth turning devices. The earliest recovered digging stick-like artifact dated back to 40,000 old according to carbon testing.

Additional reading: Burke, J. (1978). *Connections*. Boston: Little Brown Pub.

Figure 17:
Early Digging Stick

Digit
Origin: Nubia

Mathematics
Date: 3200 BCE

As far back as 3200 BCE, the Nubians developed a measuring system known as digits. The use of this mathematical function was not commonly used until 3100 BCE. The Nubian armies during their travels were thought to be the spreaders of this mathematical process during war crusades. Digits were ancient measures of length, based upon the breadth of either the first or the middle finger.

Additional reading: Smith, D. (1923). *History of mathematics*. Boston: Dover.

Dissection see Autopsies.

Distaff
Origin: Mesopotamia

Mechanical
Date: 5000 BCE

The first documents to feature the distaff, a staff on which threads of flax, wool, or copper were wound for use in spinning, came from Egypt about 3000 years BCE. A modified version from earlier models dates from the Neolithic period found in Mesopotamia

Additional reading: Lepsius, R. (1852). *Discoveries in Egypt, Ethiopia, and the peninsula of Sinai*. London: R. Bentley.

Distance Calculation
Origin: Egypt

Physics
Date: 240 BCE

Eratosthenes of Cyrene, a librarian in Alexandria around 240 BCE, was the first to calculate the diameter of the earth at about 8000 miles with the circumference at 25,000 miles. A student of Ptolemy I, he studied at Museum University, where many new and existing complex mathematical solutions were first developed.

Additional reading Pappademos, J. (1983). *An outline of Africa's role in the history of physics, in: Blacks in science*. New Brunswick NJ: Transaction Books.

Distillation
Origin: Egypt

Chemistry
Date: 3110 BCE

Distillation is the process of converting an unstable liquid into vapor by heating it, then re-condensing it by cooling. Distilled spirits are naturally-flavored solutions of alcohol in water that have been made from certain fermented liquids. In 3110 BCE, King Menes observed this process, describing the formation of mist and rain. He also noted that salt water became sweat when vaporized and did not reform as salt water if the vapor condensed.

Additional reading: Lucas, A. and Harris, J. (1962). *Ancient Egyptian materials and industries*. London: E Arnold Pub.

Divination
Origin: Mesopotamia

Medicine
Date: 2400 BCE

The early medical practice of Divination, which is the interpretation of omens perceived in natural phenomena, was used for medical purposes in Mesopotamia. The body organs of sacrificed animals were thought to reveal a patient's fate. This early medical practice was used in the northern region of Mesopotamia, and according to most records, remained in the area for a long period of time.

Additional Reading: Fox, R. (1950). *Milestones of medicine*. New York: Random House.

Diving Bell
Origin: Africa

Naval
Date: 1250 BCE

The diving bell was used in Africa as far back as 1250 BCE. When submerged under water, divers were able to breathe using a kettle or skin sack. The tank went down perpendicularly, and so did not fill up with water, keeping the air intact for a longer period of time.

Additional reading: Ross D., (1967). *Alexander and the faithless lady*. New York: Birkbeck Press.

Diving Suit Oceanography
Origin: China Date: 300 BCE

The diving suit was used in battle as a weapon as long ago as 300 BCE, in China. In order to provide a supply of air for a longer period of time and to be carried by the diver, the aqualung was developed.

Additional reading: Hsu, Cho-Yun (1965). *Ancient China in transition, 722-222 B.C.* Stanford, Cal: Stanford University Press.

Dog Domestic
Origin: Egypt Date: 8200 BCE

The origin of the domesticated dog is depicted in drawings on caves in Egypt dating back to 8200 BCE. The dog, later called hound, existed in all parts of the world. According to the earliest records, fossils found in the upper regions of Nubia were that of a domesticated dog. Carbon dating placed the age of the bones as far back as 8000 BCE.

Additional reading: Fagen, B., (1985). *New treasures of the past.* New York: Windward Press.

Doll (Toy) Entertainment
Origin: Africa Date: Antiquity

In prehistoric times, parents of small children made dolls from wood, bone, and animal skins. The earliest recovered dolls were made of wood and ivory. Later versions were made of wax and clay. Wooden images were found in Egyptians graves as far back as 200 BCE. These figures were known as paddle dolls because they were carved from a flat piece of wood. Paddle dolls were actually religious figures believed to provide Egyptians with servants in the afterlife.

Additional reading: Davidson, B. (1969). *The African genius.* Boston: Little, Brown.

Dome Construction
Origin: Mesopotamia Date: 2800 BCE

A twelve-meter high ziggurat in Ur revealed that Mesopotamians were familiar with dome-like structures as early as 2800 BCE. Corbeled arches and domes were built with layers of bricks or stone constructed so that each layer projected beyond to the one beneath it, like an upside-down staircase.

The structures were quite strong and stood for many centuries.

Additional reading: De Camp, L. (1974). *The ancient engineers.* New York: Ballantine Books.

Domino Entertainment
Origin: Iraq Date: 2450 BCE

Very little is known about different games of the early time periods. Dominos is one of the first entertainment games found. The Museum of Baghdad has an extensive collection of objects and artifacts made of bone, discovered at Ur and dating back to 2450 BCE. Archaeologists compare these artifacts to present-day dominoes. The main differences from current domino set were the numbering systems.

Additional reading: Douze, S. (1993). *Inventions and discoveries.* New York: Facts on File.

Donkey see **Ass.**

Door (Automatic) Mechanical
Origin: Egypt Date: 30 BCE

Many scholars agree that Herod was an undisputed genius of ancient high-tech engineering. Two thousand years ago, he designed doors for the temples of Alexandria that opened automatically. His design for automatic temple doors was a gift to the Egyptian priests. The automatic doors were operated by hydraulic power.

Additional reading: James, P. and Thorpe, N. (1994). *Ancient inventions.* New York: Ballantine Books.

Dove see **Air Transport.**

Drab see **Khaki.**

Drainage Civil
Origin: Nubia Date: 3700 BCE

The earliest citywide drainage and sewage system was developed in Nubia around 3700 BCE. This system moved sewage from the central part of the city to a reservoir located outside the town area. The clay tracks allowed waste and water to free flow using gravity into pits.

Additional reading: Binford, L., (1981). *Bones: Ancient man and modern myths.* New York: Academic Press.

Dress   see   Cloth.

Dressings and Bandages   Medicine
Origin: Assyria   Date: 700 BCE

The earliest identification of caring for wounds was found recorded on clay tablets dating back to the seventh century BCE. These clay tablets were discovered in the archaeological ruins of Assur and Nineveh in Assyria. Written by one of the best-known practitioners of the time, Arad-Manai, one inscription reads, "Hail to the small child whose eyes have caused him suffering."

Additional reading: Bishop, W., (1960). *The early history of surgery.* London: Roberts Hale.

Drilling   see   Oil Drilling.

Drill   see   Wood Drill.

Drill Tower   Mechanical
Origin: China   Date: 100 BCE

Drilling towers appeared in China in the first century and were designed for extracting salt from underground brine. Drilling towers were up to 40 meters high and were apparently constructed of bamboo. The drill was made of bamboo cables and wooden support structures at the ends of which were cast-iron drilling heads.

Additional reading: Shepherd, R., (1980). *Prehistoric mining and allied industries.* New York: Academic Press.

Driver   see   Chain Drive.

Drogue   Domestic
Origin: Africa   Date: 6000 BCE

Areas off the African coast were sites of heavy fishing activity, including whale hunting. A drogue and bone

constructed harpoon was discovered in the early 1500s. Carbon testing dates it back to 6000 BCE. The drogue is attached to the end of a harpoon line to check the progress of the whale running after being harpooned.

Additional reading: Graham, C. (1987). *African civilizations.* Cambridge: Cambridge University Press.

Drug   Medical
Origins: Peru   Date: 200 BCE

Evidence for the use of the stimulant coca was depicted on a vase of the Moche culture from Peru cited around 200 BCE. Drugs like coca and others stimulants were used in various religious ceremonies.

Additional reading: Melzack, R. and Wall, P. (1982). *The challenge of pain.* New York: Basic Books.

Drupe   see   Peach.

Dry Dock   Mechanical
Origin: Egypt   Date: 205 BCE

Around 205 BCE, a dry dock was constructed to accommodate a large warship built for Philopator of Egypt. The dry dock consisted of a large trench dug in the harbor and supported by wood or stone. When the ship entered the dry dock, a mechanical pump removed the water. The ship was left to settle onto a series of wooden cradles, holding it upright.

Additional reading: Daumas, M. (1969). *A history of technology and inventions. Vol. 1,* New York: Crown Press.

Duck   Domestic
Origin: Egypt   Date: 4200 BCE

The duck has its roots in the southern region of Egypt and Nubia. Inscription and symbols resembling the duck existed on many tomb walls dating as far back as 4200 BCE. Ducks were bred as a delicacy food for the royal families before becoming a popular food source for the general population.

Additional reading: Travers, B. (1996). *The Gale encyclopedia of science.* New York: Gale Group Pub.

Dye — Textiles
Origin: Egypt Date: 3000 BCE

Cloth makers learned to dye their fabrics almost as soon as they learned to weave, using an assortment of substances to produce color. Textile remnants found in Egyptian tombs show traces of blue indigo dye. However, the Phoenicians were masters of the trade, developing the rare purple dyes made from a mollusk found along the Tyrian coast. Two thousand mollusks were needed to produce one gram of dyestuff. For centuries, only monarchs could afford such garments.

Additional reading: Clark, R. , Grace, I. (1971). *Nature's colors; dyes from plants.* New York: Dover Publisher.

Dyeing — Textiles
Origin: Egypt Date: 3000 BCE

A process in which color was produced by saturating fibers with an agent, dyeing was achieved either by directly placing the materials in a solution, or by corrosive staining, a method which Pliny described as practiced among the Egyptians dating back to 3000 BCE. The Egyptians were able to dye multi-colors in a single cloth material.

Additional reading: Goodwin, G. (1982). *A dyer's manual.* London: Pelhem Books.

E

Earthenware — Construction
Origin: Babylon Date: 3500 BCE

The Babylonians were the first to make earthenware, a baked clay pottery coated with a tin-oxide base glaze. The brick friezes and their palaces were overlaid with a tin-bearing glaze. Several centuries later, the Arabs rediscovered the ancient techniques, taking them to Spain, North Africa, and then Europe.

Additional reading: Mason, O. (1966). *The origin of invention.* Cambridge: MIT Press.

Earth-house see Hut.

Earthquake Alarm — Mechanical
Origin: China Date: 132 BCE

In 132 BCE, Chang-Hing, a Chinese Imperial astronomer, mathematician, cartographer, and poet, developed an alarm system that detected trembles in the earth. The earthquake alarm was a very precise instrument and was considered one of the wonders of the Imperial Observatory. Chang-Hing's system was eight feet high and incorporated a free-swinging pendulum.

Additional reading: Chang, Kwang-chih, (1976). *Early Chinese civilization.* Cambridge: Mass. University Press.

Eclipse (Solar) — Astronomy
Origin: Babylon Date: 765 BCE

By 800 BCE, the Egyptians were tracking the movement of the sun using sundials with six time devisors to tell time. Around 765 BCE, the Babylonians were the first to record and track a solar eclipse. The Babylonians devised a system that was able to calculate when solar eclipses were to occur.

Additional Reading: Mount, E. and List, B. (1987). *Milestones in science and technology: The ready reference guide to discoveries, inventions, and facts.* Phoenix: Oryx Press.

Elasticity — Mechanical
Origin: Egypt Date: Antiquity

The earliest form of elasticity, a string-like material, dates to the time of Rameses II. A composite of horn, sinew, and wood, the improved bow proved stronger than the simple wooden bow. The Asian bow was also made of horn, wood, and sinews. When unstrung, it curved back in the opposite direction. To be bent again, it was stretched first and then crooked.

Additional reading: Parker, S. (1989). *McGraw-Hill concise encyclopedia of science and technology.* New York: McGraw-Hill.

Electrical Stimulation — Medicine
Origin: Egypt Date: 500 BCE

Before the electrical nature of nervous transmission was understood and before the coordination center of the cardiac cavity contractions was discovered, cardiac stimulation was practiced by the Egyptians. From the fifth century BCE, the Egyptians applied torpedo fish and gymnotes to the thoraxes of sick people in order to stimulate vital reflexes in them.

Additional reading: Rowling, J., (1989). *The rise and decline of surgery in Dynastic Egypt.* Antiquity 63, Saggs.

Electricity   Physics
Origin: Egypt   Date: 600 BCE

Studies in electricity date to 600 BCE, when Egyptians noted that amber would attract small objects after it was rubbed. Egyptian physicians and physicists studied electrical attraction and introduced the two states, positive and negative flow, referred to as hot and ground sources.

Additional Readings: Pappademos, J. (1983) *An outline of Africa's role in the history of physics, in: Blacks in science.* New Brunswick, N.J: Transaction Books,

Electrical Circuit   Physics
Origin: Egypt   Date: 600 BCE

Forces similar to electricity were known to flow from the negative potential, known as the cathode, as far back as 600 BCE. The Egyptian root of the word Ka is represented by raised arms, indicating the true direction of electron flow. The majority carriers, or type of charge transport, of melanin are (-) electrons as opposed to (+) protons.

Additional Readings: Pappademos, J. (1983). *An outline of Africa's role in the history of physics, in: Blacks in science.* New Brunswick NJ: Transaction Books,

Electronic Clock   Electronics
Origin: Africa   Date: 1000 BCE

The world's first electronic clock, built by Queen Makeda's engineers, was developed to represent the ancestral spirit Tet Ankh Ka Ra. The crude clock was a glowing globe that slowly rotated by the precise electromechanical movement of the arms.

Additional reading: Nur Ankh Amen, N. (1999). *The ankh: African origin of electromagnetism.* New York: A& B Publishers Group.

Electronic Conductor   Physics
Origin: Egypt   Date: 2600 BCE

The scepter conductor, or connector, is an important electronic component used in the conveyance of current through a circuit and in discharging a capacitor-like rod. In ancient Egypt, gods were often pictured holding the scepter, symbolizing their power over the lethal force of electrical discharge. This rod, having a loop at its base that allowed a free-swinging connection, was a switch and used as a control device of electrical flow to the ground.

Additional reading: Lockyer, J. (1964). *The dawn of astronomy; a study of the temple worship and mythology of the ancient Egyptians.* Cambridge: M.I.T. Press.

Electrical Power   Physics
Origin: Egypt   Date: 2100 BCE

Early studies in electrical and magnetic phenomena were conducted by Egyptians as far back as 2100 BCE. One of the most famous shrines of electrical import was the Ark of the Covenant. Once charged, this portable shrine was potentially lethal if touched. A priesthood specially trained to handle the shrine wore special clothing for protection and used a rod to ground or discharge the Ark.

Additional reading: Barber, F. (1900). *The mechanical triumphs of ancient Egyptians,* London: Trubner and Co.

Electrical Wave   see   Sine Wave.

Ellipse   see   Conic Section.

Embalming   Chemistry
Origin: Egypt   Date: 3200 BCE

Best exemplified by ancient Egyptian mummies, the process of embalming is still not fully understood. The oldest of all known mummies' dates back to about 3200 BCE, suggesting the ancient Egyptians practiced preserving corpses for thousands of years. Many archeologists believe that mummification occurred earlier in Nubia but the Egyptians are credited with its start.

Additional reading: Neuburger, O. (1930). *The technical arts and sciences of the ancients.* New York: The Macmillan Co.

Emery Plaques   see   Sand Stone.

Enamel   Chemistry
Origin: Egypt   Date: 1300 BCE

Enamel is a vitreous glaze, a compound of sand or flint, soda potash, and red lead which, when melted, becomes clear. Oxides of metals are added for color. Powdered enamel is fused with a metal base in a furnace. The earliest examples of enamel are found on gold rings in a Mycenaean tomb, dating to the thirteenth century BCE. Craftsman of the Bronze and Iron Ages made articles decorated with red, blue and yellow enamel.

Additional reading: Rice, M. (2003). *Egypt's making: The origin of ancient Egypt, 5000-2000 B.C.* 2nd ed. New York: Roulledge Pub.

Enameling   Domestic
Origin: Mesopotamia   Date: 4000 BCE

A metal vase with enamel glazing dating back to 4000 BCE, is considered the earliest example of enameling. As a means for ornamentation, the Mesopotamians dented the inlay covering of the metallic surface in order to contrast between the colors of the enamel with that of the metal. The Egyptians later developed a more advanced process of enameling.

Additional reading: Oppenheim, A. (1979). *Ancient Mesopotamia: Portrait of a dead civilization,* Rev. ed. Chicago: University Chicago Press.

Encaustic Process   Communication
Origin: Africa   Date: 1503 BCE

The use of water colors and tempera paints was developed by Queen Hatshepsut in 1503 BCE. Known as encaustic painting, it was based on burning wax-based colors into a picture. Pliny described two methods of making encaustic painting with wax or ivory using cestrum (stump).

Additional reading: Africanus, L. (1896). *The history and description of Africa.* 3 Vols. ed. London: Brown, Kakluyt Society.

Encyclopedia   Communication
Origin: Syria   Date: 1270 BCE

The earliest recorded encyclopedia, dating back to 1270 BCE, was written by Abulfaraj, a Syrian historian.

Wise men and scholars traveled great distances to use these documents. Abulfaraj was a master of many languages, in which he translated into Syrian, Arabic, and Greek.

Additional reading: James, G. (1954). *Stolen legacy.* Chicago: New York: Philosophical Library.

Endocrinology   Medicine
Origin: China   Date: 200 BCE

Developed in China during the second century BCE, endocrinology is the extraction of certain substances from human urine for therapeutic purposes. The formula, dating from 200 BCE, described this extraction process in detail, using large quantities of urine which had undergone evaporation and subsequent sublimation.

Additional reading: Needham, D. (1988). *Chinese state of medicine.* New York: Jackson Press.

End Scraper   see   Scraper.

Envelope   Information System
Origin: Iran   Date: 2700 BCE

The earliest known example of a fired clay envelope dated to 2700 BCE. It was found at Farrukhabad in what is now Iran and was used to hold counting tokens. Examples of clay envelopes, marked on the outside to denote the kind or amount of counting tokens inside, were left at sites in Syria.

Additional reading: Douze, S. (1993). *Inventions and discoveries.* New York: Facts on File.

Eohippus   see   Horse.

Equation   see   Mathematics.

Equinox   Astronomy
Origin: Turkey   Date: 150 BCE

By observing the location of a fixed star, Hipparchus of Nicea (Turkey) was first to track the sun crossing the equator, marking the equal length of night and day in all parts of the earth. In so doing, he discovered the progression of the equinoxes.

Additional reading: Parker, S. (1989). *McGraw-Hill concise encyclopedia of science and technology.* New York: McGraw-Hill Pub.

Equations (1st and 2nd Degree)   Mathematics
Origin: Egypt   Date: 1700 BCE

The Rhind papyrus, dating back to 1700 BCE, showed clear examples of solutions to first and second degree equations when attached to specific problems. Egyptian literature offered examples of solutions to these mathematical systems of equations.

Additional reading: Dickson, L., (1966). *History of the theory of numbers.* New York: Chelsea.

Escarpment   Civil
Origin: Mesopotamia   Date: 1700 BCE

Traces of the early settlement of Eridu, a Sumerian city near Ur, dated to 1700 BCE, include a building which might have been the model for later ziggurats. The structure had an escarpment, a rampart designed with slopes that angled into a ditch next to the structure. The escarpment proved over time to be a useful defense device against outside forces.

Additional reading: Phillipson, D. (1985). *African archaeology*: Cambridge: Cambridge University Press.

Explosive   Materials
Origin: China   Date: 220 BCE

The first known explosive consisted of bamboo sections which, once thrown into a fire, exploded because the air inside was suddenly heated. Various types of explosives have been used for many centuries. Around 220 BCE, the Chinese used a potassium nitrate called saltpeter for fireworks. The mixture of saltpeter, sulfur, and charcoal produced a black powder.

Additional reading: Daumas, M. (1969). *A history of technology and inventions. Vol. 3.* New York: Crown Pub.

Eye Coloring   see   Cosmetic.

Eye Surgery   Medicine
Origin: Babylon   Date: 1800 BCE

The Babylonians developed an eye surgery procedure mentioned in the famous legal code drawn up by King Hammurabi of Babylon in the eighteenth century BCE. The text refers to the "opening of a nakkapt" with a bronze lancet as a way of curing blindness. It is unclear how effective this surgerical process was during this period.

Additional reading: Pritchard, J., (1969). *Ancient near Eastern text relating to the Old Testament.* Princeton: Princeton University Press.

F

Fabrics (Knitted)   Textiles
Origin: Syria   Date: 300 BCE

The earliest surviving knitted fabrics were a pair of socks discovered in an Egyptian tomb. Dating from 1200 to 1500 BCE, the pieces were worked in round two-color knitting. Like most methods of textile production, knitting was practiced by men, who discovered a strong and flexible fabric was made by continuing a loop of yarn through itself. While no written records exist, certain New World cultures developed their own knitted fabrics. However, Assyria is considered to be the birthplace of knitting, with its traders and sailors spreading the craft throughout Europe.

Additional reading: Clark, G., and Piggott, S., (1965). *Prehistoric societies.* New York: Knopf Pub.

Face Cream   see   Cosmetic.

Faience   Materials
Origin: Mesopotamia   Date: 3000 BCE

Faience was made in Mesopotamia about 3000 BCE. By covering the surface of a talc stone powder with a copper ore, such as azurite or malachite, then heating it to a high temperature, the result was a blue-coated glass. Faience was used for the manufacture of beads and other small ornaments.

Additional reading: Ki-Zerbo, J. (1990). *General history of Africa, methodology and African prehistory. Vol. 1.* Berkeley, Calif.: University of California Press.

False Limb   see   **Limb.**

False Teeth   see   **Teeth.**

Fan   Device
Origin: Egypt   Date: 1500 BCE

Specialty fans have been in use since the reign of Pharaoh Thutnose III in 1504 BCE, when servants were employed throughout the dynastic period to fan Egyptian pharaohs using giant lotus leaves. Later, plant-like woven material functioned as a lightweight fan fabric. Other early fans were arrayed from peacock feathers.

Additional reading: Budge, E. (1895). *The book of the dead;* the papyrus of Ani in the British Museum. London: Longnans & Co.

Fantastic Tree   Agriculture
Origin: Egypt   Date: 1200 BCE

The art of topiaria, which is the creative design of trees, first appeared in Egyptian drawings in 1200 BCE. Queen Nefertari had topiaria in her gardens dating to 1292 BCE. Trees and shrubs were trimmed in a variety of fantastic, ornamental shapes, arranged in order by size and trailed over metallic frames.

Additional reading: Shanks, M.(1991). *Experiencing the past: On the character of archaeology.* New York.:

Farming   Agriculture
Origin: Kenya   Date: 9000 BCE

Early Neolithic life was based on farming and herding. The first experiments in village farming took place in Kenya about 9000 BCE. The crops grown were common to the region. The more common crops were maize, wheat, and other herbal plants.

Additional reading: Redman, C. (1978). *The rise of civilization: From early farmers to urban society in the ancient Near East.* San Francisco: W.H. Freeman.

Farm (Sea Food)   Domestic
Origin: Egypt   Date: 1375 BCE

Fishing was a favorite pastime of Akhenaten, Pharaoh of Egypt, where royals and other keen anglers would fish the Nile. Tomb paintings going back to the Eighteenth Dynasty (1550-1300 BCE) show Egyptian noblemen fishing in their gardens to relax. Many servants of the New Kingdom maintained separately enclosed ponds for the royal families, stocking fish that were later transported to favored river fishing spots of the pharaoh and other royal families' members.

Additional reading: James, P. and Thorpe, N., (1994). *Ancient inventions.* New York: Ballantine Books.

Felt   Textile
Origin: Nubia   Date: 685 BCE

The use of felt predates other textiles. Felted animal fur found at Catal Huyuk in Nubia dated from the Neolithic period. A waterproof, warm fabric, felt-making involved a simple process of first cleaning the wool, the soap acting as a catalyst that began to lock the fibers. The piece was then soaked in hot water and subjected to friction and pressure, which locked the fibers securely.

Additional reading: Clark, G., and Piggott, S., (1965). *Prehistoric societies.* New York: Knopf Pub.

Fennel   Agriculture
Origin: Mesopotamian   Date: 1200 BCE

Fennel was cultivated domestically by the Mesopotamians as early as 1200 BCE. Used in sauces and eaten with a variety of fish, fennel became so popular that it was one of the first plants grown in kitchen window gardens during the period.

Additional reading: Gouzel, D., (1975). *Mother nature's herbs and teas.* Willits, Cal.: Oliver Press.

Fermentation   Agriculture
Origin: Egypt   Date: 1800 BCE

The Egyptians discovered fermentation around 1800 BCE. They eventually learned to control the process by saving a portion of fermenting bread before it was baked and adding it to fresh dough so that dough would also ferment.

Additional reading: Anquandah, J. (1993). The Kintampo Complex; a case study of early sedentism and food production in Sub-Sahelian West Africa. In the *archaeology of Africa*: Food, metals and towns ed., T. Shaw, P. Sinclair and A. Okpoko, pp. 255-260.

Fertilizer   Agriculture
Origin: China   Date: 500 BCE

As early as 493 BCE, Chinese farmers fertilized crops with manure. The resulting increase in crop production began the process of specialized crop growth. Chou dynasty which extended China's power during this period, was mobilized by the belief that the earth should be worshipped. Many believed that the process of fertilizing crops was discovered by observation of crop growth over many seasons.

Additional reading: Chang, Kwang-chih, (1976). *Early Chinese civilization: Anthropological perspectives.* Cambridge, Mass.: Harvard University Press.

Fibula   see   **Safety Pin.**

Fig Tree   Agriculture
Origin: India   Date: Antiquity

The exact date of the fig tree being planted and grown for food is unknown. Early evidence suggests that India was the first to domestically grow and harvest figs. The fig trees of the period were grown in the southern areas of India. The fig was initially served as fruit. Later it was used as medicine.

Additional reading: Merritt, F. (1950). *Gray's manual of botany.* 8th ed. New York: D.Van Nostrand Co.

File   Tool
Origin: Egypt   Date: 1500 BCE

The earliest known file, dating from 1500 BCE, was found in the tomb of Pharaoh Thutmose III. It was made of bronze, was three sided and had cross cut ridges. The file was one of tools used by the Pharaoh's work crewmen, and was generally among the items buried with the Pharaoh at the time of his death.

Additional reading: Usher, A. (1954) *A history of mechanical inventions.* 2nd editions, Cambridge, Mass: Harvard University Press.

Fig. 18
Material file

Finger Ring   see   **Bow Ring.**

Fire Making   Domestic
Origin: Africa   Date: Prehistoric

As early as 1,300,000 BCE, Homo Erectus of Eastern Africa carefully carried and maintained fires that occurred in nature. Humans as far back as 1,300,000 BCE, developed devices that enabled them to make their own fires. As a result of these fire making devices, larger communities were settled that began to harvest plants and domesticate animals.

Additional reading: Pacey, A., (1990). *Technology in world civilization: A thousand year history.* Cambridge, Mass.: M.I.T. Press

Fire (Production)   Material
Origin: China   Date: 50,000 BCE

The first evidence of ancient man's production of fire came from the Choukoutien caves near Peking, China. Archaeologists uncovered numerous large fire hearths filled with ash and charcoal. Middle Pleistocene Peking man also left behind a lot of crude quartz choppers and coarsely trimmed deer antlers that may have served as clubs.

Additional reading: Cotterell, Y. & Cotterell, A. (1975). *The early civilization of China.* New York: Putnam Pub.

Fishhook   Tools
Origin: Africa   Date: Antiquity

Fishhooks were first recorded in central Africa around 18,000 BCE. Like the needle, the fishhook has remained essentially unchanged to this day. The original fish hook was made from animal bone and later from wood and metal.

Additional reading: Adams, W., (1977). *Nubia, corridor to Africa*. London: Allen Lane.

Fish Net   Domestic
Origin: Africa   Date: Prehistoric

The eastern sea coast of Africa was the earliest recorded region where ancient anglers interlaced plant-like fibers to make a fish net used to catch food and other water plants. Fishermen of the period cast the broad nets from the shore line and were able to capture large quantities of food. The fishhook is one of the earliest hunting devices developed by man.

Additional reading: Davidson, B. (1969). *The African genius*. Boston: Little, Brown.

Fish Trap   Mechanical
Origin: Africa   Date: 200,000 BCE

The practice of trapping is probably as old a method of catching animals as a hook or bow and arrow. Prehistoric art suggests the style and function of such traps. Early cave drawings show a crude plant-like hand woven net shaped like a box to catch fish when submerged in water. The earliest recovered trap dates back to the late Bronze Age.

Additional reading: Africanus, L. (1896). *The history and description of Africa*. 3 vols., ed. London: Brown, Kakluyt Society.

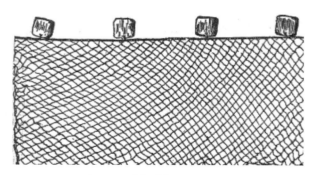

Fig 19:
Fish Net

Flail   Mechanical
Origin: Egypt   Date: 2950 BCE

The flail-like tool was one of the oldest agricultural implements—hunters and food gatherers used it before the development of farming. The earliest flail was a stick, used to separate small seeds from a coarse husk. Later, the flail developed into a two-piece hinged tool. In Egypt, the flail and crook were symbols of kingship.

Additional readings: Hart, G. (1990). *Ancient Egypt*. New York: Alfred Knopf Pub.

Flange   Mechanical
Origin: Africa   Date: Prehistoric

An axe dated to 15,000 BCE, had crude markings and rough edges resembling an old process known as flanging. A flange was the ridge along the top and bottom edges of a bronze axe-head, designed to keep the head of the axe rigid in the handle.

Additional reading: Binford, L., (1981). *Bones: Ancient man and modern myths*. New York: Academic Press.

Flax   Agriculture
Origin: Syria   Date: 7000 BCE

The region's inhabitants hunted and gathered nuts, seeds, fruits, and grains. Over a period of several thousands years, farming developed as people became less mobile. The early Syrian farms were the first to grow and cultivate flax. In many parts of the world flax was grown and consumed as a food source.

Additional reading: Bonar, A. (1985). *The Macmillan treasury of herbs*. New York: Macmillan.

Flint   Mining
Origin: Africa   Date: 50,000 BCE

A well-known European archaeologist coined the term "Southern Retouch." This method of cutting was attributed to the late Paleolithic period. Gabriel de Mortillet described the Southern region of Africa as the earliest area to apply the flint saw for cutting objects, instead of using blunt force striking.

Additional reading: Oakley, K. (1956). *Man the tool maker.* London: British Museum.

Flint Sickle   see   **Sickle.**

Float   Device
Origin: America   Date: 4000 BCE

The first fishing sticks were attached to a float, dating back to 4000 BCE. The central Eskimo harpoon and float was recovered from an ice cave. It had a harpoon stick with line and float attached, which was used for hunting. Ensuring the rate of successful throws required a float, which allowed recovery of the harpoon stick.

Additional reading: Travers, B. (1996). *The Gale encyclopedia of science.* New York: Gale Group Pub.

Floating Structure see   Bridge Floating.

Flute   Musical Instrument
Origin: China   Date: 9000 BCE

One of the oldest instruments used by tribes in central China, the flute dates to prehistoric times. Several sheep tibia bones punched full of holes have been preserved dating from the Neolithic era. Later examples of flutes rendered by the third millennium Sumerian and African peoples have also been found.

Additional reading: Holmes, P. and Coles, J., (1973). "Prehistoric Brass Instruments," *World Archaeology* 12, Macnamara.

Folsom Point   Mechanical
Origin: America   Date: Prehistoric

The early hunters of the Americas designed hunting tools in accordance with the types of animals available in the region. The Folsom point, developed by the Paleolithic hunters, was a fluted hollow-based flint arrowhead named after the site in New Mexico where they were found.

Additional reading: Palmer, G. (1968). *Archaeology a-z, a simplified guide and dictionary.* New York: Frederick Warne.

Food Preserving   Agriculture
Origin: Egypt   Date: 3200 BCE

Great quantities of preserved fish from ancient Egypt were found in a sandy desert located in the early 1800's by a Dutch expedition, stretching east of the town Ensa. The fish were wrapped in linen strips and were placed into water from the Egyptian lakes, which contained high levels of soda.

Additional reading: Derry, T. and Williams, T. (1960). *A short history of technology.* Oxford: Clarendon Press.

Foot   Mathematics
Origin: Sumer   Date: 2500 BCE

As early as 2500 BCE, the Sumerians developed a system of standard weights and concise measures, such as shekel, mina, log, homer, cubit, and foot. These standard units of measurements were adopted by successor civilizations as acceptable codes of measures.

Additional reading: Sarton, G. (1936). *The study of the history of mathematics.* Cambridge: Harvard University Press.

Foot Measurement   Measurement
Origin: Syria   Date: 2100 BCE

The oldest preserved standard for length is the foot of the statue of Gudes of Lagash, dating about 2100 BCE. Its length was divided into 16 parts at 10.41 inches each. The Sumerian system of measures included various units of capacity: the log (541 ml. or 33 cu. in.); the homer (720 logs); the cubit, and the foot, which is two-thirds of a cubit. A cubit was the distance from the tip of the middle finger to the elbow, about 17 to 22 inches.

Additional reading: Bunch, B. and Hellemans, A. (1993). *The timetables of technology: A chronology of the most important people and events in the history of technology.* New York: Simon & Schuster.

Forcep   Medicine
Origin: Nubia   Date: 3200 BCE

Early forceps were discovered in northern Nubia and date back to around 3200 BCE. Many local areas during this time period used a crude set of forceps currently on display in the National Museum of Egypt. Many medical procedures were attempted using these instruments.

Additional reading: Oliver, R. (1961). *The dawn of African history.* London: Oxford University Press.

Forest   System
Origin: Mesopotamia   Date: 2200 BCE

Dating to the late 2200 BCE, a Mesopotamian tomb housed a set of plans that look like what we know as a forest, detailing the surrounding grounds. The plans surveyed a large tract of land established and maintained in a natural setting. Other forest tracts were established by Cleopatra around 60 BCE.

Additional reading: Travers, B. (Ed.) (1996). *The Gale encyclopedia of science.* Detroit Mich.: Gale Research.

Fork and Spoon   Mechanical
Origin: Africa   Date: 7000 BCE

Based on a plethora of evidence, archaeologists from Richard Leakey to Ben Jochanan have suggested that Africans were the first to create and utilize utensils to make eating more convenient. These theories are based on the discovery of crude tools fashioned in such a way as to suggest they were eating implements.

Additional reading: Douze, S. (1993). *Inventions and discoveries.* New York: Facts on File.

Fosse   Mechanical
Origin: Africa   Date: Prehistoric

The remains of early villages show a common trench area around the perimeter lined with stone. The oldest such ditch was found in Central Africa, what is now considered the Congo. The fosse was a long, narrow defensive ditch or trench dug outside the walls of a town.

Additional reading: Erskine, B. (1927). *Vanished cities of Northern Africa.* London: Hutchinson and Co.

Foundry   see   Crucible.

Fowl   see   Chicken.

Fraction   Mathematics
Origin: Mesopotamia   Date: 2000 BCE

By 2000 BCE, the ruling power in Mesopotamia was the Semitic Hammurabic dynasty, which established schools for training priestly administrators. These administrators developed mathematics and designed fractions in a similar way as the Sumerians had represented integers. The vertical imprint made with a stylus now stood not only for 1, 60, 3600, and so on, but also for 1/600, 1/3600, etc. The arrow-headed impression stood for 1/10, 1/1,000, etc. In time, other fractions were developed into these decimal fraction units.

Additional readings: Eves H., (1953). *An introduction to the history of mathematics.* New York: Holt, Rinehart and Winston.

Fraction 2   Mathematics
Origin: Egypt   Date: 1385 BCE

Fraction 2 was developed by Akhenaten, a Pharaoh of Egypt during dynasty VXIII. The fraction 2 mathematical procedure involves a series of tables that allow one to cross-calculate two or more sums. Many mathematics scholars were using the Egyptian system of unit fractions 1000 years after the Egypt-Rhind Papyrus.

Additional reading: Gulberg, J.(1997). *Mathematics: from the birth of numbers.* New York: W.W. Norton.

Fraction Table   Mathematics
Origin: Egypt   Date: 1600 BCE

The Egyptians, as far back as 1600 BCE, developed a table which established the place values for fractions. These fraction tables were the basis for practical mathematical calculations of the period. The fraction table was based on a rotation system from right to left using floating numbers to hold place values. The Egyptians developed this table of fractions almost 800 years before Pythagoras (530 BCE), who had also been credited with creating a fraction table.

Additional Reading: Newman, H. (1956). *The world of mathematics.* New York: Simon and Schuster.

Fracture   Medicine
Origin: Egypt   Date: 3000 BCE

Introduced by Athotis in 3000 BCE, the retention

method for stabilizing fractured bones used small bands soaked in mud. Rhazes (850-932) and Averroes (1126-1198) were Arab surgeons who used cotton strips covered and made firm with egg whites. Ambriose Pare (1509-1590), the author of a treatise on the means of joining bones, employed splints made of wax, cardboard, cloth, and parchment. The damp splints were placed around the fractured limb and hardened as they dried.

Additional reading: Bennion, E. (1979). *Antique medical instruments.* Berkeley Calif: University of California Press.

Frame (Picture)   see   Cartouche.

Friction   Mechanical
Origin: Egypt   Date: 2400 BCE

The conversion of sliding friction into rolling friction was understood early in Egyptian civilization. They transported huge masses on a device called a sledge-runner. They needed to move the large stone used to build pyramids for the pharaohs of the 3rd and 4th dynasty. This process made the building process less labor-intensive. Very large round logs were placed underneath the friction pieces to reduce friction.

Additional reading: Edwards, I., (1970). *The pyramids of Egypt.* New York: Harmondsworth Press.

Fruit   Agriculture
Origin: Indochina   Date: 6000 BCE

The earliest record of fruit being domestically produced dates back to 6000 BCE, in Indochina. The specific fruit has no modern name but historical accounts show that the acid rich juice was used for medical purposes as well as human food sources.

Additional Reading: Ronan, C., (1982). *Science: Its history and development among the world's cultures.* New York: Facts on File.

Frustum   Mathematics
Origin: Egypt   Date: 3000 BCE

Egyptian scholars introduced the mathematical form frustum around 3000 BCE. The volume of the frustum, the cut-off, flattened surface of a cone or pyramid, are still determined by an Egyptian formula. The newly

developed mathematical procedure by the scholar of the Naqada III period is credited with other new mathematical innovations.

Additional reading: West, B., (1982). *The Prentice-Hall encyclopedia of mathematics.* New York: Prentice Hall Books.

Fumigating   Agriculture
Origin: China   Date: 2100 BCE

Around 2100 BCE, the Chinese fumigated houses to rid them of pests, using a quick-acting chemical that worked effectively for short periods of time. The chemical was probably harmful to humans. It is clear they had to leave their homes during the fumigation.

Additional reading: Chi Chao-Ting, (1970). Key economic areas in Chinese history, as revealed in the development of public works for water control. London.

Furnace   see   Blast Furnace.

Furrier   Domestic
Origin: Egypt   Date: 1400 BCE

The native inhabitants of Asia, Africa, and America wore animal skins as early as 35,000 BCE. The skins were not treated and didn't last long. As a result, many people died from exposure. The first record of animals being raised and harvested for their skins was under Tiye, Queen of Egypt, during 1400 BCE.

Additional reading: Gille, B. (1986). *The history of technique. Vol. 2,* New York: Research Science Pub.

G

Garden   Systems
Origin: Syria   Date: Antiquity

The Palace of the Assyrian King Tiglath-Pilesek III and Ashur-Nasir-Pal II at Nimd had exquisite architecture as illustrated by an unknown fourteenth century artist. On the River Tigris, the king's palace was surrounded with ornamental plants grown and maintained despite the arid land area.

Additional reading: Allison, P. (1962). Historical inferences to be drawn from the effect of human settlement on the vegetation of Africa. *Journal of African History,* 3(2), 241-249.

Garlic — Agriculture
Origin: Egypt   Date: 1500 BCE

King Thutmose III described techniques for planting and processing garlic. He used his specially grown garlic bulbs for both culinary and medical purposes. A bulbous plant belonging to the lily family, garlic is noted for its strong smell and a pungent, acidic taste.

Additional reading: (1983). *Medicine from the earth: A guide to healing plants.* San Francisco: Harper and Row.

Gas Lighting — Chemistry
Origin: China   Date: 340 BCE

In 340 BCE, Chang Chu described how bamboo tubes were utilized to pipe the methane gas used to illuminate villages. Travelers also used this natural gas to light their torches. By the first century BCE, the Chinese systematically bored into the earth to collect methane and capture it in containers as fuel reserve.

Additional reading: Schwartz, B. (1985). *The world of thought in ancient China.* Cambridge: Harvard University Press.

Gas (Poison) — Chemistry
Origin: China   Date: 300 BCE

Papers written by the followers of Mohists, a fifth century BCE Chinese philosopher describe the use of poisonous gas in warfare. The opposing armies were often lured into a cave or other enclosed areas where gas was released. Many died on both sides of the battle because of the unpredictable nature of the poison gas.

Additional readings: Tien, ch'ang-wu (1999). *History of chemistry in ancient China.* Shanghai: Jen-min Ch'u-pan she.

Gas Warfare — Chemistry
Origin: China   Date: 400 BCE

During the fourth century BCE, the Chinese used bombs and grenade- like devices constructed from dry lacquer, a powerful lung irritant, and arsenic and lead oxides incorporated into a combustible base such as resin or wax. Army strategies included digging tunnels just below the enemy camps and releasing poisonous fumes into them.

Additional Reading: Fitzgerald, C., (1961). *China: A short cultural history.* New York: Praeger.

Gauge   see   Balance.

Gauze — Medical
Origin: Egypt   Date: 1450 BCE

The earliest medical record describing the use of a very thin, transparent fabric comes from writings of military campaigns conducted by Thutmose III of Egypt. The doctors who attended the wounded developed a lightweight gauze material to cover wounds. The very first gauze concept was probably a derived from a sheer layer of plant or animal fiber.

Additional reading: Singer, C., and Underwood, E., (1962). *A short history of medicine.* New York: Oxford University Press.

Gear — Mechanical
Origin: China   Date: 30 BCE

Ancient Chinese manufactured toothed wheels, and/or gears, to operate various devices, such as a pulley and the water wheel. The use of gears is mentioned in the writing of Vitruvius of Italy who credited the Chinese with the development of the first gear around 30 BCE. The Chinese also investigated the nature of the inclined plane and the lever.

Additional reading: Gillispie, C., (1981). *Dictionary of scientific biography. Vol.8.,* New York: Charles Scribners & Sons.

Geology Textbook — Geology
Origin: Egypt   Date: 314 BCE

Theophrastus of Eresus is credited with writing the first known geology textbook around 314 BCE. The textbook was organized by cataloging the mineral substances then found in their natural state. Most of the natural substances were traded by merchants.

Additional reading: Barber, F. (1900). *The mechanical triumphs of ancient Egyptians.* London: Trubner and Co.

Geometry — Mathematics
Origin: Babylon   Date: 3000 BCE

Herodotus wrote, "Sesostris…made a division of the soil of Egypt among the inhabitants if the river carried away any portion of a man's lot, the King sent persons to examine and determine by measurement the exact extent of the loss. From this practice, geometry first came to be known in Egypt." The origins of geometry date back to the Babylonians at the beginning of the third millennium BCE. They worked out a system for measuring territories which was based upon units of simple surface, circumference, and squares which were using geometrical functions.

Additional reading: Struik, D., (1987). *Concise history of mathematics. 4th ed.* New York: Dover.

Geometrical Textbook   Mathematics
Origin: Babylon   Date: 3000 BCE

According to records, the Babylonians developed the first geometric problem text on clay tablets around 3000 BCE. The text included the earliest demonstrations of triangular laws, including cones, squares, circumferences and circles.

Additional reading: Gullberg, J. (1997). *Mathematics: From the birth of numbers.* New York: W.W. Norton.

Gesso   Chemistry
Origin: Egypt   Date: 960 BCE

The earliest recorded use of gesso, a mixture of ground-up chalk and beeswax that was applied to wood, was around 960 BCE. The royal workers used gesso while designing a gold leaf for Makeda, Queen of Sheba. The brick wall was covered with gesso, providing a very smooth surface after it dried that was then covered in gold leaf.

Additional reading: Lucas, A. and Harris, J. (1962). *Ancient Egyptian materials and industries.* London: E Arnold Pub.

Glass   Material
Origin: Africa   Date: 4000 BCE

As early as 4000 BCE, Africans used glass to glaze the surfaces of soapstone beads. Later, around 2500 BCE, glass was fashioned in imitation of precious stones. The glass-like materials were developed and used in craft-making and art designs of the period.

Additional reading: Davison, C. (1973). '*Glass beads in African archaeology*'. AATA, 10, 2.

Glass Blowing   Production
Origin: Syria   Date: 200 BCE

Glass blowing techniques were developed by the Syrians during the second century BCE. Glass blowing replaced the technique of molding hardening liquefied glass around a core of sand or ceramic. Glass was blown by collecting a bit of softened glass on the end of a hollow tube. The molten glass was rough-formed with a tool, after which the glass blower blew air into the tube to further form a glass glob. A similar process is used today.

Additional reading: Reynolds, T., (1983). *Stronger than a hundred men.* Baltimore: John Hopkins University Press.

Glass Eye   Ophthalmology
Origin: Egypt   Date: 300 BCE

Artificial clay eyes were created in Egypt around 300 BCE, primarily for soldiers wounded in battle. But it was not until the 1600s that John Scultetus of Germany invented the artificial glass eye. These ocular prosthetics were manufactured in bulk in Venice and later in Bohemia and France.

Additional reading: Bunch, B. and Hellemans, A. (1993). *The timetables of technology: A chronology of the most important people and events in the history of technology.* New York: Simon & Schuster.

Glass Making   Materials
Origin: Egypt   Date: 4100 BCE

Sometime around 4100 BCE, an unsung manufacturer of Egyptian faience overheated his core of quartz sand and sodium carbonate (naturally occurring in nature) and melted the whole mass. Intended or serendipitous, this meltdown caused the first recorded occurrence of glass production. The glass objects were polished and used as decorations.

Additional readings: Frank, S., (1982). *Glass and archaeology.* Academic Press.

Glazing   see   Lead (Glazing).

Glider   Aviation
Origin: Africa   Date: Antiquity

A model glider constructed of sycamore was found

in Africa, dating to 1800 BCE. The recovered antique glider model was carved from wood from a single tree. The aerodynamics appears to be in line mathematically with the modern day gliders. NASA aeronautic engineers who examined the craft deemed it to be capable of flight, marking man's earliest attempt to fly.

Additional reading: Van Sertima, I. (1983). *Blacks in science: Ancient and modern.* New Brunswick: Transaction Books.

Fig 20 Glider
This wooden glider was found in central Africa

Glue see Adhesive.

Gnomon System
Origin: China Date: 300 BCE

The gnomon was one of the first instruments used by the ancients to measure time during the day. The instrument was composed of a frame which cast a shadow on a horizontal surface. The shadow indicated the height and orientation of the sun and/or the moon above the horizon.

Additional reading: Schwartz, B. (1985). *The world of thought in ancient China.* Cambridge: Harvard University Press.

Go (Game) Entertainment
Origin: China Date: 3000 BCE

A game of mental strategy, Go was invented 3000 years ago by the Chinese emperor, Yao. This mind game was employed as social entertainment by many upper social groups and educated people. Go was introduced to Japan by way of Korea around 750 CE.

Additional reading: Cotterell, Y. & Cotterell, A. (1975).

The early civilization of China. New York: Putnam Pub.

Goat Domestic
Origin: Nubia Date: 4200 BCE

The goat was first domesticated in Nubia by land farmers as far back as 4200 BCE. The first inhabitants to settle in the Fertile Crescent migrated there from Africa. This area stretched in an arc shape from the northern end of the Persian Gulf to the valley of the Nile River in Egypt. The farmers of the region were the earliest known to domestically breed the goat for milk and food.

Additional reading: Clarke, D. and Glynn, I., (1981). *Pattern of the past: studies in honor of David Clarke.* London: Cambridge University Press.

Gold Chemistry
Origin: Mesopotamia Date: 40,000 BCE

Gold was used for making jewelry in Mesopotamia as far back as 40,000 BCE. Gold could be found as a free metal in gravel, scattered in veins of quartz, and in sea water. Today it is used primarily in jewelry-making, in certain electronics products, in restorative dental work, and in some industrial alloys.

Additional reading: Ki-Zerbo, J. (1990). *General history of Africa methodology and African prehistory,* Berkeley Calif., University of California Press.

Gold Mining Mining
Origin: Africa Date: 43,000 BCE

Around 43,000 BCE, there were more than one hundred gold mines in Africa. The ancient people there refined gold in porous clay crucibles, using blasts of air to remove impurities. The gold was mined largely for ceremonial purposes, and was also traded for goods and services, mainly within a certain area.

Additional reading: "43,000 year old mines; discovered in Swaziland" (1970).*The New York Time*s, February 8, 1970, p.6.

Golden Numbers Mathematics
Origin: Babylon Date: Antiquity

The earliest mention of the Golden Number was

recorded by Babylonian scholars. The Golden Number was the solution "X of the equation, X equals to and exists in an asymmetrical sharing when the ratio between the largest of the two parts and the smallest is equal to the ratio between the whole and the largest." Euclid, in the third century BCE, made of it a famous problem by dividing a straight line in mean and extreme ratio or "Golden Numbers."

Additional reading: Ashurst, F. , (1982). *Founders of modern mathematics*. London: Fredrick Muller.

Golf   Sport
Origin: China   Date: Antiquity

During antiquity in the southern parts of China, royal families once played the earliest form of an outdoors game similar to what we call golf. It appears that this crude ball and stick game was played in what appears to be teams. Each team had to hit a stone-like ball a certain distance and the opposite team hit the ball-like item back. When one team was closer to a predetermined hole they had the option to sink the ball-like object. This game was a popular recreation during the period.

Additional reading: Schauble, J. (1991). *"Worrying New from China: It may have invented golf."* London: *Independent Press.*

Goose   Agriculture
Origin: Egypt   Date: 5600 BCE

Farmers of the Fertile Crescent were the earliest known to domestically breed geese. The ancient goose was said to be larger than a duck and smaller than a swan. Many of the early domesticated species were distinguished by adjuncts of color, appearance, and habits.

Additional reading: Phillipson, D., (1993). *The antiquity of civilization and herding in Ethiopia*. London: Routledge Pub.

Goura   Musical
Origin: Africa   Date: 5000 BCE

The Khoikhoi of Southern Africa made music from the first known goura dating as far back as 5000 BCE. A musical bow with the addition of feathers serving as a reed, the instrument was quite difficult to master.

The oldest recovered goura is housed in the London Museum of Natural History.

Additional reading: Nketia, J., (1975). *History and the organization of music in West Africa*. Legon: University of Ghana.

Granite   Chemistry
Origin: Egypt   Date: 3500 BCE

Herodotus referred to the use of granite in the construction the pyramid of Chephren, when he wrote that as long ago as 3500 BCE, "The lowest layer of it is of variegated Ethiopian stone." Several other classical authors, including Herodotus, also mention the granite facing of the Menkaure Pyramid of Giza.

Additional reading: Petrie, W., (1900). The royal tombs of the first dynasty, 1900-1901. London: Office of the Egypt exploration.

Granulation   Chemistry
Origin: Egypt   Date: 4000 BCE

The technique was used in Egypt around 4000 BCE. Etruscan craftsmen were able to attach minuscule balls of less than 1/200 of an inch in diameter to almost any surface. From the Near East, the art of granulation spread westward around 2000 BCE. The process was highly specialized and required years of training to meet the exactness needed for royal costumes and other garments.

Additional reading: Hayes, W., (1965). *Most ancient Egypt*. Chicago: University of Chicago Press.

Grape   Agriculture
Origin: Egypt   Date: 5500 BCE

Farmers of the Fertile Crescent were the earliest known to domestically grow and cultivate a fruit known as grapes. The small seeded berry, originally called a grappo, grew wild in clusters on vines throughout the region.

Additional reading: Gwynne, M., (1975). *The origin and spread of some domestic food plants of Eastern Africa*. New York: Africana Publishing Co.

Graphite   see   Carbon.

Grass   Agricultural
Origin: Mesopotamia   Date: 6200 BCE

The valley region stretched in an arc shape from the northern end of the Persian Gulf to the Valley of the Nile River in Egypt. The soil in the Fertile Crescent was light and easy to till with simple tools. Farmers of this region were the earliest known to domestically grow and cultivate grass. The need to produce food for the livestock was most likely the motivation to domesticate and produce various species of grass and weeds.

Additional reading: De Brag L. (1978). *The wild garden: An illustrated guide to weeds*. New York: Mayflower Books.

Gray Hair Treatment   see   Almond Tree.

Great Wall   Construction
Origin: China   Date: 214 BCE

The Han dynasty was vigorous in its expansion of China's borders, and received tribute from a vast kingdom throughout Asia. So successful was the dynasty that to this day Chinese refer to themselves as the "son of Han." The Great Wall of China was begun by Emperor Shih Huang Ti, founder of the Ch'in dynasty. The Great Wall extends 500 miles from the Pacific Ocean to central Asia. It is the only man-made structure that can be seen from outer space.

Additional Reading: Schwarty, D. (2001). *The great wall of China*. London: Thames and Hudson.

Grinding Plaque   see   Tool.

Grindstone   Mechanical
Origin: Africa   Date: Antiquity

Numerous drawings on cave walls in central Africa show individuals grinding materials using hardened stone-like material. The use of these materials was wide-spread throughout the period. Many materials like wood, stone and some soft metals were ground using a designed set of grindstones.

Additional reading: (1935). *The stone age races of Kenya,* London: Oxford University Press.

Gripper   see   **Forceps.**

Grounding Rod   see   **Rod.**

Guitar   Musical
Origin: Turkey   Date: 1300 BCE

A Hittite relief in northern Turkey carved around 1300 BCE and another from central Turkey both show a musician playing an instrument with a characteristic figure-eight shaped body and frets. However, the scholarly endeavor of defining ancient musical instruments can be difficult for historians, particularly in cases where only pictorial evidence exists.

Additional reading: Rossi, N. and Rafferty, S. (1981). *Music through the centuries*. Washington, D.C.: University Press.

Gun   see   **Blow-gun.**

Gypsum (Alabaster)   Chemistry
Origin: Egypt   Date: 2500 BCE

Geologically, Egyptian alabaster is calcite, sometimes erroneously called aragonite. It has the same composition as gypsum but as a different crystalline form and different specific gravity. Originally considered to be calcium sulfate or gypsum, the material was employed extensively in ancient Egypt. This was a distinct material very similar in appearance to aragonite but consisted of calcium carbonate.

Additional reading: Lucas, A. and Harris, J. (1999). *Ancient Egyptian materials and industries*. Mineola N.Y.: Dover Publications.

H

Hair (Wig)   Cosmetic
Origin: Egypt   Date: Antiquity

Women of ancient Egypt, as early as the First Dynasty, used artificial locks of human hair to supplement their own because of age or fashion. This human hair was often supplied by local servants. This concept of wearing others hair was adopted by royalty and didn't extend to common people until it reached Europe and Asia.

Additional reading: Weigall, A. (1910). *A guide to the antiquities of Egypt.* London: Bracken Books.

Hair Coloring   see   Almond Tree.

Hair Net   see   Kell.

Halberd   Mechanical
Origin: Africa   Date: Prehistoric

The Halberd tool, characteristic of the Paleolithic Age, was used for hunting and fighting. A weapon with a heavy, dagger-like blade fixed at right angles to the shaft, it was used in battle-axe fashion.

Additional reading: Clark, J. and Brandt, S. (1983). *From hunter to farmer.* Berkeley: University of California Press.

Handle   Domestic
Origin: Tanzania   Date: Antiquity

The earliest description of a support device used for hunting and gathering food was first seen on a cave drawing in the Congo dating back to the prehistoric period. The wooden handle was approximately two feet in length and was attached to the basket by what appears to be plant strips.

Additional reading: Haaland, R., (1995). An early iron age site in the Tanzanian hinterland *Tanzania: Azania,* 29-30, 238-47.

Hand Tool   Mechanical
Origin: Africa   Date: 20,000 BCE

The first known hand tool was a sharp-edged stick or a piece of stone. The arrow were used in Africa as early as 20,000 BCE. Arrows had wooden shafts with a piece of flint attached with resin or pitch. By about 12,000 BCE, pieces of flint were stuck into wood or bone, making a simple cutting device.

Additional reading: Semenov, S., (1964) *Prehistoric technology; an experimental study of the oldest tools and artifacts from traces of manufacture and wear.* New York: Barnes and Noble.

Harbor (Boat)   Oceanography
Origin: Palestine   Date: 10 BCE

In 10 BCE, Herod the Great had the first large harbor constructed in the open sea, built to support his new town of Caesarea Palestine near present-day Haifa. The harbor was constructed of giant blocks of concrete poured into wooden forms.

Additional reading: Derry, T. and Williams, T. (1960). *A short history of technology.* Oxford: Clarendon Press.

Harness   Mechanical
Origin: China   Date: 900 BCE

Around 900 BCE, the Chinese invented a form of harness that is pushed on a horse's chest instead of his throat. This harness was especially useful for large beasts, such as elephants. It was a great improvement that was not adopted in the West until the eighth century CE.

Additional reading: Schwartz, B. (1985). *The world of thought in ancient China.* Cambridge: Harvard University Press.

Harp   Music
Origin: Egypt   Date: 3500 BCE

The harp was first seen in Egyptian drawings dating back to 3500 BCE. The harp was considered a sacred musical instrument to be used in the next life. Many versions of the harp have been recovered by archeologists. After having enjoyed great popularity, the harp fell into disuse until the eighteenth century.

Additional reading: Guillemin-Duchesne, M., (1981). "Music in ancient Mesopotamia and Egypt." World Archaeology.

Harpoon   Tool
Origin: Zaire   Date: 16,000 BCE

Archeologists found bone-shaped objects at the Ishango site in Zaire, which contained primitive examples of harpoons dating to 16,000 BCE. These hunting weapons were used primarily around water.

Additional reading: Usher, A. (1954). *A history of mechanical inventions. 2nd editions,* Cambridge: Harvard University Press

Figure 21
Harpoon
This bone and wood shaped harpoon
dates as far back as 12000 BCE

Hatchet   Tool
Origin: Africa   Date: Prehistoric

One of the most important technical advances noted in the Paleolithic period was that tools coincided with the cultural divisions in Africa. The increase in the manufacture and specialization of tools in upper Paleolithic times became more evident as the needs of the society of hunters in Africa and North Asia demanded a new set of tools. The ax was transformed into a hatchet, allowing the hunter to effectively use it with one hand. The hatchet made it possible to increase the output production and rendered less pressure on the body.

Additional reading: Adams, W. (1977). *Nubia, corridor to Africa.* London: Allen Lane Pub.

Health Care   see   Medical Practice.

Health Plan   Medicine
Origin: China   Date: 700 BCE

During the Chou dynasty, two doctrines evolved to form the basis of Chinese medicine. The first doctrine is of yin and yang. The two principles were of masculinity, light and heavy (yang), and femininity, darkness and earth (yin). The second is that of the five elements or phases: metal, wood, water, fire, and earth. It is believed by many that humans require equilibrium among the two principles and five elements.

Additional reading: Silver, G. and Sparer, M. (2004). "Health care systems," New York: *Grolier Multimedia Encyclopedia.*

Hearth   Mechanical
Origin: Africa   Date: 8000 BCE

The oldest and most common way of firing was an unenclosed fire hearth, discovered at sites of the La Terrier region of Africa. During the ancient firing process, only the most primitive methods could have been employed. In antiquity, the pots were filled with hot peat-ash and piled around with burning layers of peat. Lewis Barvas discovered the earliest firing sites in Central Africa in 1863.

Additional reading: Murry, Sir; Little, W.; Fowler, H. W.; Coulson, J.; and Onions, C. (1937). *Oxford universal English dictionary on historical principle.* London: *From the original English dictionary.*

Heat   see   Central Heat.

Helicopter Top   Mechanical
Origin: China   Date: 320 BCE

The Chinese are credited with the early development of what many consider the first helicopter top. Around 320 BCE, the Chinese developed helicopter top wooden blades, spun by pulling a cord. The recovered model appeared to have four blades. This pull-cord device led to many other mechanically activated devices based on similar principles.

Additional reading: Schwartz, B. (1985). *The world of thought in ancient China.* Cambridge: Harvard University Press.

Helmet   Military
Origin: Mesopotamia   Date: 2500 BCE

Protective head gear dates back to prehistoric times. One the earliest metal helmets were found in southern Mesopotamia. Helmets made of sheet gold were used by the Mesopotamians during war as well as for entertainment. Around 2500 BCE, helmets were formed primarily by hammer which remains the major tool for shaping metals.

Additional reading: De Camp, L., (1993). *The ancient engineers.* New York: Barnes and Noble.

Hemp   Agriculture
Origin: China   Date: 500 BCE

The early name for hemp was cannabis sativa. A plant with oil-seeds, hemp produced a secretion with narcotic properties used in the preparation of hashish. Hemp was also used to create fibers for materials in weaving, ropes, and more.

Additional reading: House, H. (1934). *Wild flowers.* New York: Macmillan Co,

Henna   **see**   **Cosmetic.**

Herb   Medical
Origin: China   Date: 2700 BCE

Around 2700 BCE, Chinese emperor Shen Nung experimented with herbs and acupuncture. The Pen Tsao herbal medical treatment process was later attributed to him. Shen Nung was considered the founder of Chinese medicine.

Additional reading: Hirth, F. (1908). *The ancient history of China.* New York: Columbia University Press.

Herbarium   Agriculture
Origin: Syria   Date: 1450 BCE

The first botanist collector of the ancient world was Pharaoh Tuthmosis III. In 1450 BCE, he invaded Syria and brought back 275 different plant species from his campaign. The ruler directed his scholars to draw a pictorial catalog of the plants in bas-relief on the great temple of Cornice. These images can still be seen today.

Additional reading: Dorland, N., (1994). *Dorland's illustrated medical dictionary,* Philadelphia; Saunders Pub.

Herding   Domestic
Origin: Iran   Date: 10,000 BCE

As long ago as 10,000 BCE, Iranians domestically raised goats for milk and food. These animals, as well as sheep and birds, were suited for the arid land and posed fewer problems than agriculture under those conditions. The herding duties were typically assumed by the young boys of the tribes.

Additional reading: Ibn Abd al-Hakam (1922). *The history of the conquest of Egypt, North Africa and Spain.* New Haven Conn. Yale University Press.

Hexagon   Mathematics
Origin: China   Date: 140 BCE

Around 140 BC, the Chinese philosopher Ham Ying made the first recorded reference to the hexagon structure of snowflakes. This was significant because it led to the study of snow and the cataloging of snowflakes. The Chinese book, *Mo Ching* written by followers of the philosopher Mo-Tzu, contained detailed descriptions of astrological data, such as law of motion, uniform motion, and effects of outside motion.

Additional reading: Yang H. (1965). *The treasury of mathematics.* London: Yang Hui's Mathematical Work.

Hieroglyphic Notation   Mathematics
Origin: Egypt   Date: 3500 BCE

Egyptian hieroglyphic numeration was easily comprehended by scribes. The system, at least as old as the pyramids, dating some 5000 years ago, was based, as might be expected, on the ten-scale. By the use of a simple iterative scheme and of distinctive symbols for each of the first half-dozen powers of ten, numbers over a stroke represented a unit. An inverted wicket or heel bone was used for 10, a snare somewhat resembling a capitol letter C stood for 100, and a lotus and a kneeling figure for 100,000.

Additional reading: Boyer, C. (1968). *A history of mathematics.* New York: John Wiley & Sons.

Hinge (Door)   Mechanical
Origin: Mesopotamia   Date: 4500 BCE

Predating door locks, ancient shelters were often secured by rocks or large structures made from a variety of materials such as wood and metal. The first stone door sockets were developed about 4500 BCE, by the Mesopotamians. The first human constructed door hinges were probably made from animal bone or wood for the royal quarters.

Additional reading: (1979). *Ancient Mesopotamia: Portrait of a dead civilization.* Rev. Ed. Chicago: University of Chicago Press.

Hoe   Tool
Origin: Mesopotamia   Date: 4000 BCE

Basic tools have existed from pre-historic times to present. Many basic tools such as the hammer, hoe and plow evolved over time. The earliest hoe was probably made in Mesopotamia around 4000 BCE. Made of flaked flint, it was used to break up the ground. Flint hoes were also made in Egypt by about 3400 BCE.

Additional reading: Usher, A. (1954). *A history of mechanical inventions. 2nd Editions,* Cambridge: Harvard University Press

Hollow Hemisphere   Medical
Origin: India   Date: 1100 BCE

During the first millennium BCE, surgery reached remarkable heights in India, where a vast array of instruments were available, including the hollow hemisphere. This medical instrument was widely used by many medical practitioners during this period. Later the hollow hemisphere was replaced by more user-friendly medical instruments.

Additional reading: Bennion, E., (1979). *Antique medical instruments.* Berkeley, Calif.: University of California Press.

Homer   Mathematic
Origin: Sumer   Date: 2500 BCE

As early as 2500 BCE, the Sumerians developed a system of standard weights and concise measurements. The ancient scholars of Sumer developed units of measures such as shekel, mina, log, homer, cubit, and foot. These standard units of measurements were adopted as acceptable codes of measures.

Additional reading: Dugas, R. (1955). *A history of mechanics.* New York: Central Books Co.

Hook (Surgical)   Medical
Origin: India   Date: 950 BCE

Around 950 BCE, medical personnel in India manufactured and used surgical hooks while performing various procedures. The Sushruta Samhita, most important of the ancient Hindu medical works, described a host of sharp and blunt medical tools, each designed to perform a different task. Many of the surgical hooks served multiple purposes.

Additional reading: Bennion, E., (1979). *Antique medical instruments.* Berkeley, Calif.: University of California Press.

Hookworm Infection   Medicine
Origin: Egypt   Date: 1600 BCE

The Egyptians were the first to make many medical, mathematical, astronomical, and scientific discoveries as far back as 1600 BCE. Egyptian medical remedies and procedures are documented in papyrus manuscripts, especially those uncovered in modern times by Edwin Smith and George Ebers in 1872. The papyrus included medical treatment for hookworm infection and gave detailed descriptions.

Additional Reading: Inglis, B. (1965). *A history of medicine.* Cleveland: World Pub. Co.

Horn   Musical Instrument
Origin: Africa   Date: Antiquity

Early records show that the horn was used both in war and hunting. Ancient horns were carved from animal bone, stone and metal. One of the early uses of the horn was to communicate over great distances. The development of the horn for a myriad of purposes was widespread throughout Africa.

Additional reading: Goldron, R. (1968). *Ancient and Oriental music.* New York: Doubleday Pub.

Horoscope   Astronomy
Origin: Babylon   Date: 400 BCE

Somewhere around 400 BCE, the Babylonians established the Zodiac Circle, the band in the sky that included the apparent paths of the sun, moon, and planets. Horoscopes became available, describing the presumed influence of the sun, moon, and planets and their position in the Zodiac at the time of one's birth.

Additional reading: Asimov, I. (1982). *Exploring the earth and the cosmos; the growth and future of human knowledge.* New York: Crown Pub.

Horse   Agriculture
Origin: Egypt   Date: 8200 BCE

The origin of the horse has sparked much debate among some archeologists. The oldest horse remains have been recovered in the lower basin of Egypt. Farmers of the Fertile Crescent were the earliest known to domestically breed horses. The horse assumed the status of being a beast of burden in the early stages of many ancient cultures, before being bred as a symbol of power and status.

Additional reading: Rice, M. (2003). *Egypt's making: The origin of ancient Egypt, 5000-2000 B.C. 2nd Ed.* New York: Roulledge Pub.

Horse Bit   Mechanical
Origin: Egypt   Date: 1200 BCE

The armies of Egypt were the first to develop a device called a horse bit to more accurately control their horses. The oldest horse bit was observed in paintings dating to 1200 BCE. Horse-drawn chariots were widely used during this period, first in battle and later for domestic transportation.

Additional reading: Bunch, B. and Hellemans, A. (1993). *The timetables of technology: A chronology of the most important people and events in the history of technology.* New York: Simon & Schuster.

Horticulture   System
Origin: Sumer   Date: 2500 BCE

Dating to 2500 BCE, the 'Oval Temple' displayed a strange arrangement of rocks, vines, and other props and was believed to be the earliest planned garden. Many of the visitors to these temples were also commercial traders, who influenced the spread of the concept of plants, water and rock gardens to many other areas.

Additional reading: Kramer, S., (1959). *History begins at Sumer.* Garden City, N.Y.: Doubleday Pub.

Hound   see   Dog.

Hourglass   Instrument
Origin: China   Date: 600 BCE

The Chinese invented the hourglass around 600 BCE. Egyptians developed a different style around 200 BCE. This crude time-keeping device didn't keep very accurate time. The early hourglass body was wooden and had a white clear-like cloth covering. The hour glass later evolved to metal and glass containment and achieved more consistent timekeeping.

Additional reading: Schwartz, B. (1985). *The world of thought in ancient China.* Cambridge: Harvard University Press.

House   Civil
Origin: Turkey   Date: 6500 BCE

As early as 6500 BCE, the architects of Turkey designed rectangular houses and they were built one against the other surrounding open courtyards. The outside of the town presented a solid wall to the world, with the only entrance being a ladder to the flat roofs, where other ladders went down through holes into the rooms. This construction was for protection against floods.

Additional reading: Ki-Zerbo, J. (1990). *General history of Africa: Methodology and African prehistory.* Berkeley, Calif.: University of California Press.

Hull (Ship)   Navigation
Origin: China   Date: 700 BCE

Dividing the hull of a ship into separate watertight compartments had been a shipbuilding practice in China as early as 700 BCE. Chalk and coal tar were used to caulk the compartments. The oldest evidence proving the great age of this invention, essential to the security of boats, was from the Tang Dynasty. Several of these boats were discovered in 1973 in the province of Jiangsu.

Additional reading: Gibson, C. (1948). *The story of the ship.* New York: Henery Schuman.

Human   Archaeology
Origin: Africa   Date: Prehistoric

The earliest human were discovered by Dr. Louis Leakey at Olduvai Gorge, Tanganyika, in 1959. The size of the teeth led to the nickname Nutcracker Man. Called Zinjanthropus, he represents the remains of the earliest known man and is possibly more than one and a half million years old.

Additional reading: Hill, P. (1917). *Prehistoric times.* New York: Harper & Row.

Hut (Reed)   Construction
Origin: Africa   Date: 20,000 BCE

The quest for shelter from the natural elements dates back to the beginning of man. The exact date of the first hut is unclear. Most scholars believe that huts were first seen in the West African rain forest. The typical hut was a dwelling of simple construction, usually smaller than a house and made of mud generally for temporary purposes.

Additional reading: Murry, Sir. Little, W.; Fowler, H. W.; Coulson, J.; and Onions, C. (1937). *Oxford universal English dictionary on historical principle*. London: *From the original English dictionary*.

Hydraulics — Mechanical
Origin: Egypt   Date: 2100 BCE

Around 2100 BCE, the Egyptians were using the siphon to transfer liquid, known as a hydraulic system, from one vessel to another. This early procedure was a common way to move large mechanical parts and equipment. Small mechanical objects were moved with this newly discovered process. Many Egyptians attempted to develop hydraulic systems that could move larger mechanical devices.

Additional reading: Butzer, K., (1976). *Early hydraulic civilizations in Egypt: A study in cultural ecology*. Chicago: University of Chicago.

Hydraulic Dam — Mechanical
Origin: Egypt   Date: 1925 BCE

Excavations of the royal cemetery at El-Kurru revealed a secret compartment with 24 horses behind the door believed to be the earliest hydraulic dam. The dam was connected to a fluid-controlled mechanical device.

Additional reading: Butzer, K., (1976) *Early hydraulic civilization in Egypt*. Chicago: University of Chicago Press.

Hydrometer — Tools
Origin: Turkey   Date: 350 BCE

Around 350 BCE, the city of Antioch (in Turkey) installed the world's first system of public lighting using a hydrometer. The early lighting systems were designed for the royal family and the ruling classes. The local living areas were not lit until almost fifty years later.

Additional reading: Bunch, B. and Hellemans, A. (1993). *The timetables of technology: A chronology of the most important people and events in the history of technology*. New York: Simon & Schuster.

Hyena   see   Dog.

Hypotenuse   see   Pythagorean Theorem.

I

Ice Pick   see   Pick.

Ice Pit   see   Refrigerator.

Ideogram — Communication
Origin: Sumer   Date: 2500 BCE

As many as two thousand ideograms were used in the earliest Sumerian records. By 2500 BCE, the number had been reduced to about six hundred. Ideograms were arbitrary representations of things which could not be depicted otherwise. Such a script still exists in China. The number of Chinese ideograms increased as the language developed.

Additional reading: Kramer S. (1956). *From the table of Sumer, twenty five firsts in man's recorded history*. Indian Hills, Colo. Falcon's Wing Press.

Immunization — Medicine
Origin: China   Date: 3200 BCE

Early Chinese writings depicted a smallpox outbreak around 3175 BCE. The Chinese practiced a form of immunization against smallpox by infecting people with scabs from a mild form of the disease. Some historical records indicate that many people who were immunized died from this medical procedure. Over many hundreds of years the immunization process improved its effectiveness.

Additional reading: Sonnedecker, G., (1976). *Kremer's and Urdang's history of pharmacy*. London: Lippincott.

Incense — Chemistry
Origin: Egypt   Date: 4500 BCE

Incense and incense burners were referred to in ancient records as early as 4500 BCE in southern Egypt. The offering of incense was shown in the illustrations in the *Book of the Dead*. The ancient incense was made from animal and bird fat.

Additional reading: Lucas, A. and Harris, J. (1999). *Ancient Egyptian materials and industries.* Mineola, N.Y.: Dover Pub.

Incense Burner — Mechanical
Origin: Egypt   Date: 4500 BCE

The Egyptians were the first to use the incense burner in ceremonies as far back as 4500 BCE. A Chinese text, dating 140 BCE, also described an incense burner, which was suspended in a system of concentric rings that kept it horizontal. Over time the incense burner design changed that enabled a slower burn for a longer lasting effect.

Additional reading: Lucas, A. and Harris, J. (1962). *Ancient Egyptian materials and industries.* London: E. Arnold Pub.

Inclined Plane — Mechanical
Origin: Africa   Date: Antiquity

The inclined plane was a convenient means of raising heavy loads. Africans were the first to develop and use this method of moving heavy objects. According to Herodotus, the pyramids were built with the help of lifting machines, the exact nature of which he did not describe. Ramps, in the form of inclined planes, served to bring the stones up to these elevated machines.

Additional reading: Parker, S. (1989). *McGraw-Hill concise encyclopedia of science and technology.* New York: McGraw-Hill Pub.

Incubator — Device
Origin: Egypt   Date: 600 BCE

Incubators were used in Egypt to hatch chicken and ostrich eggs around 600 BCE. It appears that the scholars and scientists of the period observed nature and copied it with crude man-made incubators, and by 250 BCE, the process was adopted in China and Syria.

Additional reading: Lewis, J. (2003). *Ancient Egyptians.* New York: Carroll and Graf Pub.

Inflatable Swimming Aid — Naval
Origin: Assyria   Date: 880 BCE

In 900 BCE, King Assui-Nasir-Apli II of Assyria developed an inflatable flotation device, enabling his troops to cross rivers and channels under the cover of darkness during war campaigns. The early inflatable device was made from animal skins and was designed to fit the individual for efficiency.

Additional reading: Eco, U. and Zorzoli, G. B. (1963). *The picture history of inventions, from plough to Polaris.* New York: Macmillan Co.

Ink — Communication
Origin: China   Date: 2500 BCE

The Chinese invented a liquid base ink around 2500 BCE. It was made from glue vapor and aromatic plant. Early drawings dating back to this time period show scribes writing and drawing using ink. The ink making process soon became a major part of everyday life in many areas of China.

Additional Reading: Fitzgerald, C., (1961). *China: A short cultural history.* New York: Praeger.

Inoculation — Medical
Origin: Congo   Date: 1200 BCE

Throughout history, humans have been plagued by countless unknown and strange illnesses. The medicine men of the Congo are credited with the first crude preventive treatment of unfamiliar disease. Smallpox was treated in the Congo around 1200 BCE, by taking a mixture of pustules from sick people and scratching it into the skin of healthy people, resulting in permanent immunity.

Additional reading: Imperato, P., (1977). *African folk medicine: Practices and beliefs of the Bambara and other peoples.* Baltimore: York Press.

Insect (Domestic) — Agriculture
Origin: China   Date: 1500 BCE

There were numerous species of silkworms around the world, but only the Eastern Asiatic variety has been domesticated since 1500 BCE. The Chinese silkworm, which lives on the leaves of the white mulberry tree, was China's gift to the ancient fashion world.

Additional reading: Baldwin, G.C. (1973). *Inventors and inventions of the ancient world.* New York: Four Winds.

Insecticide — Chemical
Origin: China   Date: 2100 BCE

Two thousand years before Christ, the Chinese were using dried, pounded pyrethrum found in chrysanthemum leaves to kill fleas. The use of leaf substances became widespread throughout Asia. Pyrethrin was applied as an insecticide in other regions of the world

Additional reading: Giscard d'Estaing, V. G. (1985). *The world almanac book of inventions.* New York: World Almanac Pub.

Insurance — Economics
Origin: Babylon   Date: 4000 BCE

In Babylonia, the practice of insurance consisted of borrowing funds for a commercial venture, which were then deposited with a third party who acted as banker. Smooth running of the business and the good faith of the operator were guaranteed by these funds, which the banker fully or partially owed.

Additional reading: Burke, J. (1978). *Connections,* Boston: Little Brown.

Interaction — Physics
Origin: Egypt   Date: 1700 BCE

An Egyptian scientist in antiquity identified certain particles of matter that interacted in various ways. The two forces were identified as gravitational and electromagnetic. The Egyptian priest Ahmes wrote about these charged states around 1700 BCE, describing how the interactions were incorporated in religious ceremonies.

Additional reading Pappademos, J. (1983) *An outline of Africa's role in the history of physics, in: Blacks in science.* New Brunswick Transaction Books.

Iron — Chemistry
Origin: Swaziland   Date: 43,000 BCE

Although wrought iron was a soft metal and more pliable than bronze, it was considered less valuable in ancient times. In 43,000 BCE, a tribe living in the West African region made a vital discovery. When heated repeatedly and hammered between heating, wrought iron became harder than bronze. The metal was heated by a traditional method of using charcoal. With the repetition of heating and beating the wrought iron, carbon particles on its surface were absorbed. The result was wrought iron enclosed in a casting of steel.

Additional reading: Schmidt, P. and Avery, D. (1996). *Complex iron and smelting and prehistoric culture in Tanzania.* Gainesville: University Press of Florida.

Irrigation — Civil
Origin: Egypt   Date: 2000 BCE

It is possible that early civilizations learned to encourage growth of wild plants by splashing water on the banks of a spring or stream as the earliest form of irrigation. It is certain that the shaduf, still widely used, was employed to water palms and vines, vegetable plots, and flowerbeds of Egyptians in the second millennium BCE.

Additional reading: Ki-Zerbo, J. (1990). *General history of Africa: Methodology and African prehistory.* Berkeley Calif.: University of California Press.

Irrigation Systems — System
Origin: China   Date: 1750 BCE

The Shang Dynasty in China on the flood plain of the Huang He (Yellow River) utilized the first irrigation system that redirected the flow and ultimately changed the water flow. This action was intended to save the villages from flooding. This was the earliest known system for controlling water for agriculture.

Additional reading: Baldwin, G., (1973). *Inventors and inventions of the ancient world.* New York: Four Winds Press.

Ivory — Tool
Origin: Africa   Date: Prehistoric

During the Paleolithic period, humans began to divide, cut, and process African ivory by hitting or striking with a pointed stone. Ivory and other bone materials from animals such as elephants, mammoth, hippopotamus, walrus, and narwhal became important articles of commerce.

Additional reading: Moore, F. (1931). *Ivory: Scourge of Africa.* London: Harpers & Bros.

J

Jade see **Quartzite.**

Jewelry Cosmetic
Origin: Africa Date: 45,000 BCE

The earliest recognizable jewelry consisted of ostrich shell beads from the Border Cave in South Africa, dating as early as 45,000 BCE. Crude artifacts dating back to this period that have been recovered are housed in museums around the world in locations such as London, Ethiopia, and America.

Additional reading: Carter, H. (1972). *The tomb of Tutankhamen: With 17 color plates and 65 monochrome illustrations and two appendices.* New York: Excalibur Books.

Joinery Construction
Origin: Africa Date: 1350 BCE

The art of jointing wood dates back to 1300 BCE. Several archeological digs in the lower basin region in East Africa have unearthed multiple pieces of wooden objects joined together with a variety of notches, cuts, and angles.

Additional reading: Perlin, J. (1991). *Forrest Journey: The role of wood in the development of civilization.* Cambridge Mass: Harvard Press.

Joint see **Universal Joint.**

Jubbe Domestic
Origin: Nubia Date: 720 BCE

The jubbe, a large vessel for liquor, was discovered in several tombs, including the tomb of Taharqa, the Pharaoh of Nubia from 710-644 BCE. Some jubbe were constructed from stone, clay, and metal. A number of them were created from chemically treated woods and straw.

Additional reading: Davidson, B. (1966). *Africa: History of a continent.* New York: Macmillan Co.

Junket Textile
Origin: India Date: 1450 BCE

By 1450 BCE, Indian fisherman plied their trade using the junket basket. Originally made of straw, the junket basket was designed to trap, capture, and hold fish and other sea creatures while allowing the water to escape. Early junkets were attached to bamboo and other plat-like rope. When submerged the basket was able to hold large quantities of sea food.

Additional reading: Kulke, J. (1998). *A history of India,* New York: Routledge.

Karaka Tree Agriculture
Origin: New Zealand Date: Antiquity

The karaka tree grew wild in antiquity in New Zealand and Australia. New Zealand was the first region to grow and use the seeds for domestication purposes. While the karaka fruit had an edible pulp, the kernel was raw and poisonous, and could be eaten only after roasting and drying in a running stream for a considerable length of time.

Additional reading: Babcock G. (Ed.) (2002). *Webster's third new international dictionary of the English language.* New York: Merrian-Webster.

Karate Sports
Origin: Japan Date: 3200 BCE

From pre-historic times to today, humans have used their limbs to defend themselves. The oldest records of kicking, throwing, wrestling, and punching techniques were found in Japan, dating around 3200 BCE. This warrior science laid the foundation for all martial arts systems, including kung fu and judo.

Additional reading: Iyi Kilindi, L. (1985). *African roots in Asian martial arts, Journal of African civilizations,* New Brunswick, N.J. 7 (1).

Kaross Textile
Origin: Africa Date: Antiquity

There is no exact date identifying the original development of what is now defined as the military uniform. The kaross, a kind of cloak, has existed since the Neolithic period. Nomads wore kaross, a sleeveless covering made from the skins of animals, often of different species, with the hair on. These outer garments were worn throughout Africa, Asia, India, and the Middle East as a protective covering for soldiers.

Additional reading: Clark, G., and Piggott, S., (1965). *Prehistoric societies*. New York: Knopf Pub.

Kelek   Mechanical
Origin: China   Date: 3600 BCE

The earliest evidence of the kelek dates back to China around 3600 BCE. The kelek, sometimes called a kilet, was a raft or float used to cross small bodies of water. The kelek was probably formed by inflating sheep-skins and bundling them together with reeds.

Additional reading: Schwartz, B. (1985). *The world of though in ancient China*. Cambridge: Harvard University Press.

Kell   Textile
Origin: Nubia   Date: 3000 BCE

The earliest mention of the shroud, later known as a kell, was in documents recovered in the southern region of Egypt. The kell was a woman's hair-net or cap. The style of the headdress varied from region to region. Early kell were made of feathers, beads, stones, wood, and skins.

Additional reading: Thurman, C., (1979). *The textiles, in ancient textiles from Nubia*. Chicago: Art Institute of Chicago.

Kelp   Agriculture
Origin: Africa   Date: 8000 BCE

Farmers along on the Nile cultivated kelp, a collective name for large seaweeds. Kelp was common along the sea coastal areas of the Africa. When areas became settled inland, some wild crops like corn, kelp, beans and other crops were also grown locally.

Additional reading: LeStrange, R. (1977). *A history of herbal plants*. New York: Arco Pub. Co.

Key   Mechanical
Origin: Mesopotamia   Date: 6000 BCE

Mesopotamia used locks and keys as early as 6000 BCE. This original key looked similar to a small garden rake, slightly bent around its shaft. At one end, it had teeth corresponding to the arrangement of

the pegs. When inserted, an up and down movement served to raise the pegs in such a way that the male part was freed.

Additional reading: David, A., (1986). *The pyramid builders of ancient Egypt: A modern investigation of pharaoh's workforce*. New York: Routledge.

Figure 22
Key
The illustration above shows a key made from iron that dates back as far as 1200 BCE

Keystone   Mechanical
Origin: Babylonia   Date: 1800 BCE

The Babylonians used complex mathematical concepts during the construction of the massive tomb of King Hammurabi. The last stone, placed at the summit of the arch, locked the entire structure together. This new construction locking system was considered one of the milestones of architectural design of the period.

Additional reading: (1979). *Ancient Records of Assyria and Babylon, vol I. Historical records of Assyria from the earliest times to Sargon*. Chicago: University of Chicago Press.

Khaki   Textile
Origin: India   Date: 300 BCE

As early as 300 BCE, the Indians produced a dust color drab cloth called khaki. The khaki cloth was primarily used by foot soldiers who braved the elements during military campaigns. The Indian and European armies used a woolen base khaki as late as the 1800 BCE. The khaki was a very dense and lightweight material which made it easy to carry during long journeys.

Additional reading: Kulke, J. (1998). *A History of India*. New York: Routledge.

Kiln   Mechanical
Origin: Mesopotamia   Date: 4000 BCE

A kiln was developed around 4000 BCE in

Mesopotamia. Most of the kilns were open-faced. The kiln chamber, fired by flames from a hearth located below, held the pottery. As far back as 3000 BCE, kilns in Iraq were heated to temperatures which vitrified the clay to acquire a glossy quality.

Additional reading: Baldwin, G., (1973). *Inventors and inventions of the ancient world*. New York: Four Winds Press.

Kite   Aviation
Origin: China   Date: 200 BCE

Kites were invented in the second century BCE by the Chinese general Han Sin. Kites were originally used as magical and ritualistic instruments. The Chinese armies used kites as locators and early warning systems. Some kites were color-coded, leading many researchers to conclude that the various colors had hidden meaning.

Additional reading: Hart, C., (1967). *Kites: An historical survey*. London: Faber and Faber.

Kneading (Baking)   Agriculture
Origin: Egypt   Date: Antiquity

During the time of Ramses III, the construction of a knead consisted of a wooden shaft that pointed vertically upwards. The shaft was provided with wings that reached almost as far as the inner walls of the kneading trough. These baking machines were common in many of the towns of Egypt.

Additional reading: Neuburger, O. (1930). *The technical arts and sciences of the ancients*. New York: The Macmillian Co.

Knife   see   **Ax.**

Knitting   see   **Fabric.**

Knob   Device
Origin: Palestine   Date: 3200 BCE

With the use of bowls and jars in the Middle East, the knob was developed to make the handling of these large containers possible. As the jugs became larger, the needs to attach different types of handles were

developed. The knobs and handles allowed for the hanging of pots over an open fire, carrying them, and the lifting out of ashes. The knob shape changed over time, but the same basic concept still remained.

Additional reading: Binford, L., (1981). *Bones: Ancient man and modern myths*. New York: Academic Press.

Krotala   Music
Origin: Egypt   Date: 2000 BCE

Wooden krotalas were hand-shaped instruments used in the worship of Hathor. The krotala instrument was considered to be the work of the goddess of music and love. The krotala instruments were noted for their ability to produce very pure tones that carried across great distances.

Additional reading: Grove, G. & Sadie, S, (1980). *The New Grove dictionary of music and musicians*. London: Macmillan Pub.

L

Label (text)   see   **Determinative.**

Lacquer   Domestic
Origin: Japan   Date: 600 BCE

The earliest recording of wooden sculptures being carved with a lacquer coating came from Aimu, Japan. The lacquer was a gold-colored varnish consisting chiefly of a solution of pale sap from trees. The chemically based lacquer coating sealed wooden objects, which sometimes changed the color, while preserving the life of the artifact.

Additional reading: Hitti, P. (1908). *The ancient history of China*. New York: Columbia University Press.

Lactic Acid   see   **Acacia Tree.**

Ladder   Construction
Origin: Nubia   Date: 2500 BCE

The Nubians were the first to develop a scaling ladder on wheels, depicted in a painting dating back to 2500

BCE. The ancient ladders were used in battle to scale walls, but the climbing tool was also employed by skilled craftsmen of the time.

Additional reading: Wells, H. (1922). *A short history of the world*. New York: Macmillan Co.

Lamp (Oil)   Domestic
Origin: Nigeria   Date: 50,000 BCE

The people who created cave paintings 25,000 to 50,000 years ago worked by the dim light of a sputtering animal-oil lamp. This was a lump of animal fat placed in the hollow of a stone or shell with a wick made of moss. Though burn marks on cave walls and roofs reveal that lamps were used, no lamps have survived.

Additional reading: Connah, G., (1981). *Three thousand years in Africa: Man and his environment in the lake Chad region of Nigeria*. Cambridge: Cambridge University Press.

Lasso   see   Snare.

Lathe   Machine
Origin: Africa   Date: 700 BCE

Discovered in the Lunda region of West Africa, wooden bowls, dating from the seventh century BCE, have obviously been turned on the lathe. The spring-pole innovation, which correlated two automatic actions, was a device that spun a worked piece of wood, metal, or other material, while a cutting or shaping tool was applied to its revolving surface.

Additional reading: Burke, J. (1978). *Connections*. Boston: Little Brown.

Lava   Chemistry
Origin: Africa   Date: Antiquity

The earliest recorded depiction of a volcano erupting was on cave drawings in Africa. Molten rock material formed much of the earth's surface. Two million years ago the northern region of Africa witnessed a lot of volcanic activity.

Additional reading: Parker, S. (1989). *McGraw-Hill concise encyclopedia of science and technology. 2nd Ed.*, New York: McGraw-Hill.

Lavatory   Domestic
Origin: Egypt   Date: 4500 BCE

In Egypt, lavatories were found in the bathrooms of tombs dating back to 4500 BCE. A different type of toilet was developed by the Indus Valley civilization during the same time period. The ancient metropolis of Mohenjo-Daro, dating to 2500 BCE, built an even more sophisticated style of lavatory that was enclosed and contained a series of toilet-like structures.

Additional reading: James, P. and Thorpe, N. (1994). *Ancient inventions*. New York: Ballantine Books.

Law   Legal System
Origin: Babylonia   Date: 1760 BCE

In ancient Babylonia, rules of custom were enforced because people desired to be socially accepted rather than excluded. The first relatively complete law code still read today was established by Hammurabi, king of Babylonia, who reigned from 1772-1750 BCE.

Additional reading: (1979). *Ancient records of Assyria and Babylon, vol. I. Historical records of Assyria from the earliest times to Sargon*, Chicago: University of Chicago Press.

Law of Motion   Physics
Origin: China   Date: 250 BCE

The Chinese book *Mo Ching,* written by followers of the philosopher Mo-Tzu in 250 BCE, contained a statement of the first Law of Motion that Sir Isaac Newton restated in his Principia: "A body continues in a state of rest or in uniform motion will continue until acted upon by outside forces."

Additional reading Yoke-Ho Peng, (1966). *The astronomical chapters of the Chin Shu*. Paris: Mouton.

Laxative   see   Castor Oil.

Lead   Chemistry
Origin: Egypt   Date: 3500 BCE

Lead, atomic number 82 and one of the oldest metals known to man, has been used as since 3500 BCE, starting with the Egyptians. Lead is principally found in the mineral galena. It is one of the four most largely produced and used metals. Its chief applications are in construction work, in alloys, in storage battery plates, and as a protective coating for iron and steel.

Additional reading: Diop, C. (1981). "Origin of the ancient Egyptians" *General History of Africa,* UNESCO.

Lead Glazing   Chemistry
Origin: Babylonia   Date: 800 BCE

Lead glazing was found on the brick façade of a gateway in Babylon, circa 800 BCE. Lead as an uncombined metal was too soft and unattractive to have invited many uses. However, the metal was also used as an allied ingredient of bronze, glass, and glazes. Glazes began to be applied to bricks and tiles in Mesopotamia, often with additional coloring materials such as the salts of copper.

Additional reading: Parker, S. (1989). *McGraw-Hill concise encyclopedia of science and technology in the ancient world. 2nd Ed.,* New York: McGraw-Hill Pub.

Leather   Material
Origin: Egypt   Date: Antiquity

Egypt and Nubia were early domesticators of cattle. The animal skins were harvested as body covering for functions ranging from military wear to everyday clothing. During antiquity, the Egyptians had at their disposal a fairly extensive set of tools for working leather. Knives and shoemaker's awls have been uncovered that resemble contemporary tools.

Additional reading: Bunch, B. and Hellemans, A. (1993). *The timetables of technology: A chronology of the most important people and events in the history of technology.* New York: Simon & Schuster.

Leavened Bread   see   Bread.

Leek   Agriculture
Origin: Egypt   Date: 4200 BCE

The farmers of the Fertile Crescent were the earliest known to domestically grow and cultivate the leek. The leek was and is a culinary herb used to flavor food. Closely related to the onion, it differs in that the bulbous part of the cylindrical and its leaves are flat and broad.

Additional reading: Travers, B. (1996). *The Gale encyclopedia of science,* Detroit, Mich: Gale Research.

Legume   Agriculture
Origin: Babylonia   Date: 5000 BCE

The legume plant was first grown and cultivated in Babylonia as early as 5000 BCE. A common food source among the nomadic tribes, the fruit was the edible portion of a leguminous plant. It appears that this crop was not a major food source during this historical period.

Additional reading: Bailey, L., (1950). *The standard encyclopedia of horticulture. 3 vols.* New York: Macmillan Co.

Lens   Optical
Origin: Egypt   Date: 4200 BCE

As early as 4200 BCE, the Egyptians used a clear lens-like stone to set angles and structural forms. Lenses were later adapted for correcting vision, often after some form of medical surgery.

Additional reading: Ki-Zerbo, J. (1990). *General history of Africa: Methodology and African prehistory.* Berkeley, Calif.: University of California Press.

Lentil   Agriculture
Origin: Babylonia   Date: 1790 BCE

The farmers of the Fertile Crescent were the earliest known to domestically grow and cultivate lentil. The seed of this leguminous plant was used for herbal and medicinal purposes. The lentil plant spread throughout the region.

Additional reading: Greggs, B. (1981). *Green pharmacy: A history of herbal medicine.* New York: Vicking Press.

Lettuce   Agriculture
Origin: North Africa   Date: Antiquity

The cultivation of lettuce (latuca saliva) dates back to ancient times. Its wild counterpart grew in central Africa, Asia and Europe. All ancient lettuces came from the long-leafed form and were classified as cas. Lettuce cultivation did not spread north of the Alps until the Middle Ages.

Additional reading: Beston, H. (1935). *Herbs and the earth.* New York: Doubleday, Doran and Co.

Lever   Mechanical
Origin: Africa   Date: Antiquity

Levers were natural appliances used by all prehistoric peoples. Ancient Africans employed leverage in numerous tools. There were manifold devices dependent on the action of the lever that was used for raising water. Examples of these devices are depicted on the relief at the palace of Nineveh dating from the seventh century BCE.

Additional reading: Africanus, L. (1896). *The history and description of Africa. 3 Vols.* ed. London: Brown, Kakluyt Society.

Library   System
Origin: Iraq   Date: 668 BCE

Assurbanipal, King of Assyria from 668-627 BCE, was the founder of the world's first great library at Nineveh in Iraq. His libraries took the first steps leading to information science. Texts running over more than one tablet often contained a brief summary of the contents as well as the copyist's name. Tablets were stored together on shelves in bundles or baskets bearing clay labels. Contents and locations of the various baskets were cataloged.

Additional reading: Staikos, K., (2000). *The great libraries from antiquity to the renaissance 3000 B.C. to 1600 A.D.* New Castle, Del.: Oak Knoll Press.

Life raft   see   Boat.

Lighthouse   Illumination
Origin: Egypt   Date: 285 BCE

In 285 BCE, a lighthouse was built according to the instructions of Egyptian King Ptolemy II. This lighthouse measured more than 130 meters in height. A wood fire was kept burning all night at its top. It was destroyed by an earthquake in 130 BCE.

Additional reading: Hague, D., (1975). *Lighthouse: Their architecture, history and archaeology.* New York: Gomer Press.

Limb (False)   Medicine
Origin: Egypt   Date: 1200 BCE

The strangest examples of false limbs were found on Egyptian mummies. These prosthetics were not attached for medical reasons, as Egyptian surgeons were extremely reluctant to perform amputations. Ancient Egyptians firmly believed that the physical body had to be preserved in its entirety for the immortal soul to reach the next world. However, the embalmers, when necessary, would add false limbs to restore bodies for the afterlife.

Additional reading: Bliquez, L., (1983). *Classical prosthetics.* London: Sergius Silus.

Lime   Mineral
Origin: Babylonia   Date: 1800 BCE

Prior to King Sumuabum, who ruled Babylonia from 1881 to 1849 BCE, the mortar used to construct the massive stone tombs was mixed with such items as straw, clay, gravel, and water. The builders of King Sumuabum's tomb combined an additional substance known as lime. Lime allowed the mortar to harden, making it stronger than the previous mortars of the period.

Additional reading:Rogers, R.W., (1915). *A history of Babylonia and Assyria.* Cincinnati: Libraries Press.

Limestone   Chemistry
Origin: Egypt   Date: 3100 BCE

Limestone consists essentially of calcium carbonate but contains various other ingredients, such as silica, clay, oxide of iron, or magnesium carbonate; and it differs radically in quality and hardness. Limestone was found abundantly in Egypt around the bordering hills of the Nile Valley outside Cairo. A large number of tombs of all periods were cut from limestone rock.

Additional reading: Lewin, S., (1968). 'The conservation of limestone objects and structures.' Paris: ICOMOS.

Line   see   Plumb Line.

Lines of Force   see   Electricity.

Linear
Mechanical
Origin: Mesopotamia   Date: 1250 BCE

Around 1250 BCE, the Mesopotamians converted rotary motion into back-and-forth motion, later known as linear movement in their mechanical devices. The innovation produced a variety of new mechanical devices, allowing for the development of many more compact instruments.

Additional reading: Todhunter, I. (1874). A history of mathematical theories of attraction and the figure of the earth. London:

Linear Equations
Mathematics
Origin: China   Date: 250 BCE

As early as 250 BCE, Chai-Chang Swang-Shu wrote nine chapters of the mathematical arts. The text was one of the most influential Chinese books of mathematics, containing more than two hundred problems including linear equations on engineering, surveying, calculation, and agriculture.

Additional reading: Smith, D. (1987). *A concise history of mathematics. 4 th ed.* Boston: Dover.

Linen
Clothing
Origin: Africa   Date: 6000 BCE

Flax produces a fiber that can be interwoven similar to the way twigs or bark might be interwoven to form a basket. Strong thread was made by twisting fibers together. The result was called linen. Like the word linen, the word line comes from the ancient word for flax. As early as 6000 BCE, linen cords were used for fishing. Nets were made by weaving these cords.

Additional reading: Asimov, I(1989). *Asimov's chronology of science and discovery.* New York: Harper & Row.

List
Science
Origin: Mesopotamia   Date: 290 BCE

The earliest known lists detailing a body of scientific facts dates back to 290 BCE, in Mesopotamia. This list, the first known presentation of complete scientific works, contained catalogues of signs and works, duly classified according to various criteria. The lists later expanded with a paralleled column to indicate the Akkadian equivalents.

Addition readings: Bottero J. (1987). *Mesopotamia.* Chicago: University of Chicago Press.

Literature
Communication
Origin: Syria   Date: 2500 BCE

The Sumerians, who invented cuneiform writing, were the first to put tales and stories into text. Discovered in the remains of the library of Ashurbanipal, the last king of Assyria who ruled from 668 to 626 BCE, was the story of Gilgamesh, the earliest recorded major work of literature. Written at least 1300 years before Homer wrote the *Iliad* and the *Odyssey,* it gained international importance during the mid-nineteenth century when an expert translated the Gilgamesh version of the flood. The similarity between this epic and the Biblical flood intensified the search for more cuneiform tablets.

Additional reading: Canfora, L., (1989). *The vanished library.* London: Hutchinson Radius pub.

Llama
Domestic
Origin: Peru   Date: 5000 BCE

As early as 5000 BCE, the Peruvian Indians were domesticating the llama. The llama was raised as a main food source. The local Andean nomads also employed this camelid animal as a working beast to carry small items from place to place.

Additional reading: Binford, L., (1981). *Bones: Ancient man and modern myths.* New York: Academic Press.

Lock
Mechanical
Origin: Mesopotamia   Date: 6000 BCE

The oldest known lock, dating back to 6000 BCE, consisted of two massive pieces of wood, shaped so that they fitted into each other. These pieces were held together by free pins passed through the tops of the wooden pieces and arranged in variable order.

Additional reading: (1979). Ancient *Mesopotamia: Portrait of a dead civilization,* Rev. ed. Chicago: University of Chicago Press.

Lock (Canal)   Civil
Origin: China   Date: 70 BCE

A crude sort of lock was engineered on rivers in China around 70 BCE. It consisted of a dam with a removable section called a flash lock through which a boat could be drawn. With the Chinese invention of the pound lock, the operators could raise or lower the level of an enclosed section of the waterway.

Additional Reading: Fitzgerald, C., (1961). *China: A short cultural history.* New York: Praeger.

Lock Tumbler   Devices
Origin: Syria   Date: 2000 BCE

The early process of locking prior to 2000 BCE, was done by solid pins that were notched into position. The Assyrian locksmiths replaced this process with a series of pins that were able to move in multiple positions within one contained housing. Around 2000 BCE, Assyrian locks had pin tumblers and were installed on doors and windows by using large wooden bolts. Several centuries later, lock tumblers were made from metal.

Additional reading: Derry, T. and Williams, T. , (1960). *A short history of technology from the earliest times to A.D. 1900.* Oxford: Clarendon Press.

Lodestone   Mineral
Origin: China   Date: Antiquity

Loadstones were cited in the Chinese Book of the Devil Valley Master. The book contains the first known reference to a lodestone's alignment with the earth's magnetic field. The lodestone was called a south-pointer, although it was evidently used for divination and not for locating poles.

Additional reading: Thomson, J. (1921). *Elements of mathematics theory of electricity and magnetism.* Cambridge: University Press.

Log   Mathematics
Origin: Sumer   Date: 2500 BCE

As early as 2500 BCE, Sumerian scholars developed units of measures such as shekel, mina, log, homer, cubit, and foot. These standard units of measurements were adopted as acceptable codes of measures.

Additional reading: West, B. (1982). *The Prentice-Hall encyclopedia of mathematics.* Englewood Cliff, N.J.: Prentice-Hall Pub.

Logarithm   Mathematics
Origin: Babylonia   Date: 600 BCE

The Babylonians developed many advanced mathematic concepts. The Babylonians' methods of deduction and proofs were handed down in an unbroken line of advanced mathematical functions. John Napier cites Euclid's travels through Babylon during this time period, where he explored the use of logarithms, normally computed to the base of 10 and used for shortening mathematical calculations.

Additional reading: Dickson, L. (1966). *History of the theory of numbers.* New York: Chelsea.

Loom   Textile
Origin: Egypt   Date: 4000 BCE

The loom dates back to 4000 BCE, according to carbon testing of equipment found in Egyptian tombs. For centuries, the loom's design did not change much, and weaving of cloth developed into a significant industry. Traders and others took this material production process to other areas of the world.

Additional reading: Abbot, C. (1944). *Great inventions.* New York: Smithsonian Institution Series, Inc.

Lute   Music
Origin: Sumer   Date: 2000 BCE

The Sumerian long-necked lute dates to 2000 BCE. It had two or three strings and was plucked with a plectrum, and had a small body shaped like a half pear. The shape of the lute was considered odd. The shape of the lute changed over time and ultimately took on the shape of a small guitar.

Additional reading: Fink, R., (1988). "The Oldest Song in the World." *Archaeologia Musicalis* 2.

Lyre   Music
Origin: Sumer   Date: 4000 BCE

The oldest known lyre dates to Sumer around 6000 years

ago. It was used in instrumental and choral ensembles. During this period the lyre was widely considered by many to be the musical instrument of choice.

Additional reading: Kilmer, A. (1976). *Sounds from silence: Recent discoveries in ancient near eastern music.* Berkeley: Bit Enki Pub.

Lyric   **see**   **Song.**

M

Machine   Automation
Origin: Africa   Date: 10,000 BCE

The bow drill was one of the earliest machines. It used rotation and was the "workhorse" of the period. A rod, such as an arrow shaft, was placed in the loop of a bowstring; and as the bow was moved back and forth, the linear motion was transferred into rapid rotary motion. The presence of many beads with what appear to be drilled holes suggests that the device was known in Neolithic times, or even in the late Stone Age.

Additional reading: Parker, S. (1989). *McGraw-Hill concise encyclopedia of science and technology. 2nd ed.,* New York: McGraw-Hill Pub.

Magic Spell   **see**   **Drug.**

Magnet   **see**   **Lodestone.**

Magnifying Glass   Materials
Origin: Assyria   Date: 3000 BCE

In 1853, Sir Austin Henry Layard returned from his excavations at Nimrud, one of the capitals of the ancient kingdom of Assyria in northern Iraq. Of the many treasures he submitted to the British Museum, one was a small oval piece of polished rock crystal, about one-quarter of an inch thick and shaped as a lens. It had one flat and one convex surface, the earliest known specimen of the burning and magnifying glass.

Additional reading: Rogers, R., (1915). *A history of Babylonia and Assyria. Vol 2,* Cincinnati: Books for Libraries Press.

Maize   Agriculture
Origin: America   Date: 8000 BCE

The Maya lived in the flat land areas in present Yucatan, Guatemala, Belize, and Honduras. As early as 8000 BCE, they worshipped natural things such as the wind and the rain. A number of the religious ceremonies involved foods such as salt, peas, maize, and other crops. The cultivation of maize was a large part of Mayan food production.

Additional reading: Wisseman, S. (1994) *Ancient technologies and archaeological materials,* Langhorne. Pa.: Gordon and Breach Science Pub.

Malt   Agriculture
Origin: Egypt   Date: 4200 BCE

Farmers of Fertile Crescent were the earliest known in Egypt. King Menes used barley and an assortment of grains and malt liquids, brewing and distilling them to produce a variety of malt flavors. They were used as food additives and for medical purposes.

Additional reading: Angier, B. (1974). *Field guide to edible wild medicinal plants.* Harrisburg, Pa: Stackpole Books.

Mandrake Plant   Medicine
Origin: Nubia   Date: 3800 BCE

Ancient Nubians, having discovered that many wild plants offered natural healing results, soon used them for a host of medical treatments. As early as 3800 BCE, the mandrake plant was grown and used extensively in many parts of the country as a medicinal herb. Many practitioners of the period believed that this plant could heal tooth problems and other body pains. In large doses mandrake acted as an anesthetic and in weaker amounts was said to work as an aphrodisiac.

Additional reading: Van Sertima, I. (1983). *Blacks in science: Ancient and modern.* New Brunswick: Transaction Books.

Manual (Scientific)   **see**   **Treatise.**

Manuscript (Medical)   Medicine
Origin: Egypt   Date: 2980 BCE

Imhotep, often called the world's first scientist,

wrote the first known medical manuscript as well as designed King Zoser's pyramid. Imhotep, an Egyptian physician, architect, and counselor to King Zoser, flourished around 2950 BCE.

Additional Reading: Chandler, C. (1965). *Famous modern men of medicine*. New York: Dodd Mead.

Map (Construction)   Navigation
Origin: Babylonia   Date: 500 BCE

The oldest surviving world map that was mass produced dates from around 500 BCE. Early maps were drawn on stone, wood, bone, and leather, as well as on many types of paper.

Additional reading: Harley, J., and Woodward, D., (1987). *The history of cartography*. Chicago: University of Chicago.

Map   Navigation
Origin: Babylonia   Date: 13,000 BCE

Many archeologists believed that crude maps have been inscribed on trees, animal bones and other artifacts. Many of these crude mapping charts were often carried by wanderers and traders. The oldest recovered map was unearthed in Babylon dating back to 13,000 B.C. A bone artifact containing a map found in Babylon depicted the region immediately around the site.

Additional reading: Hapgood, C., (1966). *Maps of the ancient sea kings: Evidence of advanced civilization in the ice age*. Philadelphia: Chilton Books.

Map (Relief)   Navigation
Origin: China   Date: 205 BCE

In 205 BCE, Emperor Ch'in Huang Ti constructed a relief map of his empire with the rivers formed from flowing mercury and the heavens depicted above. The map was constructed on a heavy cloth-like material that was thought to be waterproof. This map was sufficiently durable to be transported to different locations with the emperor as he travelled.

Additional reading: Travers, B. (1996). *The Gale encyclopedia of science*. New York: Gale Research.

Marble   Entertainment
Origin: Nubia   Date: 4500 BCE

Nubian marbles were discovered that date from around 4500 BCE. It is hard to determine if they were from a specific game or just a set of individual marbles. These round shape bone marbles were the earliest form of children's entertainment.

Additional reading: De Camp, L. , (1970). *The ancient engineers*. Cambridge Mass.: MIT Press..

Marble   see   Granite.

Martensite   Materials
Origin: Palastine   Date: 1300 BCE

Dating back to 1300 BCE, a miner's pick was found at Mt. Adri in northern Palestine containing martensite. Martensite was not a common nor easily found substance and craftsmen sought this element for its metallurgical uses. The analysis of the sample revealed a sophisticated manipulation of iron into steel.

Additional reading: Robinson, T. & Oesterley, W. (1932). *A history of Israel. Vols. 1-2*. Oxford: The Clarendon Press.

Martial Art   see   Karate.

Masonry   Construction
Origin: Nubia   Date: 3300 BCE

Ancient Nubian stone statues, particularly those carved from hard materials such as diorite, granite, quartzite, and schist, have long been a source of admiration because the tools that were used resulted in excellent workmanship. Modern researchers now understand the ancient method of working stone in part from the tool marks left on objects. This type of stonework method was particularly true of statues of which a number of unfinished examples still exist.

Additional reading: Payne, E., (1964). *The pharaohs of ancient Egypt*. New York: Random House.

Mass Production — System
Origin: Egypt   Date: 4000 BCE

The use of tools and jigs to produce interchangeable parts led to what is called mass production. It was employed by the Egyptians in the building of the pyramids. Skilled craftsmen were quickly employed in factory-like settings to produce dies and tools.

Additional reading: Abbot, D. (1986). *The biographical dictionary of scientist. Engineers and inventors.* New York: Harper & Row.

Massage — Medicine
Origin: Japan   Date: 600 BCE

The Japanese are credited with structuring the practice of massage as a part of medical treatment of certain illnesses. The Japanese developed written forms and procedures associated with the massage practice. The Chinese used techniques of massaging earlier as healing therapies.

Additional reading: Talbott, J. (1970). *A biographical history of medicine*: New York: Grvne & Stratton.

Mastabah — Architecture
Origin: Egypt   Date: 2600 BCE

The builders of the pharaoh tombs used the Mastabah chamber to house a large number of artifacts and mummies. The mastabah were isolated chambers and were designed for numerous purposes, such as animal collections for the afterlife. This room was usually separated and more secure. Some chambers housed precious jewelry, clothes, food, and other items needed for the afterlife.

Additional reading: Hawkes, J. (1966). *Pharaohs of Egypt.* New York. American Heritage Publishing Co.

Material (Woven) — Textiles
Origin: Jordan   Date: 3700 BCE

The oldest known woven mats were made in Beidha, Jordan, and date as far back as 3700 BCE. The wearing of the woven material was reserved for the rich and the privileged few.

Additional reading: Clark, G., and Piggott, S., (1965). *Prehistoric Societies*. London: Penguin.

Mat Covering   see   Carpet.

Mathematics (Numbers) — Mathematics
Origin: Egypt   Date: 900 BCE

Since the invention of the abacus, Egyptians developed the use of numbers for a series of mathematical functions. In the ninth century BCE, the Egyptian scholar, Al-Jabr Wal Mugabalah's textbook brought Arabic-Hindu numbers and other parts of the world. His textbook was considered by some as the mathematical model for mathematics functions from addition to geometry.

Additional reading: Turnbull, H.W., (1969). *The great mathematicians.* New York: New York University Press.

Mattock — Mechanical
Origin: Syria   Date: 400 BCE

The mattock was a digging tool, affixed with a blade at right angles to the handle and used during the harvesting of crops such as corn, peas and others. Although the date of its origin is unknown, the mattock appeared in Syrian literature as early as 400 BCE.

Additional reading: Semenov, S., (1964). *Pre-historic technology; an experimental study of the oldest tools and artifacts from traces of manufacture and wear.* New York: Barnes and Noble.

Measurement — Mathematics
Origin: Sumer   Date: 200 BCE

Around 200 BCE, the Sumerian system of measures included the shekel and mina, as well as units of capacity (the log, 541 ml. or 33 cu. in., and the homer, equal to 720 logs) and units of length (the cubit and the foot, which is two-thirds of a cubit).

Additional reading: Ashurst, F., (1982). *Founders of modern mathematics.* London: Fredrick Muller.

Measuring Instrument   see   Ruler.

Medical Book — Medicine
Origin: Egypt   Date: 2000 BCE

The earliest Egyptian medical texts listed drug mixture

of recipes for practicing physicians. The various diseases of the day were vaguely referred to in the texts. Ebers medical papyrus, dating from 1600 BCE, described forty-seven diseases, including symptoms, diagnoses of different cases, and prescriptions for treatments. Later texts described causes of an illness ascertained by the examination of omens and how the patients should be treated.

Additional reading: Singer, C., and Underwood E., (1962). *A story history of medicine.* New York: Clarendon Press.

Medical Diagnosis — Medicine
Origin: China   Date: 2595 BCE

The Chinese emperor Huang-Ti lived and developed the medical text Nei Ching. In the medical text, Emperor Huang-Ti in 25 BCE, described the four steps to a medical diagnosis: observation, auscultation (listening to the sounds that arise within organs), interrogation, and palpation (touching). As time passed and this medical diagnosis process spread, it became known as look, listen, ask, and feel.

Additional Reading: Castiglioni, A. (1941). *A history of medicine.* New York: A.A. Knopf.

Medical Ethics — Medical
Origin: Mesopotamia   Date: 1775 BCE

As early as 2000 BCE, the Mesopotamian physicians were governed by the Code of Hammurabi, this document included the earliest known system of medical ethics. The code of medical ethics document remained in practice for many years. When modern medicine refers to medical ethics many of the ethical principles date back to the Code of Hammurabi writings.

Additional reading: Singer, C., and Underwood, E., (1962). *A short history of medicine.* New York: Oxford University Press.

Medical Instrument — Medical
Origin: Babylonia   Date: 1800 BCE

The description and use of medical instruments came from the Babylonian Code of Hammurabi, which listed more than fifty medical instruments used by doctors. It contained a scale of fees and punishments for surgeons. For example, "If the doctor shall open an abscess with a bronze knife and kill the patient… his hand shall be cut off."

Additional reading: Bennion, E., (1979). *Antique medical instruments.* Berkeley, Calif: University of California Press.

Medical Manuscript — Medical
Origin: Egypt   Date: 2980 BCE

Imhotep, an Egyptian physician to King Zoser, lived around 2980 BCE, and was refered to as the world's first scientist. He wrote the first known medical manuscript, the forerunner to the first medical textbook.

Additional reading: Van Sertima, I. (1983). *Blacks in science: Ancient and modern.* New Brunswick: Transaction Books.

Medical Practice — Medical
Origin: Iraq   Date: 2700 BCE

The first known doctor was named Lulu, who practiced in the country of Sumer around 2700 BCE. In Egypt, fifty doctors were known to have their own practices during 2600 BCE. Around 2400 BCE the first medical papyri were written, describing some of their operations.

Additional reading: Bishop, W., (1960). *The early history of surgery.* London: Robert Hale Pub.

Medical Procedure (Manual) — Medical
Origin: Egypt   Date: 1600 BCE

A medical procedure manual was developed about one hundred and seventy five years after the Code of Hammurabi developed a code of ethics. The Egyptians wrote a textbook detailing medical procedures for different illnesses. Topics included arthritis, hookworm, infection, and surgery for head injuries. This medical textbook had over five hundred medical procedures outlined in detailed. The medical historians believe that during translation numerous other medical procedures were apparently lost.

Additional reading: Van Sertima, I. (1983). *Blacks in science: Ancient and modern.* New Brunswick: Transaction Books.

Medical School Medicine
Origin: Egypt Date: 250 BCE

The first medical school was started in Alexandria, Egypt, around 250 BCE, and lasted until massive military invasions caused it to close in 48 BCE. It was the only center in the ancient world where the human body was studied as a pure science.

Additional Reading: Castiglioni, A. (1941). *A history of medicine.* New York: A.A. Knopf.

Medical Transplant Medical
Origin: India Date: 600 BCE

The reconstruction of a nose was performed in India as early as 600 BCE. The new nose was constructed from stiff cloth. The transplanted nose was fully functioning. The transplant practice was only done for the ruling class and wealthy.

Additional reading: Kulke, J. (1998). *A history of India.* New York: Routledge.

Mercury Chemistry
Origin: Egypt Date: 1500 BCE

The silver-white liquid was used in Egypt as early as 1500 BCE. The most common source was from the processing of cinnabar, found primarily in the eastern regions of Egypt. Its most important use during the period was in pesticides and herbicides.

Additional reading: Considine, D. and Considine, G., (1983). *Van Nostrand's scientific encyclopedia.* 6th Edition, New York: Reinhold, Co.

Meridian Astronomy
Origin: Mesopotamia Date: 2000 BCE

The concept of equal latitudes was first used by the Mesopotamians to calculate the precise direction of the north point. The early theory about astronomy deals with the points, before and after, at which the shadow just touched the circle traced on the sand around the shadow clock were noted, and the arc was bisected. The device was used to chart stars.

Additional reading: Parker, S. (1989). *McGraw Hill concise encyclopedia of science and technology. 2nd edition,* New York: McGraw-Hill Pub.

Metal Chemistry
Origin: Egypt Date: 4000 BCE

The exact date in which metal was mined for domestc uses is unclear. Some historical records indicate that around 4000 BCE, man processed metal. A metal, somewhat black in color, comprised of any number of alloys of sulfur with silver lead and copper, was used to decorate metallic objects by means of inlay.

Additional Readings: Schmidt, P. and Avery. D., (1996). *Complex iron smelting and prehistoric culture in Tanzania.* Florida: University of Florida Press.

Metal (Casting) see **Cast Iron.**

Metal Leaf Chemistry
Origin: Egypt Date: 3500 BCE

Exactly when humans first selected gold as the metal of choice is unclear. Gold leaf was found almost everywhere in prehistoric times. Goldsmiths used gold as far back as 3500 BCE. Proper gilding, with the help of gold leaf, occurred in the Egyptian kingdom.

Additional reading: Sutton, J., (1997). The African lords of the intercontinental gold trade before the Black Death. London: *Antiquaries Journal,* 77, 221-42.

Metal Pipe Material
Origin: Egypt Date: 400 BCE

About 400 BCE, the Egyptians designed the pipe. Originally made of baked clay, the pipe was used to supply water to various areas and houses in the towns of the Empire. Chalk mixed with olive oil was used to make the pipe watertight.

Additional reading: Lucas, A. and Harris, J. (1960). *Ancient Egyptian materials and industries.* London: E. Arnold Pub.

Metal Plating Chemistry
Origin: Egypt Date: 4000 BCE

The Egyptians used equal parts of silver, copper, and sulfur in their metal plating process. Tin-plating, known since prehistoric times, was effected by dipping objects in molten tin and so skillfully done by the

Gauls that tin-plated objects were not distinguishable from silver ones.

Additional reading: Shore, D. (1983). Steel-making in ancient Africa. *Journal of African civilizations*. [New Brunswick, N.J: Douglass College, Rutgers University] 5 (1-2).

Metallurgy   Material
Origin: Syria   Date: 1200 BCE

Metallurgists in Syria discovered that the addition of tin ore to copper before smelting produced a harder, more useful metal and was easier to cast. The usefulness of the new metal, known as bronze, was such that the era became known as the Bronze Age.

Additional reading: Wisseman, S. (1994). *Ancient technologies and archeological materials.* New York: Gordon and Breach Pub.

Meteorite   see   Comet.

Micralith   see   Triangle.

Migration (Group)   Transportation
Origin: Africa   Date: Prehistoric

In East Africa, the humanoid (human like) species were the first to make tools and use wood sticks for walking aids. They were also the first to leave Africa in large migration units to far off places such as Asia and eventually Europe. The earliest firm evidence of human artifacts were found in East Africa were from archeological digging that showed common skeleton structures.

Additional Reading: Trefil, J. (1992). *1001 things everyone should know about science.* New York: Doubleday Pub.

Military   see   Army.

Milk   see   Dairy.

Mill   see   Rotary Mill.

Millet   see   Cereal.

Millstone   Mechanical
Origin: Egypt   Date: 100 BCE

Invented around 100 BCE, the millstone was two heavy disk-like stones, one atop the other. With the bottom stone fixed, the top stone rotated by means of hand bars protruding from its circumference. Set on a horizontal wooden frame above a swift-running stream, a vertical shaft or axle was fastened to the center of the upper stone. The millstone was used in early construction sites

Additional reading: Usher, A., (1954). *A history of mechanical inventions.* 2nd editions, Cambridge: Harvard University Press.

Mina   Mathematics
Origin: Sumer   Date: 2500 BCE

As far back as 2500 BCE, the Sumerians developed many mathematical firsts. They, over the next few centuries, developed a system of standard weights and measures, including such units as the shekel, the mina, the log, the homer, the cubit, and the foot. These forward-thinking mathematicians have been acknowledged as pioneers in the field of architecture, mathematics, astronomy, and science.

Additional Reading: Parkinson, C. L. (1985). Break-throughs: A chronology of great achievements in science and mathematics. Boston: G.K. Hall.

Mineral compound   see   Chemical Textbook.

Mining   Mining
Origin: Swaziland   Date: 43,000 BCE

Organized mining began in Egypt around 3000 BCE, Gold, silver, and copper were some of the most popular materials sought. The early mining process was human intensive. Over a wide period of time the mining process became more dependent on tools and newly developed machines.

Additional reading: "43,000 year old Mines Discovered in Swaziland." (1970) New York. *The New York Times*, p 6.

Mint — Agriculture
Origin: Egypt Date: 6000 BCE

The Nubians used mint as a healing substance but the Egyptians are credited as the first to plant and cultivate the plant. Farmers of Fertile Crescent were the earliest known to domestically grow and cultivate the mint plant. The leaves of the mint plant were brewed as early as 6000 B.C. for their soothing flavor.

Additional reading: Dyer T., (1889). *The folklore of plants*. New York: Appleton and Co.

Mirror — Materials
Origin: Nubia Date: 3000 BCE

The concept of image reflection has engaged humankind from the beginning of time. Prehistorically, many natural objects such as still water, later reflective artifacts, have allowed man to see himself. The Nubians are credited with being the first society to construct reflective mirrors. The first mirrors were made of silver, gold, and bronze. Egyptians were crafting mirrors of tin and polished steel during the third millennium.

Additional reading: Gosse, A. (1923). *The civilization of the ancient Egyptians*. London: T.C. and E.C. Jack, Ltd.

Fig. 23
Reflective mirror

Money (Clay Token) — Economics
Origin: Syria Date: 8000 BCE

The earliest forms of clay tokens dating back to 8000 BCE, were found at sites near present-day Syria. The tokens measured the values of farming yields. Tokens evolved over the next 5000 years and were used as a kind of currency in some locations until 1500 BCE.

Additional reading: Finley, M., (1973). *The ancient economy*. Berkeley, Calif.: University of California Press.

Money (Coinage) — Economics
Origin: China Date: 3000 BCE

Different objects at various times were used as a means of monetary exchange. In China, as early as the year 2697 BCE, issued paper money, produced from the fiber of the mulberry tree. Currency of metal had to be weighted in order to determine its value. There were, for example, rings made from precious metal and were weighed and used as money.

Additional reading: Finley, M., (1973). *The ancient economy*. Berkeley Calif.: University of California Press.

Mongoose — Domestic
Origin: Nubia Date: 800 BCE

The problem of pest and rodent control has vexed humans since prehistoric times. The Nubians experimented with different wild animals in efforts to control the population of pests. The first known domestically-raised animal deployed to restrain rodents was the mongoose. A small and agile mammal, the mongoose was raised to subdue the spread of small rodents and their eggs; it was also kept in some homes to be eaten.

Additional reading: Alexander, J. (1993). *Beyond the Nile: The influence of Egypt and Nubia in Sub-Saharan Africa*. New York: Expedition vol. 2. 35, 51-61.

Mortar — Material
Origin: Egypt Date: 600 BCE

The early Egyptians were noted for the production of wheat, corn, and barley. The Egyptians developed a mortar, a cup-shaped container in which grain and other foodstuffs were ground. The mortar was constructed out of thin, lightweight metal and formed into shape using an anvil and chase.

Additional reading: Anquandah, J. (1993). The Kintampo Complex: A case study of early sedentism and food production in West Africa. *The archaeology of Africa: food, metal and towns*, New York: T. Shaw, P. Sinclair, A. Okpoko, pp. 255-260.

Mortar   Construction
Origin: Egypt   Date: 350 BCE

Depending on the nature of the construction, mortar in ancient Egypt was one of two kinds: clay dried by the sun or gypsum containing calcium. Clay, which has been dried to form bricks, is still used as a most suitable construction material. Gypsum is no longer used as mortar, having been replaced by lime, a sand mixture, or cement.

Additional reading: Petrie, W. , (1996). *The arts and crafts of ancient Egypt.* London: Bracken Books.

Mortise   Mechanical
Origin: Egypt   Date: 900 BCE

The process of building long lasting mega-structures has been a challenge for ancient architects for thousands of years. The Egyptians developed the material now known as mortise around 900 BCE. Developed during the rule of Makeda, Queen of Sheba, the mortise was used as a jointing process. A small hole was cut in the surface of a piece of wood to form a firm joint and to support the massive stones placed atop these large structures.

Additional reading: Hill, N. (1930). *The intimate life of the Queen of Sheba.* New York: Putnam.

Moth   see   **Silkworm.**

Mouse Trap   Mechanical
Origin: Nubia   Date: 3000 BCE

An early example of a mouse trap can be traced back to Nubia around 3000 BCE. Illustrations in the Hebrew Book of *Parables* documented the rodent problem in ancient Nubia. A crude mousetrap design was made of two wooden sticks tied together with a vine that would release after tension was applied. Nubians also kept weasels to reduce the rodent population.

Additional reading: Babcock G., (2002). *Webster's third new international dictionary of the English language.* New York: Merrian Webster Books.

Multiplication   Mathematics
Origin: Sumer   Date: 3000 BCE

Before 2500 BCE, the Sumerians had drawn up multiplication tables, which they used to determine the area of fields (by multiplying length time's breadth) and to estimate the volumes of such things as brick stock (by multiplying the length times the breadth times the height). In calculating the area of a circle and the volume of a cylinder, they rounded off the direct measurement to a whole number.

Additional reading: Bell, E., (1945). *The development of mathematics.* 2nd ed. New York: McGraw Hill.

Multiplication Table   Mathematics
Origin: Babylonia   Date: 1800 BCE

The Babylonians are credited with many mathematical discoveries and modifications. As early as 1800 BCE, the Babylonians developed a concise table of multiplication facts. The tables were used in the construction and development of civil and mechanical devices and structures.

Additional reading: West, B. (1982). *The Prentice-Hall encyclopedia of mathematics.* New York: Prentice Hall Pub.

Mummification   see   **Embalming.**

Music (Charting)   Musical
Origin: China   Date: 400 BCE

The Chinese are recorded in history as introducing many instruments to the family of music. Around 400 BCE, the Chinese were the first to develop a chart of the hand, which showed the twelve fundamental notes. They developed numerous musical scripts around this formation.

Additional reading: Rossi, N. and Rafferty, S. (1981). *Music through the centuries.* Washington D.C.: University Press of America.

Musical Note   see   **Notation (Musical).**

Musical String (Gut)   Music
Origin: Egypt   Date: 3000 BCE

The earliest example can be traced to the prehistoric period. In ancient Egypt the strings and base of musical instruments were constructed from the thong of animal tissue. Two small twisted pieces of gut were recovered from the Step Pyramid at Saqqara built in the Third Dynasty.

Additional reading: Mahmoud, Z. (1959). *The land and people of Egypt*. New York: J.B. Lippincott Pub.

Mustard   Agriculture
Origin: Egypt   Date: Antiquity

During the III Dynasty of Dira Abu'N Nega, Egyptians customized the development and use of mustard to season food. Three species of mustard plants were cultivated during this period, black mustard (Sinapis Nirga), field mustard (S.Anuensis), and white mustard (S. Alba). The spread of the mustard seed is evident in locations like Marmakiahi, where some seeds were found in an animal skinned bag as far back as 2300 BCE.

Additional reading: Wilson, J. (1951). *The ancient culture of Egypt*. Chicago: University of Chicago Press.

N

Nail   Mechanical
Origin: Mesopotamia   Date: 3500 BCE

Mesopotamia created the first nails designed from bone and later in metal. Because the nails were costly, most ancient furniture was made with carved joints. The nail became plentifully when towns and villiages grew and became stable and inhabitants didn't move as often as they did earlier.

Additional reading: Cotterell, A. (1975). *The encyclopedia of ancient civilizations*. London: Penguin Books.

Nation   System
Origin: Egypt   Date: 3100 BCE

The first large scale areas that we called nations came into being around 3100 BCE. Under the rule of Menes, the first king of the First Dynasty, the city states of the Nile delta in Lower Egypt were united with those in Upper Egypt. About 300 BCE, the Egyptian priest Manetho had written a history of Egypt, detailed the various dynasties, each representing a family whose members ruled over Egypt for a period of time.

Additional reading: Asimov, I. (1989). *Asimov's chronology of science and discovery*. New York: Harper & Row.

Natron   Mineral
Origin: Egypt   Date: 1500 BCE

The land in and around the Nile Valley is rich with natural deposits such as natron. Natron is a form of sodium carbonate and is found in the ground naturally. During the period of 1504 to 1450 BCE was mined in Egypt.

Additional reading: Hart, G. (1990). *Ancient Egypt*. New York: Alfred Knopf Pub.

Natural Gas   Chemistry
Origin: China   Date: 350 BCE

A text by Chang Chu, dating from 347 BCE, described the construction of bamboo pipes, which served to transport methane gas to towns. The presence of numerous pockets of this natural gas on the surface of the soil, and the spontaneous combustion eventually resulted in gas reserved fields.

Additional reading: Schwartz, B. (1985). *The world of thought in ancient China*. Cambridge, Mass.: Harvard University Press.

Navigation   Navigation
Origin: Japan   Date: 100,000 BCE

The first proofs that early prehistoric man crossed a substantial body of water were stone tools found in Africa and Japan made of similar materials, dating from 100,000 BCE. Not much is known about the makers of the tools, but the mainland at that time was probably inhabited by a late population of homo erectus.

Additional reading: Neuburger, O. (1930). *The technical arts and sciences of the ancients*. New York: The Macmillan Co.

Needle (Surgical)   Medical
Origin: India   Date: 1100 BCE

The Indians are credited with the development of a style of needle which was used to close open wounds. The ancient Hindus developed a series of needle-like surgical instruments around 1100 BCE. The Hindu surgeons had a vast array of instruments available to them, many forged from steel.

Additional reading: Singer, C., and Underwood, E., (1962). *A short history of medicine.* Oxford: Oxford University Press.

Negative Numbers
Mathematics
Origin: China   Date: 250 BCE

The earliest form of negative and positive numbers were developed in China around 250 BCE. The Chui-Chang Suan-Shu is nine chapters in the Mathematical Arts, one of the most influential Chinese books of mathematics. It contains more than two hundred problems on engineering, surveying, calculation, agriculture, and right triangles, as well as solutions to problems in simultaneous linear equations using the earliest known form of positive and negative numbers.

Additional reading: Dickson, L., (1966). *History of the theory of numbers.* New York: Chlesea.

Net
Material
Origin: Africa   Date: 5000 BCE

Prehistoric men have left evidence that they inventively used natural occurring materials like vines plants and trees to make traps and nets to capture food. Small fragments of nets dating back to 5000 BCE, have been recovered from African peat deposits. Nets of similar timeframe have also been found preserved in the dry valleys of Egypt.

Additional reading: Neuburger, O. (1930). *Illustrated science and inventions encyclopedia.* New York: Macmillan Co.

Network   see   Road Network.

Nilometer
Mechanical
Origin: Nubia   Date: 3200 BCE

Records suggest that the nilometer was used as early as 3200 BCE. A graduated pillar or vertical surface that served as a scale, a nilometer indicated the height the Nile rose during the flood season. This was an important device used for forecasting crops harvest based on seasonal flooding levels.

Additional reading: Oakley, K., (1956). *Man the tool-maker.* London: British Museum.

Noose   see   Snare.

Nose (Transplant)
Medicine
Origin: India   Date: 750 BCE

As early as 750 BCE, nose transplants were performed in India. Women were sometimes punished by having their noses amputated, the physicians who treated them realized that the skin grafted to the mutilated nose had to come from the same person and had to be irrigated by the same blood. Accordingly, the physicians transplanted a skin fragment taken from the forehead of the patient.

Additional reading: Basham, A., (1954). *The wonder that was India* (a survey of the culture of the Indian sub-continent before the coming of the Muslims). New York: Macmillan Co.

Notation (Musical)
Music
Origin: Syria   Date: 1300 BCE

The earliest full length musical score was composed in Syria around 1300 BCE. Discovered on clay tablets, the musical notation was based on themes of love and war. This full length written musical was transcribed with specific musical and vocal parts.

Additional reading: Guillemin-Duchesne, M., (1981). "Music in ancient Mesopotamia and Egypt." *World Archaeology* 12:3.

Notation   see   Positional Notation.

Nova (Super)
Astronomy
Origin: China   Date: 350 BCE

As far back as 350 BCE, the Chinese astronomer Shin Shen prepared a star catalog with over eight hundred entries. Most notably the Super Nova was discussed in detail describing its heavenly appearance. This was the earliest record of such novas. The Europeans later describe novas around 250 BCE.

Additional Reading: Fitzgerald, C., (1961). *China: A short cultural history.* New York: Praeger.

Null   see   Zero.

OBOE

Number Theory — Mathematics
Origin: Egypt   Date: 300 BCE

The Egyptian mathematicians Euclid studied in Alexandria, Egypt, for many years, where they developed the number theory. In 300 BCE, the Elements textbook was written, summarizing mathematical theories. Their work included a theory of numbers and was accepted as a basic reference until the modern age.

Additional reading: Weil, A., (1984). *Number theory, an approach through history.* Boston: Birkhavoer.

Numeral — Mathematics
Origin: Iraq   Date: 3500 BCE

As early as 3500 BCE, counting was performed by using a soft clay ball, inside of which were placed as many clay beads as there were items to be cataloged. It is clear that counting had been happening for a period of time, but this was the first standardized numerical system developed. Written numbers date back to 3000 BCE, as attested by clay tablets found at Susa and Uruk in modern day Iraq.

Additional reading: West, B., (1982). *The Prentice Hall encyclopedia of mathematics.* Englewood Cliffs, N.J.: Prentice-Hall.

Numerical Record — Accounting
Origin: Egypt   Date: 8000 BCE

Tokens of simple geometric shapes or representations of jars and animals were used for keeping numerical records as far back as 8000 BCE. Around 4400 BCE, tokens had marks and were a variety of shapes for grouping large numerical sums.

Additional reading: Ashurst, F., (1982). *Founders of modern mathematics.* London: Fredrick Muller.

Numerical System — Mathematics
Origin: Sumer   Date: 3000 BCE

The earliest records of the Sumerians dealt with accounts of produce stored in the temple storerooms or handed out. Priests made permanent records by making imprints on clay tablets, which were baked and preserved for future reference. Imprints consisted of numbers and abbreviated pictures of the produce enumerated.

Additional reading: Midonick, H., (1965). *The treasury of mathematics.* New York: Philosophical Library.

O

Oar — Naval
Origin: Egypt   Date: 5000 BCE

The use of oars to power ships began in Egypt circa 5000 BCE. Ships began to use more than one bank of oars to transport more people and materials. The trireme was invented as a fighting ship around 700 BCE, and had three rows of more than one hundred rowers.

Additional reading: Daumas, M. (1967). *History of technology and inventions.* New York: Crown Press.

Oat — Agriculture
Origin: Africa   Date: 8000 BCE

Black oats appeared in the northern part of Africa around 8000 BCE. Some evidence exists that prehistory Africans throughout the eastern region also cultivated an indigenous oat strand that originated in Ethiopia. Oats are among the first grasses domesticated by Neolithic humans in Asia, Eastern Europe, and southern locales in the Americas.

Additional reading: Travers, B.(1996). *The Gale encyclopedia of science.* Detroit Mich: Gale Research.

Obelisk — Mechanical
Origin: Egypt   Date: 2100 BCE

An obelisk was a narrow, solid, four-sided shaft of stone, usually cut from a single block of granite. The top was pyramid-shaped and covered with electrum. Pairs of obelisks were placed before the entrances to Egyptian temples associated with sun worship.

Additional reading: Barber, F., (1900). *The mechanical triumphs of ancient Egyptians.* London: Trubner and Co.

Oboe — Music
Origin: Egypt   Date: 2100 BCE

The instruments from the oboe family were known in

— 81 —

Egypt as early as 2100 BCE. Like many instruments of the period, they were constructed with double reeds. A special bamboo was cultivated for its high quality and long lasting wood form.

Additional reading: Rossi, N. and Rafferty, S. (1981). *Music through the centuries.* Washington D.C.: University Press of America.

Observatory   Astronomy
Origin: Babylonia   Date: 505 BCE

The earliest known observatory was erected around 500 BCE, on top of the temple of Belus in Babylon. This observatory was affixed with reflective material and was used to steer ships as well as to study the skies above.

Additional reading: Rogers, R., (1915). *A history of Babylonia and Assyria. Vol 2,* Cincinnati: Books for Libraries Press.

Oil Drilling   Mechanical
Origin: China   Date: 200 BCE

As early as the second century BCE, the Chinese bore oil wells using bamboo stems and later bronze pipes. The depths of these oil wells were limited, estimated to be around one hundred feet deep.

Additional reading: Needham, J. (1958). *The development of iron and steel technology in China.* London: Newcomen Society,

Oil and Fat (Production)   Agriculture
Origin: Africa   Date: Antiquity

The olive tree and the oil obtained from it are mentioned in the early Egyptian records from the Eighth Dynasty. The cultivation of the olive tree prospered because it yielded the oil necessary for preparing foods, filling lamps, anointing the body, cleaning purposes, and producing perfumes and cosmetics.

Additional reading: Dorsey, G. (1931). *The story of civilization; man's own show.* New York: Halcyon Publishing House.

Oil Lamp   Illumination
Origin: Africa   Date: 20,000 BCE

During an archeological expedition in the 1930s,

a team discovered a crude artifact that was later described as a lit torch, also referred to as the oil lamp. Housed within the device was an oil residue that some believed was some sort of burning agent. Carbon testing dates this artifact back to over 20,000 years ago. Oil lamps consisted of a container for the oil and a wick, perhaps twisted plant fiber. To obtain more light, lamps held up to twenty wicks.

Additional reading: Hodder, I. and Issac, G. 1981. *Patterns of the past studies in honor of Davis Clark.* Cambridge, Mass: University Press.

Oil seed   see   Hemp.

Ointment   Chemistry
Origin: Egypt   Date: 2100 BCE

Ancient Egyptians prepared ointments by mixing oils and fats with various perfumes, usually consisting of solid plant oils. They had melting points above ordinary temperatures. Ointments were obtained from various vegetable substances, including tree oil, rose oil, almond oil, sweet calamus, cinnamon, incense, sesame, marjoram, lily, iris, cypress, amaravain, malabathrum, honey, and oenanthe.

Additional reading: Hart, G. (1990). *Ancient Egypt.* New York: Alfred Knopf Pub.

Olive   Agriculture
Origin: Egypt   Date: 3100 BCE

The early farmers during the Naqada III dynasty plated and cultivated several varieties of olives. In the southern region of Egypt farmers were the earliest known to domestically grow and cultivate the olive tree. The seed of the olive tree was eaten for food and olive juice was used as body oil.

Additional reading: Balsam, M. and Sagarin, E. (1972). *Cosmetic science and technology.* New York: Wiley Interscience.

Onion   Agriculture
Origin: Syria   Date: 6000 BCE

Farmers of this Fertile Crescent were the earliest known to domestically grow and cultivate onions.

The edible, rounded bulb of Allium Cepa consisted of a close concentric coat with a strong flavor and smell. Its color varied from black to white and varied in size depending on the region where it grew.

Additional reading: Spoerke, D. (1980). *Herbal medications.* Santa Barbara: Woodbridge Press.

Organ
Origin: Egypt

Music

Date: 300 BCE

During the Ptolemaic Period, many musical instruments were in use in Egypt including a rather large instrument called an organ. A hydraulic organ was developed around 300 BCE by Ktesibios of Alexandria. Its name was derived from the hydraulic mechanism that fed the pipes with air.

Additional reading: Williams, P., (1980). *A new history of the organ from the Greeks to the present day.* Bloomington: Indiana University Press.

Ornament
Origin: Turkey

Jewelry

Date: 7000 BCE

By 7000 BCE, people in southern Turkey were making implements and ornaments out of native copper, tin and iron. The early ornaments were used as body armor. Within a few centuries, copper was heated and hammered into different shapes to accomodate the various regional needs.

Additional reading: Stewart, J. (1960). *An archaeological guide and glossary.* London: Phoenix House.

Oscillator
Origin: Egypt

Physics

Date: 3500 BCE

Components of a typical oscillator date to the Amen priesthood in 3500 BCE. Symbols in many hieroglyphic reliefs were meant to convey knowledge of the hidden force of electromagnetism to future generations of the Order of the ancient priesthood. The symbols only held supreme religious significance to the descendants of this race of photonic beings.

Additional reading: Nur Ankh Amen, N. (1999). *The ankh: African origin of electromagnetism.* New York: A&B Publishers Group.

Ovine
see
Sheep.

Oxen
Origin: Turkey

Domestic

Date: 6400 BCE

The earliest record of oxen being domesticated dates as far back as 6400 BCE. Cattle domesticated in Turkey were probably bred from the longhaired wild ox called the Auroch or Uru. The oxen were a food source as well as a beast of labor. This strand of oxen (Aurochs) became extinct in 1627.

Additional reading: Diamond, J. (1993). *The third chimpanzee: The evolution and future of human animals.* New York: Harper.

Oyster Farming
Origin: China

Domestic

Date: 200 BCE

The first oyster farmers in recorded history were the Chinese. A Roman named Sergius Orata was the first to make a commercial enterprise from oyster farming. At the beginning of the second century, Orata built an oyster bed on his property in Lake Lucrin near Naples. He built fish ponds that connected with the sea but protected the young oyster brood from the waves. They were provided with posts on which they clung and grew in proper conditions of temperature and light. Sergius Orata's acumen was such that he made a fortune selling oysters. Lake Lucrin disappeared in 1583 CE, after an earthquake and a volcanic eruption —common occurrences in that area.

Additional reading: Schwartz, B. (1985). *The world of thought in ancient China.* Cambridge Mass.: Harvard University Press.

P

Paint
Origin: Africa

Material

Date: 15,000 BCE

The earliest evidence of processing and application of pigments for other than body decoration was discovered in painted caves dating back to 15,000 BCE. A recent promising find of apparent mixing tools and dye ingredients in a South Africa cave may dial back the record to 100,000 years ago. Around 1500 BCE, the Egyptians used dyes to make blue and red pigments. In the Orient, organic pigments, which included such materials as egg white and beeswax, were blended as early as 6000 BCE.

Additional reading: Buritt, M. (1928). *South Africa's past in stone and paint.* Cambridge: Cambridge University Press.

Painting (Artistic) — Design
Origin: Africa   Date: 40,000 BCE

The inhabitants of East Africa were the world's first artists, inventing not only painting, but sculpture and carving as well. Many of their most striking works were made on the walls, ceilings, and floors of caves. This first great art movement lasted some fifteen to twenty thousand years. It reached its peak during the middle and latter part of Magdalenian period. They soon graduated to engraving and carving small figurines or statuettes out of bone, horn, ivory, and stone.

Additional reading: Clark, D. (1964). "Prehistoric Origins of African Culture," *Journal of African History,* vol. 1.

Paint (Tempera) — Material
Origin: Egypt   Date: 3400 BCE

Early wall paintings depict images of workers using a coloring substance now known as tempera. This new coloring substance appeared during the Naqada II dynasty. Binding substances in which the colors are mixed and made to adhere the to ground first appeared around 3400 BCE. These substances were usually classified as carbohydrates, albumens, or a mixture of both.

Additional reading: Barber, F., (1900). *The mechanical triumphs of ancient Egyptians:* London: Trubner and Co.

Painted Cloth — Textile
Origin: Egypt   Date: 2000 BCE

A fragment of painted linen found in Egypt dates from the Twelfth Dynasty, between 2000 and 1788 BCE. The practice of painting on cloth was widespread and in many areas was the primary form of communication. With the invention of paper, the art of painting was limited to art and public viewing.

Additional reading: Huffman, T. (1971). Cloth from the iron age in Rhodesia. *South Africa: Annual Review of Anthropology II* pp133-150.

Pancrace   see   Boxing.

Paper — Material
Origin: China   Date: 140 BCE

The Chinese made paper as early as 140 BCE, and used it as a packing material for clothing and personal hygiene. The process of paper making was confined to China for many years because of the lack of travel through China at the time.

Additional reading: Fitzgerald, C., (1961). *China: A short cultural history.* New York: Praeger.

Papyrus — Communication
Origin: Egypt   Date: 1800 BCE

The Egyptians are usually credited with the invention of papyrus. The stem of a reed cultivated in the Nile Valley constituted the raw material. Scholars, who accompanied Bonaparte on his Egyptian campaign in 1798, discovered sheets of papyrus dating back to 1800 BCE.

Additional reading: Giscard d'Estaing, V. (1985). *The world almanac book of inventors.* New York: World Almanac Pub.

Parachute — Aviation
Origin: China   Date: 200 BCE

The parachute was described in the annals of the Chinese historian, Sseu-ma Ts'ien (Sima Qian), written about 90 BCE. The parachute was described as being relatively old, and therefore it was thought to have dated from the preceding century. Joseph Needham, an English specialist in Chinese history, found descriptions of a parachute jump dating from 1214 BCE. Jumping from the top of a minaret in Canton, China, the jumper was aided with the help of two umbrellas without shafts.

Additional reading: Schwartz, B. (1985). *The world of thought in ancient China.* Cambridge, Mass.: Harvard University Press.

Parchment — Communication
Origin: Asia Minor   Date: 200 BCE

Legend has it that the inhabitants of Pergamum in Asia Minor invented parchment during the second century BCE. The oldest example of written parchment was a fragment probably dating from the end of the first century. Many items were made from the skins of sheep, goats, and lambs. There was no widespread use of parchment because only a few people of the period were able to write.

Additional reading: Derry, T. and Williams, T. (1960). *A short history of technology from the earliest times to A.D. 1900*. Oxford: Clarendon Press..

Paved Street   Construction
Origin: Assyria   Date: 3200 BCE

The Assyrians used paved roads as early as 2000 BCE. They built roads using two paved strips 1.5 meters apart. In 1460 BCE, the Cretans conveyed people, animals and materials on paved roads. The Romans were the first to cover their roads with a hard surface, such as granite or lava slabs.

Additional reading: Rogers, R., (1915). *A history of Babylonia and Assyria*. Vol 2, Cincinnati: Books for Libraries Press.

Pea   Agriculture
Origin: Egypt   Date: 4200 BCE

The Egyptian farmers were the earliest known to domestically grow and cultivate pea seeds. Pisum Sativum was a hardy, climbing, leguminous annual, existing in many varieties in the wild. Early transcriptions indicate that when Egyptian farmers grew peas, it soon became a food substance that was traded to many areas of the region.

Additional reading: Kowalchik, C. and Hylton, W., (1998). *Rodale's illustrated encyclopedia of herbs*. Pennsylvania: Rodale Press.

Peace Treaty   Communication
Origin: Egypt   Date: 1272 BCE

The earliest known surviving peace treaty between two countries happened in 1272 BCE, between Egypt and Hittites. The peace treaty was inscribed on a stone slate and spelled out the details which led to the end of the war between the two armies.

Additional reading: Wright, Q. (2004). "Peace Treaty" Encyclopedia Americana Grolier Online.

Peanut   Agriculture
Origin: India   Date: 7500 BCE

The peanut was often used as a food source in India. Akachis Hypogaea grew wild in the West Indies, India, and West Africa. Its fruit was a pod that ripened underground and contained two seeds similar to peas. The peanut was one of the most valued foods of the period.

Additional reading: House, H. (1934). *Wild flowers*. New York: Macmillan Co.

Peach   Agriculture
Origin: Mesopotamia   Date: 3200 BCE

During the Naqada II Dynasty dating back to 3200 BCE, the Egyptian farmers were the first known to domestically grow peach trees. The fruit of the tree was a large drupe, usually round, with a white to yellowish color. The peach was cultivated throughout the entire region and existed in many varieties.

Additional reading: Blunt, W. (1979). *The illustrated herbal*. New York: Thames and Hudson.

Pear   Agriculture
Origin: Persia   Date: 5500 BCE

Derived from the wild plant, pyrus communis, pears were being cultivated as early as the late Neolithic period. Seeds were found in several dwelling sites, such as Badmon, Mondsee, and Wangen.

Additional reading: Contenau, G. (1954). *Everyday life in Babylon and Assyria:* London: Edward Arnold Pub.

Pease   see   **Pea.**

Pedestal Urn   Domestic
Origin: Africa   Date: Prehistoric

An archeological dig during early 1900s in Eastern Africa turned up a crude pedestal urn found in a mud basin. The pedestal urn was a tall pot with a narrow base used by people of the Iron Age to hold items ranging from water to soil.

Additional reading: Stewart, J. (1960). *An archaeological guide and glossary*. London: Phoenix House.

Pen
Communication
Origin: Egypt   Date: 550 BCE

The predecessor of the fountain pen originated in Egypt around 550 BCE. The shaped reed was filled with ink which, when pressed lightly, ran down to the point. A shaped bamboo, filled with ink in a similar manner, was used in China. In the fourth century BCE, Aristotle used a silver reed.

Additional reading: Giscard d'Estaing, Valerie-Anne; (1993) *Inventions and discoveries. What's happened, what's coming, what's that?* New York: Facts on file.

Pepper
Agriculture
Origin: Mexico   Date: 7000 BCE

As far back as 7000 BCE, on the North American territory known as Mexico, widespread plant cultivation had been taking place. A wide variety of plants was being grown for food sources. The earliest known harvesting of the pepper dates back to 7000 BCE.

Additional Reading: Coe, M. (1994). *Breaking the Maya code.* London: Penguin.

Peppermint
Agriculture
Origin: Africa   Date: 6000 BCE

Tribes settling in the northern region of Africa were the earliest known to domestically grow and cultivate the peppermint tree. The seeds of the peppermint tree were eaten for food and the juice was as an additive for drinks.

Additional reading: Dyer, T., (1989). *The folklore of plants.* New York: Appleton and Co.

Perfume
Cosmetic
Origin: Egypt   Date: 1400 BCE

The Egypt's perfume production started prior to the New Kingdom Dynasty including the 'Amarna Period.' It wasn't until around 1400 BCE, that perfume products were mass produced. There was a powerful perfume industry in Egypt, where fragrances were used to seal royal tombs such as that of Pharaoh Tutan-khamen, which when opened in 1922, was still pleasingly fragrant.

Additional reading: Genders, R. (1972). *A history of scent.* London: Hamilton.

Percussion Instrument
Music
Origin: Africa   Date: Antiquity

The earliest recorded description of man producing an echo sound by hitting an object came from Africa. Numerous artifacts have been recovered that were struck, scraped, shaken, or banged together. In every region of Africa, percussion instruments have been found dating back to prehistoric times.

Additional reading: Ki-Zerbo, J. (1990). *General history of Africa, methodology and African prehistory.* Berkeley Calif.: University of California Press.

Pesticides
Chemistry
Origin: China   Date: 202 BCE

The earliest records of pesticides came from China, which was one of the wealthiest agricultural societies in the ancient world. In the third century BCE, special officers were appointed to take charge of pest control. Books describing the precautions needed to safeguard crops at every stage of the agricultural cycle from sowing to storing the harvest have survived from the Han Dynasty (202 BCE – 220 BCE). Pesticides were sprayed on the ground before planting to kill off insects and weeds and on the seeds themselves to keep birds from eating them.

Additional reading: McGrew, R. and McGrew, M. (1985). *Encyclopedia of medical history.* New York: McGraw-Hill Pub.

Petroleum
Chemistry
Origin: Mesopotamia   Date: Antiquity

The first users of petroleum using the latest dating process of carbon testing show that they lived in the Middle East. The first recorded use of hydrocarbons came from the North African region, where many tools have petroleum coatings. It is believed that petroleum-base oil lamps were used in the early mining industry.

Additional reading: Burlingame, R. (1938). *March of the iron men; a social history of union through invention.* New York: C. Scribner's sons.

Phi Mathematics
Origin: Sumer Date: 2500 BCE

Around 2500 BCE, the Sumerians used multiplication tables to determine the areas of fields by multiplying length times breadth. They estimated the volumes of such things as brick stacks by multiplying the length, breadth, and height. In calculating the area of a circle and the volume of a cylinder, they took the value of phi as a numerical value as three, probably determining the value by direct measurement and rounding it off to a whole number for simplicity.

Additional reading: West, B. , (1982). *The Prentice-Hall encyclopedia of mathematics.* New York:

Phonetic Communication
Origin: Syria Date: 1600 BCE

As written early as 1600 BCE, the Phoenicians invented a phonetic alphabet, a system based on symbols for sounds. The alphabet is considered the ancestor of all modern western alphabets. There were written slate text that had lettering characters but the phonetic sounds were not spelled out as they were with the Syrian phonetic alphabet system.

Additional reading: Fischer, S. (2001). *A history of writing.* London: Reaktion Books.

Phonetic Language Communication
Origin: Mesopotamia Date: 2000 BCE

Around 2000 BCE, the Semitic Akkadian peoples transcribed their phonetic language into cuneiform script. This form of language practice was imitated by every culture that established its rule in Mesopotamia until the time of the Greeks.

Additional reading: (1979). *Ancient Mesopotamia: Portrait of a dead civilization.* Rev. ed., Chicago: University of Chicago Press.

Physiotherapy Medical
Origin: Sumer Date: 4000 BCE

Human efforts to heal themselves by discovering and extracting the medicinal properties of plants are probably as old as humankind. Slate tablets inscribed during the Sumerian societies of around 4000 BCE, provide the earliest written formulas for plant-based medications. An early collection of slate tablets, rendered incomplete due to the wars and invasions of the period, are housed in the Egyptian Museum of History and show that there are over fifty medical formulas listed using the process of phytotherapy.

Additional reading: Kramer S., (1956). *From the table of Sumer, twenty five Firsts in man's recorded history. Indian Hills,* Colo: Falcon's Wing Press.

Pi Mathematics
Origin: Egypt Date: 4000 BCE

The Naquda I Dynasty has been credited for many mathematical first. Around 4000 BCE, the Egyptians developed the ratio of the circumference of a circle to its diameter, called pi. This discovery occurred centuries before Pythagoras developed his theorem.

Additional reading: Dauben, J., (1985). *The history of mathematics from antiquity to the present.* London: Garland.

Pick (Antler) Tool
Origin: Africa Date: Prehistoric

The pick as an implement dates back to the dawn of man. The exact date is undetermined. During the Neolithic age, humans used bones such as antlers to make clubs, spears, and shovels. The antlers of the deer were used as spades. Many historical records show that the pick was one if not the earliest of man made devices used.

Additional reading: Noel H. (1969). *Historical archaeology.* New York: Knopf Pub.

Pictogram see **Art.**

Pier see **Quay.**

Pig Agriculture
Origin: Egypt Date: 7200 BCE

Farmers of ancient Egypt were the earliest known to domestically breed pigs for their meat. The early name for pig was pygue and was described as the young of a swine. They were also called young sows and boars.

Additional reading: Travers, B. (1996). *The Gale encyclopedia of science*. Detroit Mich. Gale Research.

Pigeon — Domestic
Origin: Nubia   Date: 2100 BCE

The Nubians trained pigeons as communication carriers. During war campaigns, pigeons were trained to delivery military messages. One of the most unique features of this bird was its ability to find its way back home from great distances.

Additional reading: Gunther, J. (1955). *Inside Africa*. New York: Harpers Brothers.

Pin — Domestic
Origin: Egypt   Date: 4000 BCE

Man has long fabricated nature-supplied pins in the form of sharp thorns and fish bones, but the first man-made pins were of copper. Egyptians also used bronze to make round-headed pins. The early man-made pin was carved from bone and was used to hold plant leaves in place on constructed shelters.

Additional reading: Hitti, P. (1943). *The Arabs*. Chicago: Gateway Press.

Pincer — Medical
Origin: India   Date: 1000 BCE

Around 1000 BCE, the ancient Hindus excelled in the manufacture of surgical instruments including surgical pincers. Surgery reached remarkable heights during this period. In a Samhita medical textbook, pincers were described as a tool used by medical personnel.

Additional reading: Singer, C., and Underwood, E., (1962). *A short history of medicine*. New York: Clarendon Press.

Pipe (Tobacco) — Domestic
Origin: America   Date: 1000 BCE

The earliest pipes in the Americas were those found on Marajo Island at the mouth of the Amazon and at Poverty Point, the region known as Louisiana, dating to the early first millennium BCE. The most elaborate ancient pipes were those of the Hopewell culture (100 BCE–700 BCE) of the eastern United States. Its craftsmen carved their smoking pipes out of rare stones

imported from sources spread across North America.

Additional reading: Spencer, L. (1913). *The myths of Mexico and Peru*. London: Dover.

Pipe (Street) — Civil
Origin: Pakistan   Date: 2500 BCE

The earliest recorded street drainage pipes date back to 2500 BCE. The largest street drain found intact was discovered in the diggings of Mohenjo-Daro, Pakistan. Palaces were equipped with an elaborate network of drains for sewage disposal.

Additional reading: Bunch, B. and Hellemans, A. (1993). *The timetables of technology: A chronology of the most important people and events in the history of technology*. New York: Simon & Schuster.

Piston (Double Acting) — Mechanical
Origin: China   Date: 310 BCE

In 310 BCE, the Chinese invented the double-acting piston bellows, which produced a continuous stream of air. This device was considered quite productive for maintaining air flow. Such a bellows were not known in the West until the fourth century.

Additional reading: Schwartz, B. (1985). *The world of thought in ancient China*. Cambridge: Harvard University Press.

Plane — Manufacturing
Origin: Egypt   Date: 300 BCE

Used as early as the third millennium BCE in Egypt, the plane was used to shave a wood surface in order to make it level or smooth. The jack plane had a flint blade housed in a multi-piece wooden design and was used on the surfaces of objects.

Additional reading: Barber, F. (1900). The mechanical triumphs of ancient Egyptians. London: Trubner and Co.

Plane Geometry — Mathematics
Origin: Egypt   Date: 300 BCE

The Egyptian mathematicians who studied in Alexandria, developed many mathematical theories. In 300 BCE. they wrote the first draft of what is known as Elements, a textbook summarizing and systematizing mathematics, including plane geometry. This work was accepted in the West as a basic reference.

Additional reading: Barrow, I. (1916). Geometrical lectures. Chicago: (Trans. and edited by J.M. Child),

Planning (City)   see   Urban Planning.

Plaster
Origin: Egypt

Construction
Date: Antiquity

The ancient Egyptians used a cement composition similar to contemporary mortar, consisting of clay and gypsum. While the structures of antiquity have long since been destroyed, among the ruins of the palace of Amenophis III and of El Amarna was found plaster similar to that found in some of the ancient Egyptian tombs and temples.

Additional reading: Weigall, A. (1910). *A guide to the antiquities of upper Egypt, from Abydos to the Sudan Frontier.* London: Methuen & Co.

Plough
Origin: Nubia

Agriculture
Date: 3600 BCE

The Nubians and Egyptians developed the plow between 4000 BCE and 3000 BCE. Adapted from the digging stick, the junction of the forks acted as a plowshare and dug into the soil. Humans probably dragged the first plows before they enlisted pairs of oxen or other beasts of burden.

Additional reading: Hart, G. (1990). *Ancient Egypt.* New York: Alfred Knopf Pub.

Plum
Origin: Syria

Agriculture
Date: 6000 BCE

The Syrians were the first to plant and harvest plum for their food and drink as early as 6000 BCE. The fruit of the plum tree, prunus domestic, was a round, fleshy drupe varying in size and color with a somewhat flat, pointed stone and sweet pulp. The plum was dried and often used as a pudding food.

Additional reading: Hill, L. (1976). *Food and remedy.* New York: Universe Books.

Plumb Line
Origin: Egypt

Mechanical
Date: 3000 BCE

Egyptian builders were the first to use a plumb line, a weighted cord used to ensure that construction stood exactly upright when with the line. Plumb lines were used in complex mathematical equations for alignments of large structures that were typically spread out over a distance.

Additional reading: Murray, M. (1963). *The splendor that was Egypt.* New York: Hawthorn Books, Inc.

Poem
Origin: Babylonia

Communication
Date: 700 BCE

Gilgamesh, a poem of the seventh century BCE, was inscribed in cuneiform on clay tablets and found in pieces in the ruins of the Royal Library of Ashur-bani-pal at Nineveh. The epic, which is divided into twelve parts, tells how Gilgamesh conquered his environment and sought the secret of eternal life. It includes the Babylonian story of the flood taken from Sumerian sources.

Additional reading: James, P. and Thrope, I. (1993). *Centuries of darkness: A challenge to the conventional chronology of Old World archaeology.* New Brunswick, N.J.: Rutgers University Press.

Poisonous Gas
Origin: China

Chemistry
Date: 500 BCE

Poisonous gases have occurred in nature since the dawn of man. The Mohists, followers of the fifth century BCE, Chinese philosopher Mo-Tzu, described the use of poisonous gas in warfare. The gas caused people to weaken. Further development of the gas made people sleep. The early production of poisonous gas was manufactured in central Europe during the late 1700's.

Additional reading: Hirth, F. (1908). *The ancient history of China:* New York: Columbia University Press.

Poker
Origin: Persia

Entertainment
Date: 3000 BCE

The Persians invented and played a series of adult games such as poker as early as 3000 BCE. The goal of the game was to come up with pairs, three of a kind, full house, or four of a kind. This early card game was laid out on small slate tablets using a host of unique images carved into each. The precise rules have been lost to history, but many believed that this game was similar to our current poker games.

Additional reading: Binford, L., (1981). Bones: *Ancient man and modern myths*. New York: Academic Press.

Police Force   Domestic
Origin: Egypt   Date: 1200 BCE

The Egyptian police force was formed around 1320 BCE. Prior to this, the military performed security functions. In times of war, this left many demilitarized areas without protection. The military assigned and trained a civilian militia rather than use standing military police to monitor various localities. The militia also guarded the tombs of the pharaohs, notably those in the Valley of the Kings at Thebes.

Additional reading: James, P. and Thorpe, N., (1994). *Ancient inventions*. New York: Ballantine Books.

Polygonal Areas   Mathematics
Origin: Babylon   Date: 1900 BCE

In 1936, a group of mathematical tablets were unearthed at Susa, a couple of hundred miles from Babylon, and these include significant geometric formulations. True to the Mesopotamian penchant for making tables and lists, one tablet in the Susa group compares the areas and the squares of the sides of the area of the regular polygons of three, four, five, six, and seven sides. The ratio of the area of the pentagon, for example, to the square on the side of the pentagon is given as 1;40, a value that is correct to two significant figures. For the hexagon and heptagon the ratios are expressed as 2;37,30 and 3;41 respectively.

Additional reading: Boyer, C., (2000). *A history of mathematics*. New York: John Wiley.

Pomegranate (Tree)   Domestic
Origin: Egypt   Date: 6200 BCE

The pomegranate tree, containing large berry-like fruit bearing numerous plump seeds, grew wild in the southern areas of Egypt and was used as a food source. Each seed was enveloped in a pleasantly acid, juicy pulp, enclosed in a tough orange rind. A bas relief

work at the tomb-chapel of Chaty Ramose in Thebes featured Ramoses's parents, Neby and Apuya, holding a pomegranate fruit standing near a tree.

Additional reading: Krochmal, A. and Korchmal C. (1984). *A field guide to medicinal plants*. New York: Time Books.

Poppy   Agriculture
Origin: Egypt   Date: 1750 BCE

In a wall drawing dating back to 1750 BCE, Nefertiti, Queen of Akhenaten, was accompanied by one of her daughters carrying poppy plants. The poppy grew in temperate and sub-tropical regions and consisted of a milky juice that had narcotic properties.

Additional reading: Hickey, M. and King, C. (1981). *100 families of flowering plants*. Cambridge Eng.: Cambridge University Press.

Porcelain   Materials
Origin: China   Date: 90 BCE

Porcelain originated in China. There are three kinds of porcelain: hard past, translucent, and Dresden or Meissen. Hard-past porcelain was made around 90 BCE, Kaolin and China stone were used to produce translucent, china-like glass.

Additional reading: Schwartz, B. (1985). *The world of thought in ancient China*. Cambridge, Mass.: Harvard University Press.

Porch   Construction
Origin: Africa   Date: 200 BCE

Early in the 1400s, Prince Henry of Portugal had ships exploring southern parts of Africa. The explorers realized that Africans had lived quite differently. One major difference was building designs. The early European explorers observed structures that were time-tested to enhance lives and minimize discomfort in a tropical climate. Dwellings often featured an exterior space that functioned like a room, but was open on three sides, with the hut serving as the back wall. During the day, when interiors reached oven-like temperatures, the porches provided a comfortable space in which to prepare food, mind children, sleep, and hold ceremonies for the village. These hut-like dwellings have appeared in cave drawings dating back to 200 BCE.

Additional reading: Dolan, M. (2002). *The American porch: An informal history of an informal place.* Guilford Conn.: Lyons Press.

Portrait — Communication
Origin: Sumer — Date: 3000 BCE

Around 3000 BCE, Sumerians used clay tablets for pictographic writing and portrait images. This clay tablet continued until parchment replaced it. By all indications only the royal families and the very wealthy could afford to have portraits done.

Additional reading: Schmandt, B. (1992). *Before writing.* Austin: University of Texas Press.

Positional Notation — Mathematics
Origin: Babylonia — Date: 2000 BCE

The Babylonians are credited with the development of many mathematical equations dating back to as early as 3200 BCE. Around 2000 BCE, the Babylonians developed positional notation based on the number 60. This new mathematical process was very useful because it provided structure to the country's economic system.

Additional reading: Bell, E., (1945). *The development of mathematics. 2nd ed.* New York, McGraw Hill.

Positive Number — Mathematics
Origin: China — Date: 250 BCE

The Chui-Chang Suan-Shu is comprised of nine chapters in the Mathematical Arts, one of the most influential Chinese books of mathematics. It contains more than two hundred problems on engineering, surveying, calculation, agriculture, and right triangles as well as solutions to problems in simultaneous linear equations using the earliest known form of positive and negative numbers. The development of positive and negative numbers was a gateway to an array of mathmatical solutions.

Additional Reading: Midonick, H. (1965). *The treasury of mathematics.* New York: Philosophical Library.

Post — Communication
Origin: Persia — Date: 550 BCE

Cyrus the Great (558-528 BCE), the King of Persia, invented the post. Cyrus had conquered an enormous empire, wherein the practice of individually dispatched messengers bearing letters and other information was no longer efficient. The king organized a series of relay stations located at regular intervals, with personnel responsible for tending to the couriers' horses after a reasonable daily run.

Additional reading: Scheele, C., (1970). *A short history of the mail service.* Washington D.C.: Smithsonian Institution Press.

Post Office — see — Post.

Postal System — Communication
Origin: Egypt — Date: 500 BCE

In Egypt, a postal system for royal and administrative messages consisted of a relay system in which messages were passed from one courier to the next. The earliest post office was a military outpost, and the first postal workers were military personnel.

Additional reading: Forbes, R. (1958). *Man, the maker; a history of technology and engineering.* New York: Abelard-Schuman.

Poster — Communication
Origin: Egypt — Date: 3000 BCE

Dating from 3000 BCE, the first known poster was an Egyptian papyrus offering a reward for finding escaped slaves. Posters featured sales, rentals, shows, and festivities. In Nubia, news for the public to read was painted on wooden tablets and displayed in the public squares, during the same time period.

Additional reading: Giscard d'Estaing, V. (1985). *The world almanac book of inventions.* New York: Ballantine Books.

Potato — Agriculture
Origin: Peru — Date: 8000 BCE

With the harnessing of fire and large villages beginning to form, the domestication of animals and the planting of crops began to spread throughout many regions. As far back as 8,000 BCE, the Peruvians were the first to plant and cultivate the potato. The potato crop was used for a food substance for both humans and later domesticated animals.

Additional reading: Coe, M. (1994). *Breaking the Maya code.* London: Penguin.

Pottery   Art
Origin: Turkey   Date: 7000 BCE

Pottery was invented in the Middle East, perhaps in Anatolia, about 6500 to 7000 BCE. During the next few thousand years, the methods of making pottery spread throughout most of Africa, Asia, and Europe. In the New World, both Peruvian and Mexican Indians discovered how to make pottery around 2500 BCE.

Additional reading: Redman, C. (1978). *The rise of civilization from early farmers to urban society in the ancient near East.* San Francisco: Freeman;

Potter's Wheel   Mechanical
Origin: Egypt   Date: 3000 BCE

The earliest mass pottery making device dating as far back as 3500 BCE, have been found in Africa, Asia and Europe. The potter's wheel was developed as long ago as 3000 BCE, in Egypt. The earliest potter's wheel was spun by hand. By 2000 BCE, a second wheel was placed under the first wheel, and as such, was powered by the foot.

Additional reading: Perlman, I. & Isaro, F. (1969). Pottery analysis by neutron activation,'*Archaeometry.* II.

Power (Numerical)   Mathematics
Origin: Sumer   Date: 3100 BCE

Around 3000 BCE, Sumerians developed a process of using a small reed to designate units of ones and tens. A large reed was used to represent units of six hundred. By 2500 BCE, the power system was no longer used, and the reeds were replaced by the wedge-shaped stylus used in writing the cuneiform script. A single vertical imprint was used to designate any power of 60-1, 60, 3600, and so on. The particular value which these signs denoted was determined by their position or place in the Arabic numeral system.

Additional reading: Van Sertima, I. (1983). *Blacks in science: ancient and modern.* New Brunswick: Transaction Books.

Prefabricated Building   Construction
Origin: Babylonia   Date: 1300 BCE

The Babylonians developed a series of mobile, prefabricated temples for the tribe of Dan. The early versions of these structures housed military generals in the field. Prefabricated temples housed the tabernacle, ark, mercy seat, candle-sticks, and priests' garments.

Additional reading: Low, A. (1947). *Your world tomorrow.* London: Hutchinson.

Pregnancy Test   Medical
Origin: Babylonia   Date: 700 BCE

A Babylonian tablet dating from about 700 BCE, explained the method used to detect pregnancy. The test was carried out by midwives and involved placing a woolen tampon soaked with the juice of certain plants into the woman's vagina. The color change was an indication of pregnacy.

Additional reading: Reiner, E. (1989). *Babylonian birth prognosis.* Zeitschrift: Assyriologie.

Press   see   Bag Press.

Probe   Medical
Origin: India   Date: 1000 BCE

According to ancient surgeon Sushruta, the Hindu Samhita, an Ayurvedic compendium, describes well-defined probes for various medical procedures. The medical people who used the probe had a variety of styles and types. Their selection of probe type, according to the Samhita was based on the specific medical problem posed, such as ear infection or urethral blockage.

Additional reading: Noel H. (1969). *Historical archaeology.* New York: Knopf Press.

Propeller   Navigation
Origin: Nubia   Date: 400 BCE

The Nubians used propeller devices to move heavy stone block on the Nile. The devices were attached to floating barges and required several men to maintain it when heavy loads were being transported. Around 300 BCE, Hero of Alexander developed a screw-like propeller that required less manpower.

Additional reading: Adams, W., (1977). *Nubia: Corridor to Africa.* Princeton, N.J: Priceton University Press.

Psychiatry   Medical
Origin: Babylonia   Date: 1950 BCE

The earliest reference to psychiatry can be traced to 1950 BCE, in the Code of Hammurabi, King of Babylon. The Code recommended opium and olive oil to treat psychiatric disorders, which were believed to be demonic possession.

Additional reading: Murray, D. (1983). *A history of Western psychology.* Englewood: Prentice-Hall.

Psychology   Medicine
Origin: China   Date: 500 BCE

Chinese philosopher Confucius discussed human nature. He also developed a set of plans detailing how human behavior can be modified. The treatments ranged from medication, surgery and natural medicine. Over time the concept did gain popularity but not until hundreds of years later.

Additional reading: Foley, R. (1991). *The origins of human behavior.* New York: Hyman Pub.

Pulley   Mechanical
Origin: Assyria   Date: Antiquity

The pulley was used by the Assyrians and the Egyptians. Entertainers used a combination of several pulleys of unequal size for altering the rate of movement of dancing figures. From these pulleys, the Romans adapted the compound pulley or tackle of pulleys.

Additional reading: Williams, T. (1987). *The history of invention.* New York: Facts on File.

Puppet   Entertainment
Origin: Nigeria   Date: Antiquity

Early toy-like images were found in Africa as early as 20,000 BCE. The concepts of puppets were introduced much later for specific purposes. Puppets were first created in Nubia and used in religious festivals. While the exact date is unknown, many references were made to the existence of strange life-like dancing images in antiquity.

Additional reading: Connah, G., (1981). *Three thousand years in Africa: Man and his environment in the lake Chad region of Nigeria.* Cambridge: Cambridge University Press.

Pyramid (Structures)   Civil
Origin: Egypt   Date: 3700 BCE

These massive structures were designed to be safe tombs for the remains of Egyptian pharaohs. Imhotep is believed to have been the builder of the first pyramid, constructed in Egypt around 2700 BCE. It was 200 feet high with a base of 358 by 411 feet. The most famous surviving example of a pyramid is the Great Pyramid of Giza, which has a height of about 463 feet. Some native cultures in the Americas, including the Mayan and Aztec, also built pyramids.

Additional reading: Edwards, I., (1970). *The pyramids of Egypt.* New York: Viking Press.

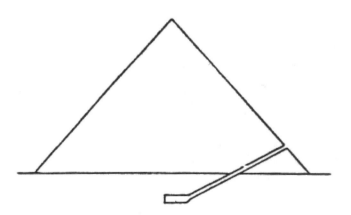

Figure 24
Pyramid
This depicts an early example of small pyramid structure.

Pyrethrum   see   Pesticide.

Pythagorean Theorem — Mathematics
Origin: Mesopotamia   Date: 2200 BCE

The Mesopotamians were the first to publish in text form the use of the Pythagorean triplets of integers ($a2 + b2 = c2$), i. e., the sums of the squared sides of a right-angled triangle equals the square of the hypotenuse (the line opposite the triangle's right angle). This equation appeared in a mathematics text dating to 2200 BCE.

Additional reading: Smith, D. and Karpinski, L. (1911). *The Hindu-Arabic numerals.* Boston: Ginn & Co.

Q

Qanat — Construction
Origin: Iraq   Date: 2200 BCE

In Assyria, the practice of digging underground tunnels called qanat, began in 2200 BCE. These qanat led to subterranean ground water and were used for irrigation purposes. The quality of the water was good, and the qanat often supplied large areas. The Romans took this method of irrigation to the Mediterranean region.

Additional reading: Straub, H. (1952). *A history of civil engineering:* London: Leonard Hill Pub.

Quadratic Equation — Mathematics
Origin: Babylonia   Date: 2500 BCE

The quadratic equation was developed by the Babylonians in 2500 BCE. The primary use of this mathematical process was in the development and construction of large structures. Using fractions, the calculation of division was carried out by multiplying the number to be divided by the reciprocal of the divisor. Tables of reciprocals were drawn up for this purpose, although the places for awkward numbers such as 1/7 were left blank. Tables of squares of numbers, their square roots, were also drawn up, and the tables were used to solve problems involving quadratic and cubic equations. In the field of geometry, the Babylonians were aware that all triangles inscribed in a semi-circle were right-angled triangles, this being generally true and not just for specific cases.

Additional reading: Newman, J. (1956). *The world of mathematics.* New York: Simon and Schuster.

Quarry — Material
Origin: Egypt   Date: 3200 BCE

The rock quarry was a vast deposit of stones that were retrieved to build large structures. The use of stone on a large scale for building purposes became practicable in Egypt about 3200 BCE. The stone used earlier for vases and other comparatively small objects had been procured from blocks that were detached from the cliffs by natural processes or from boulders that had been found in the ancient dry water courses and at the sides of the river in cataract areas.

Additional reading: Barber, F. (1900). *The mechanical triumphs of ancient Egyptians.* London: Trubner and Co.

Quartzite — Chemistry
Origin: Asia   Date: Prehistoric

Quartzite is a hard, compact variety of sandstone that is formed by the depositing of crystalline quartz between sand grains. It varies considerably both in color and in texture. Quartzite also occurred in various locations, notably at Gebel Ahmar, which is situated in the northeast and close to Cairo.

Additional reading: Lucas, A. and Harris, J. (1999). *Ancient Egyptian materials and industries.* New York: Dover Pub.

Quay — Navigational
Origin: Africa   Date: Antiquity

In the northern regions of Africa, many naturally occurring small islands surrounded the coastal waters. When small bands of seamen went out to fish, they were met close to shore by other members of the village on manmade quays. The quay was an artificial landing place built for unloading the catch. The use of quays spread quickly down the coastal regions of western Africa.

Additional reading: Binford, L., (1981). *Bones: Ancient man and modern myths.* New York: Academic Press.

Quern — Agricultural
Origin: Persia   Date: 6000 BCE

The quern, a hand mill first used to grind grains, appeared around 6000 BCE in Persia. It consisted of two stones configured in the shape of a saddle, making a saddle quern. The rotary quern, a revolving hand mill, appeared in the Mediterranean region between 5000 BCE.

Additional reading: Hitti, P. (1943). *The Arabs*. Chicago: Gateway Ed.

R

Radish   Agriculture
Origin: Babylonia   Date: 8500 BCE

The farmers of the Fertile Crescent were the earliest known to domestically grow and cultivate the radish for a food additive. The radish was eaten raw and often cooked for its juices. It was also used for medical treatments.

Additional reading: Krzyzaniak, L. (1977). Early farming cultures on the lower Nile: The predynastic period in Egypt. *Varsovie*: Scientifiques de Pologne.

Raft   Navigation
Origin: Africa   Date: 6000 BCE

The first humans established living areas near lakes and rivers, which served as a source of food. People learned to swim and soon found that wood could float. By 6000 BCE, they had lashed logs together to form rafts. By paddling with their hands or a crude oar, they crossed small stretches of water.

Additional reading: Africanus, L. (1896). *The history and description of Africa. 3 vols, ed.* London: Brown, Kakluyt Society.

Raisin   see   **Plum.**

Rattan   Agriculture
Origin: Syria   Date: 5200 BCE

With the advent of small villages and towns, many plants that grew in the wild were grown domestically by the Syrians dating as far back as 5200 BCE. Farmers of the Fertile Crescent were the earliest known to domestically grow and cultivate Rattan. Rattan was one of several species of climbing palms, notable for its long, thin, jointed, and pliable fronds. This plant was used as food and often for ropelike projects.

Additional reading: Huggins, W. (1937). *An introduction to African civilizations in current Ethiopian history.* New York: Avon House.

Rauwalfia   see   **Reserpine.**

Razor   Medicine
Origin: Egypt   Date: 2600 BCE

Relatively sophisticated surgical instruments such as razors came from Egypt, an area regarded by the ancient Greeks and Romans as the cradle of medicine. The Egyptians used copper surgical blades that were sharp enough for simple operations.

Additional reading: Dayagi-Mendele, M. (1989). *Perfumes and cosmetics in the ancient world.* Jerusalem: Israel Museum.

Reamer   see   **Drill.**

Record System   see   **Numerical System.**

Reflection Device   see   **Mirror.**

Refrigeration   Mechanical
Origin: China   Date: 221 BCE

The Chinese developed a process of food preservation by using a device that formed an ice pit. Built by H. Sienyang for the first emperor, Shih H. Wang Ti, the ice pit was made from giant terra cotta rings about three feet high and five feet, eight to twenty-four inches in diameter and extended forty-three feet below ground level.

Additional reading: Schwartz, B. (1985). *The world of thought in ancient China.* Cambridge: Harvard University Press.

Reindeer   Domestic
Orgin: America: Date: 1500 BCE

The reindeer was domesticated around 1500 BCE. Domesticated reindeer were later used as decoys to lure wild reindeer into traps. An undercover hunter held the tamed deer by ropes and approached the herd of wild reindeer against the wind until the hunters were close enough to shoot bows and arrows.

Additional reading: Gille, B. (1986). *The history of technique*. New York: Gordon and Breach Science Pub.

Repair (Surgery)   Medical
Origin: India   Date: 49 BCE

In 49 BCE, the Hindu surgeon Susruta carried out an operation that consisted of treating intestinal perforations and obstructions by joining together the damaged or occluded part of the intestine after cutting into the abdomen below the navel. Susruta sutured the segments of the intestine by placing the freshly cut heads of giant black ants on the edges of the opposing sections.

Additional reading: Dorland, N. (1994). *Dorland's illustrated medical dictionary*. Philadelphia: Saunders.

Reserpine   Medicine
Origin: India   Date: 1250 BCE

The ancient Hindus were credited with originating production of the treatment known as reserpine, which is the first sedative-anti-hypertensive. This treatment, derived from the root of the Rauwalfia serpentina plant, was mostly provided to the well to do of the period. Other treatments often led to serious injuries and even death for those suffering hypertensive illness.

Additional reading: Piggott, S. (1950). *Prehistoric India to 1000 B.C.*. Harmondsworth: Middlesex.

Rice   Agriculture
Origin: Indochina   Date: 8000 BCE

Over time, humans in low-lying areas with plentiful rainfall throughout Asia and Africa gathered different varieties of wild rice. Indochina was the first region to grow and cultivate rice as a domestic crop. Rice was grown in several strands and varied from dark brown to light tan in color. Though rice is now grown in many areas in the world, the cereal was and continues be a major food source for and export product of Indochina.

Additional reading: Robert, J., (2003). *The complete history of China*. England: Sutton Pub.

Right Angle Instrument   Mathematics
Origin: Egypt   Date: 2500 BCE

By 2500 BCE, Egyptian surveyors used the three-four-five right triangle instruments to establish right angles. The construction of right angles in the major pyramids suggested that the method probably predated 2500 BCE.

Additional reading: Van Sertima, I. (1983). *Blacks in science: Ancient and modern*. New Brunswick: Transaction Books.

Rigveda (Hymn)   Music
Origin: India   Date: 1500 BCE

The principles of musical performance were first set out in the Rigveda (Veda of Hymns) and the Samuveda (Veda of Chants), two of the four sacred Veda books dating from 1500 BCE. The Vedic scale corresponded to the seven stages in the descent of the divine word into the realm of substance.

Additional reading: Kilmer, D., (1976). *Sounds of silence: Recent discoveries in ancient Near Eastern music*. Berkeley: Bit Enki Pub.

River Boat   Oceanography
Origin: Nubia   Date: Antiquity

Because water offered less friction than land, the Nubians were the earliest known society to move heavy loads. The Nile flowed almost due north, while the wind was almost always from the north. A boat moved effortlessly downriver and, when the time came to return, a sail was hoisted to catch the wind, and the ship was blown upstream.

Additional reading: Asimov, I. (1989). *Asimov's chronology of science and discovery*. New York: Harper & Row.

Riveting   Mechanical
Origin: Israel   Date: 1460 BCE

The joining of two or more metal pieces to form a single large piece was effected by riveting or clamps. At some unknown date, these methods were supplanted by the more intimate union obtained by soldering. Some metal structures were unearthed during the 1930's during archeological expeditions in the area now known as Israel. The folding shields were joined by what appears to be rivets.

Additional reading: Robinson, T. and Oesterley W. (1932). *The history of Israel. Vols. 1-2,* Oxford: The Clarendon Press.

Road   Mechanical
Origin: Mesopotamia   Date: 4000 BCE

The earliest roads were found in Mesopotamia around 4000 BCE. Few traces of roads have been found in Mesopotamia that provide a clue as to their original appearance, condition, or how they were constructed. The sparse remains of a stone-paved road that led to Nineveh were not sufficient to determine what road building technology had been employed. For the most part, these routes were initially caravan tracks that gradually became crude roads.

Additional reading: Derry, T. and Williams, T. (1960). *A short history of technology from the earliest times to A.D. 1900.* Oxford: Clarendon Press.

Road Network   Civil
Origin: Mesopotamia   Date: 2100 BCE

In 2100 BCE, the Ur-Nammu of Mesopotamia developed an elaborate road-networking system used during peacetime for the transportation needs of the populace. In times of war, the soldiers were able to use the networking system to rapidly deploy their troops and surround the aggressors.

Additional reading: (1979), Ancient *Mesopotamia: Portrait of a dead civilization.* Rev. ed. Chicago: University of Chicago Press.

Robotic   Mechanical
Origin: Egypt   Date: 3000 BCE

In the eighth century BCE, Homer referred to the Egyptian king Hephaestus and the animated gold statues that served him. These statues shared intelligence, voice, and movement. Many philosophers wrote about fictitious animated machines in ancient times. Egyptian sermonizers impressed their followers with accounts of these inventions. The

early tabletop automation was the first of its kind and could move small objects from point A to point B.

Additional reading: Low, A. (1947). *Your world tomorrow.* London: Hutchinson.

Rock (Igneous)   see   Lava.

Rod (Grounding)   Electrical
Origin: Egypt   Date: 1500 BCE

The Egyptians attached masts to pylons, which were gateways in front of their temples, to function as grounding rods. Inscriptions from the temple at Edfu, completed by Ptolemy IV in 212 BCE in Egypt, recorded how copper-covered masts were built into pylons.

Additional reading: Lockyer, J. (1964). *The dawn of astronomy: A study of the temple worship and mythology of the ancient Egyptians.* Cambridge: M.I.T. Press.

Rod   Mathematics
Origin: China   Date: 300 BCE

As early as 300 BCE, it was written that the Chinese used a system of "rod" symbols for numerals described in the Chou Pei Suan Ching. The rod is a system of volume and physical measurements. The system involved sometimes written and/or by physical rods to carry out calculations of large numbers.

Additional readings: Kramer, E., (1970) . *The nature and growth of modern mathematics.* New York: Hawthorn.

Rope   Materials
Origin: Egypt   Date: 3000 BCE

As depicted in temple hieroglyphics, ancient Egyptians invented and manufactured rope sometime around 3000 BCE, in constructing the pyramids, as well as ocean-faring ships. Egyptian rope dating about that time was woven from strands of papyrus reeds. Recent digs at a dried-up lagoon in the seaport town of Mersa Gawasis may dial the date back further; researchers uncovered there remarkable coils of thick rope twisted very much like modern rope, along with a 3,800 year old grassy mat. Down through the centuries, other plant materials served to make rope, including flax, jute, vanilla, and sisal.

Additional reading: Sanford, E. (1938). *The Mediterranean world in ancient times*. New York: Ronald Press Co.

Rosetta Stone   Chemistry
Origin: Egypt   Date: 190 BCE

In 1799, French soldiers discovered an odd stone-like object, now know as the Rosetta Stone near Rosetta in the West Delta of the Nile. It bore inscriptions in three languages, including Egyptian hieroglyphs, demonic, a simplified form of hieroglyphic writing, and Greek. Knowledge of Greek made it possible to decipher the hieroglyphs. The inscriptions were versions of a decree passed by a Council of Priests at Memphis in 196 BCE, declaring that Ptolemy V was the rightful ruler of Egypt.

Additional reading: DeBono, E. (1974). *Eureka!: How and when the greatest inventions were made: An illustrated history of inventions from the wheel to the computer*. London: Thames & Hudson.

Rotary Mill   Agriculture
Origin: Israel   Date: 500 BCE

The area around what is now considered Israel is credited with being the first to invent the rotary mill. The first rotary mill appeared in the Mediterranean region during the fifth century BCE. Donkeys and other beasts of burden drove the mill used to grind grain and the resulting increases in productivity.

Additional reading: Curwen, E. and Hatt, G. (1953). *Plough and pasture, the early history of farming*. Pt. 1: *Prehistoric farming of Europe and Near East*. New York: H. Schuman.

Rudder (Boat)   Oceanography
Origin: Egypt   Date: 3000 BCE

The earliest rudder-like device was used since the dawn of time in Africa. The first manmade rudder was designed and used to steer boats probably began in Egypt circa 3000 BCE. Around 2000 BCE, the Chinese positioned an oar in an opening carved into the overhanging deck of their boats. By 1000 BCE, Arabs started to hang solid pieces off the sterns of their ships.

Additional reading: Cornwell, P.D. (2007). Book of the dead. New York: G.P. Putnam's Sons.

Ruler   Mechanical
Origin: Mesopotamia   Date: 1950 BCE

The first known standard measure of length was a heavy copper bar, unearthed at Nippur on the Euphrates River. Marked with four large units, each unit was divided into 16 smaller units, much like feet and inches. The early rulers were made from bone, ivory, and other materials.

Additional reading: Burke, J. (1978). *Connections,* Boston: Little Brown.

Rye   Agriculture
Origin: Persia   Date: 5000 BCE

The domestication of rye dates back to 5000 BCE. Its wild form was Ancestrale, found in Persia, Afghanistan, and Syria. It had a brittle form like other wild grasses. The Persians had many uses for the raw rye crop. The crop spread quickly to other regions of the world.

Additional reading: Saggs, H., (1965). *Everyday life in Babylonia and Assyria.* London: B.T. Batsford.

S

Safety Pin   Tool
Origin: Sumer   Date: 3000 BCE

Around 3000 BCE, Sumerians used pins made from iron or bone to hold painted cloth together. During that time period these safety pins also served as support for the hand-fashioned garments worn by the general population.

Additional reading: Kramer S., (1956). *From the table of Sumer, twenty five firsts in man's recorded history*. Indian Hills, Colo.: Falcon's Wing Press.

Saffron   Agriculture
Origin: Nubia   Date: 2500 BCE

Saffron grew and was cultivated during the rule of King Khufu of Nubia in 2500 BCE. The plant was orange-red, consisting of the dried stigmas of crocus, and was used as food flavoring. Medically, it was used as a cordial and soporific.

Additional reading: Windsor, R. (1969). *From Babylon to Timbuktu: A history of the ancient black race including the black Hebrews.* New York: Exposition Press.

Sail　　　　　　　　　Navigation
Origin: Nubia　　　　　Date: 5000 BCE

The oldest known depiction of a sail was found in a 5000-year-old Nubian drawing of a Nile river craft. Ancient ships dating back many thousands of years were nearly all under sail. Early sails were likely made from interwoven branches. Cloth sails were known to be used by the Sumerians as early as 3500 BCE.

Additional reading: Gilfillan, S. (1935). *Inventing the ship.* Chicago: Follett Pub. Co.

Saltgylic Acids　　see　　**Aspirin.**

Salt　　　　　　　　　Chemistry
Origin: Tanzania　　　Date: Prehistoric

As far back as 1,000,000 years ago, the first humans used salt in some form. Many archeological sites in what is now Tanzania have shown concentrated areas of salt rock. Chemically known as sodium chloride, salt was one of the most abundant substances in both solution and crystalline form.

Additional reading: Chittick, N. (1975). An early salt-working site on the Tanzanian coast, *Azania* 10, p. 151-3.

Sampu　　　　see　　　　**Boat.**

Sandal　　　　　　　　Domestic
Origin: Nubia　　　　　Date: 3600 BCE

The custom among ancient Nubians circa 3500 BCE, was to walk barefooted, using their sandals only when necessary, such as for special ceremonies. The first sandals were all the same size and made from plaited papyrus and palm fiber. Records indicate that mostly wealthy Nubians wore custom-made sandals.

Additional reading: Adams, W., (1977). *Nubia, corridor to Africa.* Princeton, N.J.: Princeton University Press.

Sandpaper　　　see　　　**Abrasive.**

Sandstone　　　　　　Chemistry
Origin: Egypt　　　　　Date: 3200 BCE

Sandstone is comprised of quartz sand derived from the disintegration of older rocks, cemented together by very small proportions of clay, calcium carbonate, and oxide of iron or silica. By 3200 BCE, sandstone formations were known to exist near Sabaia at Aswan. The rock, however, was not widely employed until the Eighteenth Dynasty when it was used for foundations, pavements, pillars, roof slabs, and walls of the hall in the mortuary temple. Sandstone was the material of choice for the massive building projects and enormous cultural statuary erected during Egypt's New Kingdom. Almost all of the existing temples in Upper Egypt were built of sandstone.

Additional reading: Connah, G., (1981). *Three thousand years in Africa: Man and his environment in the lake Chad region of Nigeria.* Cambridge: Cambridge University Press.

Sarbacane　　　see　　　**Blowpipe.**

Saronic Cycle　　　　Astronomy
Origin: Mesopotamia　Date: 400 BCE

Mesopotamians discovered that lunar eclipses occurred every eighteen years and called this period of time the Saronic Cycle. In the fourth century BCE, they developed an algebraic method for analyzing the complex celestial phenomena and to predict eclipse cycles. They found that the average lunar month was twenty-nine and a quarter days, and that the deviations from this average were periodic. Modern astronomers still use the method.

Additional reading: Nur Ankh Amen, N. (1999). *The ankh, African origin of electromagnetism.* Brooklyn New York: A&B Publishers Group..

Saw　　　　　　　　　Mechanical
Origin: Egypt　　　　　Date: 4000 BCE

One of the earliest Stone Age instruments, the saw, had jagged edges that were attached to shafts of wood or bone used for cutting skins or for harvesting. The earliest known saw made first of copper then later of bronze was used in Egypt around 4000 BCE. However, their V-shaped heads did not allow an even cut to be made through thick materials. The oldest known saws, made first of copper and later of bronze, were used in Egypt around 4000 BCE. Progressive improvements in the length, sharpness, and durability of the saws resulted in longer and more even cuts.

Additional reading: Barber, F. (1900). *The mechanical triumphs of ancient Egyptians*. London: Trubner and Co.

Scale	**see**	**Music.**

Scale (Balance)   Tool
Origin: Egypt   Date: 2000 BCE

Around 2000 BCE, balance scales were used in Egypt and Mesopotamia. Because the evidence of these balance scales found in drawings and paintings was not sufficiently detailed, it cannot be ascertained how the scales were pivoted or whether they could be adjusted.

Additional reading: Bunch, B. and Hellemans, A. (1993). *The timetables of technology: A chronology of the most important people and events in the history of technology.* New York: Simon & Schuster.

Scalpel   Medical
Origin: Nubia   Date: 1000 BCE

The ancient Hindus developed an array of surgical instruments known as scalpels. The earliest mention of surgical instruments was in the ancient Hindu medical works of Sushruta Samhita, in which twenty surgical tools were described in detail, along with their various uses.

Additional reading: Bennion, E., (1979). *Antique medical instruments*. London: Sotheby Parke Bernet Pub.

Scrapper	**see**	**Burin.**

Scarab   Domestic
Origin: Egypt   Date: Antiquity

The scarab was an amulet first used in the Sixth Dynasty of ancient Egypt. It was made in the form of a scarab beetle, which the Egyptians associated with the power that drove the sun across the sky. Scarabs were worn as necklaces and were buried with the dead, in both cases as a protective charm. In the Twelfth Dynasty, the seal-scarab came into use with the owner's name cut into it.

Additional reading: Palmer, G. (1968). *Archaeology a-z, a simplified guide and dictionary*. New York: Frederick Warne.

Scoop	**see**	**Shovel.**

Script	**see**	**Notation.**

Scroll	**see**	**Cuneiform.**

Sculpture   Domestic
Origin: Africa   Date: Prehistoric

The earliest formed figures were depicted on hill side drawings in the lower valley of Africa. The images showed sculptures carved out of wood. The images were of manmade tools and various foods of the period. The earliest human-like figure dates back to the Neolithic period.

Additional reading: James, P. (1993). *Centuries of darkness: A challenge to the conventional chronology of old world archaeology.* New Brunswick, N.J: Rutgers University Press.

Seal (Cylinder)   Mechanical
Origin: Mesopotamia   Date: 3500 BCE

The Mesopotamians are credited with being the first to develop an air tight cylinder. The cylinder seal was developed to increase the efficiency of the water-powered instruments around 3500 BCE.

Additional reading: Ecco, U. and Zorzoli, G. B. (1963). *The picture history of inventions: From plough to polaris.* New York: Macmillan.

Seal   Communication
Origin: Israel   Date: 1250 BCE

Around 1250 BCE, Israelis began to use seals to identify property, carving the seals into wet clay.

Throughout history symbols have been used to identify artifacts. Many identifying seals have been analyzed many years before the Israelis developed a process for producing air tight seal. The uniform markings were the first known systematic identification form.

Additional reading: Gordon, C., (1974). *Riddles in history.* New York: Crown Press.

Seaweed   see   **Kelp.**

Security   see   **Police Force.**

Sedative   see   **Reserpine.**

Seed Drill   Agriculture
Origin: Africa   Date: 2000 BCE

About 2000 BCE, the first seed drills were made by placing a funnel through a hole drilled in a wooden plow. Seeds that poured into the funnel were directed out of the hole and deposited into a plowed furrow.

Additional reading: Africanus, L. (1896). *The history and description of Africa.* 3 Vols, ed. London: Brown, Kakluyt Society.

Senet   Entertainment
Origin: Egypt   Date: 2000 BCE

During this period, entertainment games were common throughout northern Africa. Games such as checkers, senet, and bowling started in this geographical region. At one time, senet was the most popular game in ancient Egypt, played by peasants and artisans as well as by the pharaohs. An early representation of the playing board figures were found on the tomb of Ramses.

Additional reading: Hart, G. (1990). *Ancient Egypt.* New York: Alfred Knopf Pub.

Sesame   Agriculture
Origin: China   Date: 1600 BCE

As early as 1600 BCE, Chinese farmers cultivated sesame. The sesame seeds were processed into thick oil and used for a variety of foods and other domestic purposes. Sesame was a common trading item of the region.

Additional reading: Schwartz, B. (1985). *The world of thought in ancient China.* Cambridge: Harvard University Press.

Sewer   Mechanical
Origin: Syria   Date: 800 BCE

Sewers were used to contain excess rainwater and waste. During the second Assyrian Empire, in the eighth century BCE, gutters were dug in the center of the town streets. The Assyrians dug sewers and installed their main sewers underground.

Additional reading: Badawy, A., (1966). *A history of Egyptian architecture.* Berkeley: University of California Press.

Sexagesimal Fractions   Mathematics
Origin: Babylon   Date: 3200 BCE

The secret of the primacy of Babylonian mathematics over that of the Egyptians undoubtedly lies in the fact that those who lived "between the two rivers" took the most felicitous step of extending the principle of position to cover fractions as well as whole numbers. The Babylonians had at their command the computational power of the modern scholar and the modern engineer. The addition or the multiplication of 23.45 and 9.876 was essentially no more difficult than was the addition or multiplication of the whole numbers 2345 and 9876; and Mesopotamians were quick to exploit this important mathematical development.

Additional reading: Boyer, C. (2000), *A history of mathematics.* New York: John Wiley.

Sex Manual   Medical
Origin: India   Date: Antiquity

Kama Sutra, a sex manual from ancient India, began to infiltrate the Western world after its translation by British Orientalist, Sir Richard Burton, who also translated The Arabian Nights. The Kama Sutra was written to inform the leisure class of ancient India about the practical details of conducting their love affairs. While not ashamed of seeking the pleasures of sex,

Hindu society recommended that it be experienced within marriage. The manual outlined social conduct, virtue and gracious living.

Additional reading: Vatsyayana, B.R., (1964). *The Kama Sutra of Vatsyayana; the classic Hindu treatise on love and social conduct.* New York: E.P. Dutton & Co.

Shaduf   Agriculture
Origin: Mesopotamia   Date: 3000 BCE

Sometime after 3000 BCE, farmers in both Mesopotamia and Egypt began to use the shaduf. The device lifted water from a river or canal to the higher level of a field. The shaduf was a long pole balanced on an upright post with a rock or other counterweight tied to one end of the pole and a container on a rope fastened to the other. The container was lowered by hand into the water, raised by hand with the counterweight doing most of the lifting, emptied into either a cistern or a canal, and then lowered into the water again.

Additional readings: Hart, G. (1990). *Ancient Egypt.* New York: Alfred Knopf Pub.

Shawabit   Construction
Origin: Nubia   Date: 800 BCE

The earliest shawabits were found in Nubia dating back to 800 BCE using carbon testing. During the early part of the twentieth century, archeologists discovered at the ancient pyramids in Meroe a variety of smaller stone casket figurines, called shawabti (or sometimes ushabti), in the tombs. Excavators found more than 1,000 sepulchral shawabti in King Taharka's tomb.

Additional Reading: Edwards, I., (1985) *The pyramids of Egypt.* Harmondsworth: Viking Press.

Sheep   Agriculture
Origin: Egypt   Date: 7200 BCE

Egypt and other northern Africa countries are credited with the early domestication of grazing animals. Livestock such as sheep, camels, and goats were a favorite of the region. During Egypt's Badarian period, farmers of the Fertile Crescent were the earliest known to domestically breed sheep for food

and milk. The sheep was one of the animals selected to travel with communities that migrated from region to region.

Additional reading: Gille, B. (1986). *History of technique.* New York: Gordon and Breach Science Pub.

Shekel   Mathematics
Origin: Sumer   Date: 2500 BCE

As far back as 2500 BCE, the Sumerians developed many mathematical firsts. They, over the next few centuries, developed a system of standard weights and measures, including such units as the shekel, the mina, the log, the homer, the cubit, and the foot. Sumer's forward-thinking mathematicians have been acknowledged as pioneers in the field of architecture, mathematics, astronomy, and science.

Additional reading: Black, M (1934). *The nature of mathematics.* New York: Harcourt Brace and Co.

Ship   Naval
Origin: Egypt   Date: 4000 BCE

Large floating vessels have been around for many years. It wasn't until the Naqada I Dynasty that large floating vessels were designed and constructed by ship builders. Ships were sailed by the Egyptians as early as 4000 BCE. Whether powered by sail or by oars, ships enabled worldwide exploration and trade to take place.

Additional reading: Johnstone, P. (1988). *The sea-craft of prehistory.* New York: Routledge.

Shoe   Material
Origin: Egypt   Date: 4000 BCE

During the predynastic period, known as the Archaic period, the earliest known constructed pair of foot covering was made. The Roman Museum contains a pair of Egyptian shoes made of papyrus dating to 4000 BCE. The invention of shoes occurred much earlier, however, probably during Neolithic times.

Additional reading: Glanville, S. (1942). *The legacy of Egypt.* Oxford: Clarendon Press.

Shorthand   Communication
Origin: Africa   Date: 63 BCE

As early as 63 BCE, a primitive system of shorthand was developed by what some archeologists believe was a former slave. Early records show that certain stone carvings recovered in the early 16th Century had a series of symbols that were shorter written expressions from other symbol writings of the area.

Additional Reading: Gardiner, A. (1957). *Egyptian grammar; being an introduction to the study of hieroglyphs.* London: Oxford University Press.

Shovel   Tool
Origin: Africa   Date: Prehistoric

A prehistoric tool made of antler with the characteristics of a shovel, the first of its kind, was discovered in Central Africa. Oval in shape with three perforations down its center for the attachment of the handle, the shovel was made from the wide palmation at the bottom of an elk antler.

Additional reading: Peckham, S. (1960). A guide for highway salvage programs in archaeology, history and paleontology. *Society for Archaeology.* Publication No. N.P.

Shower   Mechanical
Origin: Egypt   Date: 1350 BCE

The adoption of specially-made shower stalls dates back to 1350 BCE. At Akhenanten, the ancient capital of Egypt, archaeologists discovered a shallow slab, which some believed to be the first shower pan. This early shower was designed as a wooden enclosure with a ceramic lining.

Additional reading: James, P. and Thorpe, N., (1994). *Ancient inventions.* New York.: Ballantine Books.

Shroud   see   **Cloth.**

Sickle   Agriculture
Origin: Palestine   Date: 6000 BCE

Evidence of the earliest sickle was found in Mount Carmel in Palestine. Dating to some time before 6000 BCE, it was probably used by Mesolithic hunters and gatherers to cut grasses and made of flint mounted on carved bone or wooden handles.

Additional reading: Forbes, R. (1967). *Studies in ancient technology.* New York: Leiden, E.J. Pub.

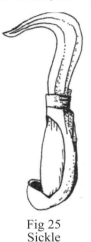

Fig 25
Sickle

Sign (Texts)   see   **Determinative.**

Signaling (Formal)   Communication
Origin: Africa   Date: Prehistoric

The act of communicating dates back to the dawn of mankind. In the southern region of Africa, hollow trees or hardened surfaces were often used to communicate warnings of danger and returning home from long campaigns.

Additional reading: Adams, W. (1977). *Nubia, corridor to Africa.* Princeton, N.J., Princeton University Press.

Silk   Material
Origin: China   Date: 3000 BCE

The Chinese were the first to understand that the average length of 1500 meters of thread made by the silk worm could be unwound and woven. The cultivation of the silkworm, called sericulture, in China was well-documented. According to the Chinese tradition, Lei-Tzu, the wife of the Asian emperor Houang-Ti, revealed the secret of silk weaving to her subjects in 2698 BCE.

Additional reading: Basalla, G. (1988). *The evolution of technology.* Cambridge Eng.: University Press.

Silk Thread — Material
Origin: Egypt   Date: 1000 BCE

Around 1000 BCE, silk thread found in an Egyptian mummy's hair provided evidence that silk was being manufactured by this time. Small amounts of Chinese silk reached Egypt by way of Persia through merchant trade.

Additional reading: Parker, S. (1984). *McGraw-Hill concise encyclopedia of science and technology.* New York: McGraw-Hill.

Silkworm — Domestic
Origin: China   Date: Antiquity

The earliest evidence that the Chinese raised silk worms reaches back to antiquity. The silk worm, also known as Bombyx mori, were first domesticated in northern China more than 5000 years ago, before the breeding practice later spread throughout Asia and to the West. This economically vital insect is able to change into a pupa state and spin a cocoon made of silken filament. It was this raw silk filament that was, and continues to be so harvested and used in the production of fine silk items.

Additional reading: Schwartz, B. (1985). *The world of thought in ancient China.* Cambridge: Harvard University Press.

Silo — Agriculture
Origin: Syria   Date: 2600 BCE

The process of preserving food dates back to prehistoric times. The oldest silo was discovered in Syria and dates back to 2600 BCE. The early silo was a pit used to store grain like flax, maize, rye, and wheat. Many of these underground silos were lined with animal fur that kept grain dry from natural elements.

Additional reading: (1979), *Ancient records of Assyria and Babylon, vol I. historical records of Assyria from the earliest times to Sargon.* Chicago: University of Chicago Press.

Silver — Chemistry
Origin: Asia Minor   Date: 3000 BCE

Silver, a white metal with atomic number 47 and chemical symbol Ag, is softer than copper and harder than gold. It is superior to all other metals as a conductor of electricity and heat. Slag dumps in Asia Minor showed that silver had been separated from lead as early as 3000 BCE. Silver can be found all over the world and, in some areas, it exists as a compound. Most silver is obtained as a by-product of the processing of lead, copper, or gold.

Additional reading: Considine, D. and Considine, G. (1983). *Van Nostrand's Scientific Encyclopedia. 6th Edition,* New York: Reinhold, Co.

Silver Mining — Mining
Origin: Syria   Date: 3000 BCE

Since time immemorial, humans have adopted some medium of exchange between themselves to acquire goods and services. Silver was a medium of exchange in Assyria as far back as 3000 BCE, and thereafter became a valuable and sought-after resource for flourishing civilizations in the region. At that time, donkey-driven mills were used to crush the ore. By the Middle Ages, the amount of silver being mined had increased significantly due to discovery of new silver lodes and improved extraction technologies.

Additional reading: Phimister, I.R. (1975). *History of mining in Southern Rhodesia to 1953,* Dissertation Thesis (D. Phil)—University of Rhodesia.

Sine Wave — Physics
Origin: Egypt   Date: 2100 BCE

The first mathematical description of a sine wave is attributed to Fourier, one of the assistants who attended the first pharaoh of the Middle Kingdom of Egypt. He described a wave as a distinctive sum of sine waves, defined by their frequency, amplitude, and phase.

Additional reading: Nur Ankh Amen, N. (1999). *The ankh: African origin of electromagnetism.* Brooklyn New York: A&B Publishers Group.

Siphon — Mechanical
Origin: Egypt   Date: Antiquity

According to depictions on wall carvings, ancient Egyptians were the first to use siphons to move fluids from one container to another location. There is evidence that in the production of wine, Egyptians used a siphon to keep the dregs that settled at the bottom of the vat segregated from the wine to be served. The forerunner of the siphon may have been a pipe-like device used for sucking. Not to be regarded as a true siphon, it made use of the atmospheric pressure on liquids to raise them out of a vessel and to the level of the mouth.

Additional reading: Barber, F. (1900). *The mechanical triumphs of ancient Egyptians*. London: Trubner and Co.

Sistrum (Music Rattle)   Musical
Origin: Egypt   Date: 2400 BCE

The Egyptians during the old Kingdom are credited with the earliest development of the musical instrument known as a sistrum. Many believe that different forms of rattle existed prior to the sistrum, but the earliest recovered rattle is housed in the Egyptian Museum and dates back to 2400 BCE. Considered a sacred instrument, the sistrum was used in ceremonial activities by the spiritual leaders who accompanied the priest.

Additional reading: Hart, G. (1990). *Ancient Egypt*. New York: Alfred Knopf Pub.

Skin Dressing   see   Gauze.

Skin Grafting   Medicine
Origin: India   Date 1500 BCE

As early as 1500 BCE, Indian doctors performed surgery under controlled conditions. Hindus were the first to perform the surgical procedures for skin grafting. This procedure led to plastic surgery on different parts of the body.

Additional reading: Van Sertima, I. (1983). *Blacks in science: Ancient and modern*. New Brunswick. Transaction Books.

Slate   Material
Origin: Africa   Date: Prehistoric

Pestles for pulverizing materials like jade, quartz, shell, and slate plaques were used during the Mesolithic period. Early slate plaques came from Malta region. The slate plaque was rare because the tools for pulverizing minerals were found in many ancient settlements.

Additional reading: Semenov, S. (1964). *Prehistoric technology; an experimental study of the oldest tools and artifacts from traces of manufacture and wear*. New York: Barnes & Noble.

Sledge   Transportation
Origin: Africa   Date: 30,000 BCE

The first land vehicles, found in southern Africa, were simple sledges that were often made from two parallel poles joined by strips of hide or bark and used to transport animal kills. Runners were later added to reduce the friction.

Additional reading: De Camp, L. (1974). *The ancient engineers*. New York: Barnes & Noble.

Sling   Mechanical
Origin: Africa   Date: 10,000 BCE

The earliest record of a hunting tool known as the sling was recorded in Western Africa, dating back to 10,000 BCE. A crude model was discovered by archeologists during an excavation in 1913. This sling is currently housed in a London museum. Made from vines and given its size, it was used to hunt only small animals.

Additional reading: Hill, P. (1917). *Prehistoric times*. New York: Harper & Row

Slot Machine see Coin Operated Machine.

Smelting   Chemistry
Origin: Egypt   Date: 2900 BCE

Dating as far back as 2900 BCE, during the Archaic Dynasty, the Egyptians and Sumerians were smelters, extracting metals from ores by melting and refining them. Of the base metals known during prehistory such as silver, iron and copper, ancient metallurgists applied heating and chemical reduction processes, including oxidization, to extract the desired metals from the ore.

Additional reading: Binford, L. (1981). *Bones: Ancient man and modern myths*. New York: Academic Press.

Snare   Tool
Origin: Africa   Date: 20,000 BCE

The snare was an ancient trapping tool first used by the highlander nomads of Africa, dating back to 20,000

BCE. The early snares were made with treated vines coated with tree sap or hardened mud. Eventually, the material composition of the snare changed to metal. The lasso-like snare was essentially a long cord with a running noose.

Additional reading: Semenov, S. (1964). *Prehistoric technology; an experimental study of the oldest tools and artifacts from traces of manufacture and wear.* New York: Barnes and Noble.

Snowflake   Chemistry
Origin: China   Date: 140 BCE

The Chinese philosophers Han Ying devoted most of his adult life to the study natural phemonena such as snowflake patterns. He was the first to make a reference to the hexagonal structure of snowflakes. Han Ying was also the first to attempt to catalog the different shapes of snow flake as they appeared in nature. Historical records show that the limited cataloging of the different shapes was due to his inability to store snowflakes in their natural form.

Additional reading: Hsu, Cho-Yun, (1965). *Ancient China in transition, 722-222 B.C.* Stanford Cal.: Stanford University Press.

Soap   Chemistry
Origin: Sumer   Date: 2500 BCE

The Sumerians are credited with the invention of soap. A clay tablet from 2500 BCE described the use and manufacture of soap. Later soap re-appeared in Israel among the Gauls and in Islamic countries.

Additional reading: Hassall, W., (1962). *How they lived.* Oxford: Blackwell Pub.

Soda (Extraction of)   Chemistry
Origin: Egypt   Date: 1600 BCE

In the sixteenth century BCE, the Egyptians used native sodium carbonate and alkali as components of very advanced glass-making techniques. The Egyptians were followed by other peoples of the Near and Middle East who extracted soda from the ashes of plants. The ashes were washed in sieves and soda was left as a residue once the water had evaporated.

Additional reading: Derry, T. and Williams, T. (1982). *A short history of technology.* New York: Oxford University Press

Sodium Carbonate   see   Natron.

Solar Calendar   Astronomy
Origin: Egypt   Date: 800 BCE

The Egyptians invented the solar calendar, dividing the year into twelve months of thirty days each and five or six days remaining at the end of the year. During the reign of Numa king from the eighth to the seventh century BCE, two months were added to the calendar to develop the a 355-day year.

Additional reading: Neugebauer, O. (1945). "The history of ancient astronomy, problems and methods." *Near Eastern studies*, vol. 4. Egyptian Exploration Society.

Solar Device   Astronomy
Origin: Egypt   Date: Antiquity

The Disk of Aten is an example of ancient solar devices used to focus sunlight to a point or beam of extreme intensity. These large domed disks were made of highly polished metal. A stone block was exposed to a narrow beam and, when heated, cold water was poured, causing the stone to split in precise dimensions along the heated lines. With the rise of the Atenism, the technology was adopted to concentrate other invisible electromagnetic waves. The disks were dismantled during the reign of Tutankhamen.

Additional reading: Nur Ankh Amen, N. (1999). *The ankh: African origin of electromagnetism.* Brooklyn New York: A&B Publishers Group.

Solar Eclipse   see   Eclipse.

Solar Energy   Mechanical
Origin: Nubia   Date: 600 BCE

The earliest recorded history of ancient Nubia lists the use of an energy collecting device using the sun. The ruins of buildings in Nineveh contained lenses and mirrors, which were presumably used to focus the rays of the sun as early as 600 BCE.

Additional reading: Strandh, S. (1979). *A history of the machine.* New York: A.& W. Publishers.

Solar System
Astronomy
Origin: Egypt   Date: Antiquity

Prehistoric African astronomers from Egypt to the Congo region proposed various models depicting the relative positions of the sun, earth, and the planets. The ancient sky watchers designed numerous monoliths and extant religious structures to interact with the solar system. The Egyptians believed the earth was a fixed body at the center of the universe around which the sun and fixed stars revolve.

Additional reading: Downs, R. (1982). *Landmarks in science: Hippocrates to Carson*. Littleton Colo.: Libraries Unlimited.

Soldering
Metallurgy
Origin: Nubia   Date: 2500 BCE

Dating as far back as 2500 BCE, the Nubians used a form of soldering to join gold and other metallic sheets together in an apparent seamless manner. Solder was a metal alloy with a melting point lower than that of the metals to be joined.

Additional reading: Neuburger, O. (1930). *Illustrated science and inventions encyclopedia*. New York: Methuen & Co. Ltd.

Solid Geometry
Mathematics
Origin: Egypt   Date: 300 BCE

The Egyptian mathematics was credited with several mathematical theories including solid geometry. The Ahmose papyrus used extant methods to calculate the area of a circle and the value for pi. In 300 BCE, Euclid, presumably while working at the university in Alexandria, wrote the celebrated Elements, a textbook outlining the principles and process of the mathematical functions of solid geometry. The general application of this mathematical theory was primarily for use in the construction and civil design fields.

Additional reading: Rene D. (1968). *The treasury of mathematics*. London.

Song (Written)
Communication
Origin: Babylonia   Date: 4000 BCE

Tens of thousands of tablets, including entire libraries, were unearthed from Babylonia and its northern neighbor Assyria. The wedge-shaped, cuneiform script and language of the texts was intelligible to the philologists deciphering them. Tablets containing musical texts from Babylonia were deciphered as early as 1919 BCE. However, it took years before the terminology could be translated and interpreted.

Additional reading: Fink, R. (1988). "The Oldest Song in the World," *Archaeologies Musicalis 2*.

Sow   see   Pig.

Spade
Tool
Origin: Africa   Date: 50,000 BCE

Several types of manmade spades have been found made of animal bone dating back to pre-historic times in Central Africa. The spade, a handheld tool dates back to prehistoric Africa. It came into use when humanity progressed from gathering edible plants from the wild to farming. Some of the earliest spade artifacts were made from animal bone and later stone carvings shaped into spades.

Additional reading: Douze, S. (1993). *Inventions and discoveries*. New York: Facts on File.

Spawning   see   Artificial Spawning.

Spear
Weapon
Origin: Africa   Date: 25,000 BCE

Most anthropologists believe that crude forms of spears have existed in some form or fashion since the dawn of human. The earliest known spear was found in West Africa. This spear was constructed in two parts, a shaft and a pointed arrow-like shape made of animal bone. Carbon testing dated the spear at about 25,000 BCE, and confirmed that it was made from an animal's antler.

Additional reading: Allman, W. (1994). *The stone age present: How evolution has shaped modern life: From sex, violence, and language to emotions, morals, and communities*. New York: Simon & Schuster.

Fig 26
Wooden Spear

Spear Thrower   Military
Origin: Africa   Date: 13,000 BCE

The first spear thrower similar to the harpoon was developed as early as 13,000 BCE. This early weapon was used for hunting and defense and made of wood and animal skins. Stick-like objects have been drawn on cave walls, but the first confirmed carved spear was found in the western region of Africa. This recovered animal bone-like spear's carbon test dated as far back as 13,000 BCE.

Additional reading: Oakley, K. (1957). *Man the tool-maker*. Chicago: University of Chicago.

Speculum   Medical
Origin: India   Date: 900 BCE

The ancient Hindus developed a series of surgical instruments around 900 BCE. One of the many medical instruments was a tool known as the speculum that used to dilate the orifices of the body. Early records show that the speculum was used by medical and religious members of the community with little success. Records show that many people died from complications associated with this instrument.

Additional reading: Singer, C., and Underwood, E., (1962). *A short history of medicine*. New York: Oxford University Press.

Spice   Agriculture
Origin: Africa   Date: Prehistoric

The first inhabitants who settled the region later known as the Ivory Coast, were the earliest known to domestically grow and cultivate plants and herbs

stocked to season and/or preserve foods. Many different spices made from plants such as herbs were produced throughout the region. The spread of these food additives traveled with nomadic tribes.

Additional reading: Travers, B. (1996). *The Gale encyclopedia of science*. Detroit Mich.: Gale Research Pub.

Spike   see   **Nail.**

Spindle Whorl   Mechanical
Origin: Iraq   Date: 6500 BCE

The people at Jarmo in northern Iraq were spinning thread as early as 6500 BCE. The presence of stone and clay spindle whorls in ancient ruins indicated to researchers that the people had performed some kind of spinning and weaving, although no cloth or other perishable fabric were uncovered at the site. The action of the spindle produced a more uniform thread than could the unaided hand. The twisting process was repeated and threads were spun into tighter and finer threads.

Additional reading: Stewart, J. (1960). *An archaeological guide and glossary*. London: Phoenix House.

Spinning   see   **Distaff.**

Spinning Wheel   Material
Origin: Middle East   Date: 1100 BCE

The art of spinning dates to prehistoric times. A stick with a conically-shaped point was used to spin wool and flax. This slow method allowed only a meter of thread to be spun at one time. The spinning wheel originated in the Middle East and allowed great lengths of thread to be spun without interruption. Toward the beginning of the thirteenth century, the spinning wheel was introduced to the West.

Additional reading: Lucas, A. and Harris, J. (1962). *Ancient Egyptian materials and industries*. London: E. Arnold Pub.

Spoon   see   **Fork.**

Spring   Mechanical
Origin: Egypt   Date: 2200 BCE

The earliest spring was developed around 2200 BCE,

and apparently made of rolled metal. It was used on a tomb door leading to a burial chamber. This spring-like device was approximately six inches in length and was not very strong in its spring action.

Additional reading: Barber, F. (1900) *The mechanical triumphs of ancient Egyptians*. London: Trubner and Co.

Spring Balance — Mathematics
Origin: China   Date: 1000 BCE

The balance scale with two unequal arms was invented by the Chinese around 1000 BCE. It was probably brought to the West by nomadic horsemen. The Chinese style of balance is still used today.

Additional reading: Parker, S. (1989). *McGraw-Hill concise encyclopedia of science and technology*. New York: McGraw-Hill.

Square — Mathematics
Origin: Sumer   Date: 1700 BCE

The Sumerians, as far back as 1700 BCE, were the first known to develop and use the mathematical development of squares and square roots and, over the next century, the mathematical principles and functions associated with the square. These ancient mathematicians have been acknowledged as pioneers in the field of astronomy and science.

Additional reading: Boyer, C. B. (1968). *A history of mathematics*. New York: Wiley Press.

Square Root — Mathematics
Origin: China   Date: 100 BCE

The oldest known example of the extraction of square roots was found in the compiled Chinese work, Nine Chapters on Mathematical Art. Its extraction of the number 1,860,867 yielded a square root of 123. In 1245 CE, Chin Chiusao's Mathematical Treatise in Nine Sections included some equations with terms to a power greater than three (e.g., -x to the second power minus 40,642,000 = 0).

Additional reading: Van Sertima, I. (1983). *Blacks in science: Ancient and modern*. New Brunswick: Transaction Books..

Square (Construction)   see   **Try Square.**

Squash — Agriculture
Origin: Mexico   Date: 7000 BCE

As far back as 7000 BCE, in the North American territory now known as Mexico, plant cultivation had been taking place in villages and river-based communities. The earliest known cultivation of squash dates as far back as 7000 BCE. This crop was used as a food source for the area.

Additional reading: Coe, M. (1992). *Breaking the Maya code*. New York: Thames & Hudson.

Stain   see   **Varnish.**

Stamp   see   **Seal.**

Stamping — Material
Origin: China   Date: 800 BCE

The stamping of metal money dates back to eighth century BCE, China. Coins were made by inserting small preheated ingots of metal between two hard-metal molds. The top mold was hammered down, and the pressure exerted by the mold stamped the coin. This process was also used in India until the nineteenth century.

Additional reading: Derry, T. and Williams, T. (1960). *A short history of technology*. Oxford: Clarendon Press.

Star (Catalog) — Astronomy
Origin: Egypt   Date: 1130 BCE

The first map documenting the positions of the stars was made around 1130 BCE, by Egyptian astronomers, who created the catalog on the walls of tombs. Around 150 CE, Claudius Ptolemy expanded what was known about the stars and included a study of the orbits of the planets and other phenomena.

Additional reading: Asimov, I. (1982). *Asimov's biographical encyclopedia of science and technology: the lives and achievements of 1510 great scientists from ancient times to the present chronologically arranged*. Garden City, N.Y.: Doubleday Pub.

Starch   Chemistry
Origin: Egypt   Date: 400 BCE

Pliny stated that starch, which was made from wheat flour and mixed with boiling water, was used in connection with the manufacture of papyrus. If the plants had been freshly gathered, no adhesive except the natural juice was necessary to make small sheets of papyrus.

Additional reading: Lucas, A. and Harris, J. (1962). *Ancient Egyptian materials and industries.* London: E. Arnold.

Steel   Mechanical
Origin: Mesopotamia   Date: 4200 BCE

The Mesopotamian scientist Hayas produced carbon steel with preheated, forced-draft furnaces. The furnace pits were usually in the ground and used to make weapons. A similar technology was developed by a European scientist, but not until the nineteenth century.

Additional reading: (1979), *Ancient Mesopotamia: Portrait of a dead civilization.* Rev. ed. Chicago: University of Chicago Press.

Stellar Observatory   see   Armillary Ring.

Stellar Deck   see   Armillary Ring.

Stone Building   Architecture
Origin: Egypt   Date: 1500 BCE

Egypt possesses both the oldest and largest stone buildings in the world. The earliest examples of the use of stone for building dates to the First Dynasty. Such examples include the lining and roofing with roughly cut slabs of limestone on a number of small chambers in a tomb at Saqqara; limestone portcullis in the tomb of Hemaka at Saqqara; and a pavement of roughly dressed granite slabs in the tomb of Den (Udimu) at Abydos. 'A great deal of worked limestone in large slabs' was found in the large First Dynasty mastaba of Senar at Tarkhan. Limestone slabs were used in First Dynasty cemetery at Helwan.

Additional reading: Lucas, A. and Harris, J. (1962). *Ancient Egyptian materials and industries.* London: E. Arnold.

Story (Written)   Communication
Origin: Sumer   Date: 2500 BCE

The epic of Gilgamesh, written between 2700 and 2500 BCE, was the earliest surviving major work of literature. It was written at least 1300 years before Homer wrote the *Iliad* and *Odyssey.* Many historians believe that the epic of Gilgamesh was written in two sections. The second version was apparently lost in history. The most complete version of the epic tale, first discovered in 1853, was written on clay tablets and has since been translated from cuneiform into many languages.

Additional reading: Gordon, C., (1974). *Riddles in history.* New York: Crown Publishers.

Straw   Device
Origin: Nubia   Date: 2500 BCE

The earliest drinking straw was depicted on a Nubian seal dating back to 2500 BCE. The seal showed several men using straw-like devices to drink a liquid substance. Straws also appeared in Egypt and Mesopotamia during the same period.

Additional reading: Singer, C. (1956). *A history of technology.* Oxford: University Press.

String   Domestic
Origin: Iraq   Date: 6500 BCE

Man discovered how to make string and ropes for hunting, fishing, and trapping by twisting grass and plants into lengths strong enough to be connected and woven. As far back as 6500 BCE, the people of Jarmo in northern Iraq spun thread from grass and plant fibers.

Additional reading: Lucas, A. and Harris, J. (1962). *Ancient Egyptian materials and industries.* London: E. Arnold.

Structures (Living)   Architecture
Origin: Tanzania   Date: Prehistoric

Certain archaeological sites in the Olduvai Gorge in Tanzania contain structures that suggest human existence dates back to 1,600,000 BCE. Tools and hominid remains have been found at these sites, which may have been campsites. Paleoanthropologists conjecture that these sites may have been used as camps by nomadic tribes who wandered from place to place rather than establishing a home base.

Additional reading: Burke, J. (1978). *Connections.* Boston: Little Brown Press.

Stylus   Communication
Origin: Mesopotamia   Date: 2900 BCE

The earliest form of communication began with pictures and symbols. Writing on structured clay tablets with set charters has been traced to ancient Mesopotamia. The Mesopotamians developed a stylus tool set to write pictorial drawings that evolved in cuneiform on clay tablets. The stylus was wedge-shaped and custom-made to form fit the particular writing plate.

Additional reading: (1979), *Ancient records of Assyria and Babylon, vol. I. historical records of Assyria from the earliest times to Sargon.* Chicago: University of Chicago Press.

Sugar   Agriculture
Origin: India   Date: 1130 BCE

Sugar cane was cultivated in India around 1130 BCE. However, as early as antiquity, the Greeks and Romans referred to refined sugar as Indian salt and honey of India. Refined sugar was probably brought to the West by the Christians during the Crusades. Since the earliest times, the Chinese employed processes for the extraction and refining of cane sugar, operations which were not developed until much later in the West.

Additional reading: Kulke, J. (1998). *A history of India.* New York: Routledge.

Sugar Cane   Agriculture
Origin: New Guinea   Date: 7000 BCE

As early as 7000 BCE, New Guinea was cultivating a form of sugar cane. Sugar cane was processed and used initially as a food additive. Later the sugar cane became a common food source. Around 4100 BCE, the leaf from the sugar cane was processed and used for medical purposes in the Americas and Europe.

Additional reading: Spencer, L. (1913). *The myths of Mexico and Peru.* London: Dover.

Sulfur   Chemistry
Origin: China   Date: 900 BCE

Sulfur has atomic number 16 and is one of the few elements found in elemental form. Known as far back as 800 BCE, sulfur was used in medicine, metallurgy, and as a fumigant. Many Chinese records show that the chemical occurred naturally and was used in warfare because of its explosive properties.

Additional reading: Fitzgerald, C. (1961). China: *A short cultural history.* New York, Praeger Pub.

Sundial   Horology
Origin: Egypt   Date: 4000 BCE

For thousands of years, Egyptians and others in the Middle East measured time by the position of the shadow cast by an upright post called a gnomon. Around 4000 BCE, the hours of the sundial were devised by the Egyptians.

Additional reading: Erman, A. (1971). *Life in ancient Egypt.* New York: Dover pub.

Sunspot   Astronomy
Origin: China   Date: 165 BCE

Sunspots, dark areas visible on the sun's surface, have been viewed and recorded for centuries. The Chinese recorded the phenomenon as early as 165 BCE. Evidence suggests that sunspots peak in occurrence every eleven years. As a way to standardize measurements, observers use a formula called the Aurich Sunspot Number.

Additional reading: Considine, D. and Considine, G., (1983). Van Nostrand's scientific encyclopedia. 6th Edition, New York: Reinhold, Co.

Supernova   Astronomy
Origin: China   Date: 352 BCE

The Chinese reported the first supernova as early as 352 BCE. Chinese astronomer Shin Shen prepared a star chart with over eight hundred astrological entries. This early supernovas were charted over many years. Many supernovas were charted over many hundreds of years.

Additional Reading: Swihart, T. (2004). "Supernova." Grolier multimedia encyclopedia.

Surgery   Medicine
Origin: Africa   Date: 50,000 BCE

The first recorded surgical operation was an amputation, dating back to 50,000 BCE. However, the skeleton of a Neanderthal man was found in the Zagros mountains of Iraq who had undergone the amputation of his right arm around 47,000 BCE. Scarring has been found on a few trepanated skulls. Prehistoric surgeons used instruments such as knives, blades, and triangular points made of stone and bone.

Additional reading: Hellemans, A. and Bunch, B. (1988). *The timetables of science.* New York: Simon & Schuster.

Surgery (Brain)   Medicine
Origin: Africa   Date: 1500 BCE

Africans performed brain surgery as early as 1500 BCE. Several writings explain this surgical procedures by African surgeons. Boring holes in the skull to treat epilepsy, the surgeon removed skull fragments, compressed the brain, and relieved chronic headache.

Additional reading: Newsome, F. (1979); *Black Contributions to the History of western medicine.* New York.

Survey   Mechanical
Origin: Egypt   Date: 3600 BCE

The Egyptians used the heavens as a clock and calendar as far back as 3600 BCE as depicted in drawings in early tombs. The process demanded absolute accuracy when surveying the positions of heavenly bodies. Queen Nefertari's scientists designed an instrument consisting of a plumb-like forked stick to find an accurate north-south line. By timing the exact moment a star crossed the Meridian, they were able to map the position in the sky.

Additional reading: Ronan, C. (1975). *Lost discoveries.* New York: McGraw-Hill Pub.

Surveying   Civil
Origin: Babylon   Date: 3600 BCE

Surveying was known as far back as 3600 BCE, in Babylonia. Egyptian pyramids built around 2900 BCE also used surveyors. Plane surveying assumes that the areas surveyed are on a horizontal plane while geodetic surveying takes into account the curvature of the earth.

Additional reading: Moorey, P. (1992). *Ancient Egypt:* Oxford: University of Oxford.

Surveyor's Instrument   Mechanical
Origin: Egypt   Date: 600 BCE

Egyptian surveyors checked the straightening of walls and fences by viewing them through the merkhet, or slit palm leaf. They invented the groma, a simple cross of wood held horizontally, to set out squares and rectangles. Plumb lines hanging from each stick allowed the surveyor to sight along lines at exact right angles.

Additional reading: Childe, V., (1950). The urban revolution, *Town Planning Review,* 21. No. 1, London.

Suspension (Bridge)   Mechanical
Origin: China   Date: 25 BCE

The first account of a suspension bridge dates back to 25 BCE. A Chinese text mentioned a span of 15 meters and consisted of several similar bridges that spanned the San Chih-pan gorge in the Himalayas. A later account dating from 399 CE described the same region and cited a bridge span of 120 meters.

Additional reading: Smith, S. (1953). *The world's greatest bridges.* London: Phoenix,

Swine   see   **Pig.**

Sycamore   Agriculture
Origin: Egypt   Date: 6200 BCE

Egyptian farmers were the earliest known to domestically grow and cultivate sycamore trees, a species of a figtree common to dry areas. The sycamore tree had leaves that resembled the mulberry plant. The Egyptians cultivated the sycamore tree as a shady ornamental tree and used its wood for tools and other artifacts.

Additional reading: Gille, B. (1986). *History of technique.* New York: Gordon and Breach Science Pub.

Symbol — Communication
Origin: Sumer   Date: 2900 BCE

Many historical sources have credited the first structured form of transportable writing to the Sumerians. The Sumerians used a crude form of symbols which later evolved into syllables. This was a vital step in the evaluation of writing. The limited set of syllables was common to the region and later spread to Asia and Europe where new symbols and modifications were added.

Additional reading: Gordon, C. (1974). *Riddles in history.* New York: Crown Pub.

Syringe — Medical
Origin: India   Date: 975 BCE

The earliest known syringe was used around 975 BCE, according to the medical textbook of Sushruta Samhita, which detailed the practice of medicine in India. There were many written accounts describing the successes and failures of the early syringe tools. It seems that many individuals lost their lives using these crude devices. The syringe was later improved and was successful in many medical procedures.

Additional reading: Bennion, E. (1979). *Antique medical instruments.* London: Sotheby Parke Bernet Press.

T

Table	see	Dais.
Table Cloth	see	Carpet.
Table (Math)	see	Multiplication.
Tablet	see	Dictionary.
Talc	see	Calcite.

Tank — Construction
Origin: Nubia   Date: 900 BCE

The Assyrians were masters of the Near East region during 900 BCE, due in large part to their army. Assyrian memorials depicted tank-like vehicles mounted on four to six wheels. The impressive structures were sheathed in wickerwork for protection.

Additional reading: Adams, W., (1977) *Nubia, corridor to Africa.* Princeton, N.J.

Tanning — Chemistry
Origin: Egypt   Date: 4000 BCE

Leather played an important part in clothing and body armor. Untanned hides, which were probably the oldest form of dress among all peoples, tended to decay and often lasted only a short time. While it is not known what the earliest methods of tanning were, it is thought that the skins were first softened in water so that the hairs were readily removed. They were then treated with juices extracted from plants, possibly with juice from periploca secamone, still in use for tanning today.

Additional reading: Dorland,. W. (1994). *Dorland's illustrated medical dictionary.* Philadelphia,: Saunders.

Tattoo — Communication
Origin: Africa   Date: 4000 BCE

African tribes had many languages and various forms of communications. One of the earliest was a process of recording tribal history on their bodies with an ink-like substance. This form of tattooing dates back to 4000 BCE, as observed on a cave wall in Western Africa.

Additional Reading: Spindler, K., (1977). *The man in the Ice: The discovery of a 5,000-year-old body reveals the secrets of the stone age.* New York: Harmony Books.

Tea — Agriculture
Origin: China   Date: Antiquity

As far back as antiquity, leaves of the tea plant were mixed with water and brewed into a stimulating drink. In China, drinking tea became a ceremony, poured from gracefully-shaped teapots into beautifully painted cups. The custom spread to Japan in which the drinking of tea was accompanied by ritual. Many of these customs still exist today.

Additional reading: James, P. and Thorpe, N. (1994). *Ancient inventions*. New York: Ballantine Books.

Teeth (False)   Medical
Origin: China   Date: 3300 BCE

The first implantation of a tooth that had fallen out of its socket was performed in China in 3216 BCE. Most individuals of that era lost their teeth at an early age. The implantation caused an improvement in the health and life expectancy of people during of the period.

Additional reading: Woodforde, J., (1968). *The strange story of false teeth*. New York: Universe Books.

Telegraphy (Vocal)   Communication
Origin: Persia   Date: 520 BCE

Around 500 BCE, King Darius I of Persia found that when he shouted orders from hilltops, his voice amplified and was heard by his troops. Mountain horns, trumpets, and drums were used to project non-vocal, coded communications across distances. Other forms of non-vocal telegraphy included fires, smoke signals, and reflecting mirrors.

Additional reading: Wilson, G., (1976). *The old telegraphs*. London: Phillimore.

Tektite   Mineral
Origin: Africa   Date: 6100 BCE

Tektite, a form of naturally occurring glass created by the melting and cooling of terrestrial rock, was discovered in West Africa, dating back 6000 years. Although the origin of tektite remains somewhat controversial, these distinctive glassy pebbles emanating exclusively from a few strewn fields in Africa and elsewhere inspired manual glass production around 4100 BCE.

Additional reading: Parker, S. (1984). *McGraw-Hill concise encyclopedia of science and technology*. New York: McGraw-Hill Pub.

Testing   see   Pregnancy Test.

Textbook   see   Chemical Textbook.

Theodolite   Astronomy
Origin: Egypt   Date: 200 BCE

The theodolite, a modern instrument used for measuring reduced horizontal angles, zenithal distances, and azimuths, originated as an antique invention. In the second century BCE, Hipparchus invented the diopter which was used for measuring the apparent diameters of the sun and moon.

Additional reading: Parker, S. (1984). *McGraw-Hill concise encyclopedia of science and technology*. New York: McGraw-Hill.

Theorem   see   Pythagorean Theorem.

Throwing Stick   Military
Origin: Australia   Date: 10,000 BCE

A crude form of a throwing stick was used by Australian hunters as early as 10,000 BCE. The earliest throwing stick was recovered intact from a basin in central Australia. Used for close-range hunting of small animals, the stick's shape changed over time in adaptation of the different attributes of the animals that were hunted.

Additional reading: Semenov, S. (1964). *Prehistoric technology; an experimental study of the oldest tools and artifacts from traces of manufacture and wear*. New York: Barnes and Noble.

Thyme   Agricultural
Origin: Sumer   Date: 4700 BCE

Farmers of the Fertile Crescent grew thyme as early as 4700 BCE. Thyme is a shrubby herb with fragrant aromatic leaves. One of the early uses was in a sour tasting beverage that some scholars believe was a form of intoxicating substance. Another use was as a perfume because of its aromatic scent.

Additional reading: Hickey, M. and King, C. (1981). *100 families of flowering plants*, Cambridge, Eng.: Cambridge University Press.

Tide   Astronomy
Origin: Egypt   Date: 650 BCE

Around 650 BCE, an Egyptian geographer and scholar became the first to recognize that tides were caused by the influence of the moon. He also noted that tides came at different times in different parts of the world.

Additional reading: Downs, R. (1982). *Landmarks in science: Hippocrates to Carson.* Littleton, Colo.: Libraries unlimited.

Timekeeper   see   **Clock.**

Tin   Chemistry
Origin: Egypt   Date: 3500 BCE

Tin, atomic number 50 and chemical symbol Sn, is a silver-white metal with a bluish tinge. Artifacts made of bronze, a tin-containing alloy, reveal that tin was known in Egypt as long ago as 3500 BCE. Tin was produced by treating the mineral known as cassiterite. It was used extensively as an alloy, in coatings, and in compounds.

Additional reading: Parker, S. (1984). *McGraw-Hill concise encyclopedia of science and technology.* New York: McGraw-Hill.

Tobacco   Medical
Origin: America   Date: 1502 BCE

The Maya of Mexico used tobacco for medical purposes, treating asthma, nasal congestion, headaches, indigestion, toothache, boils, snakebite, and even problems experienced during childbirth. The Aztecs mixed tobacco with pulverized charcoal, adding flowers and other sweet-smelling substances.

Additional reading: Wilbert, J., (1987). *Tobacco and shamanism in South America.* Princeton: Yale University Press.

Toilet   Domestic
Origin: Nubia   Date: 4100 BCE

The earliest identified toilet was found around 4100 BCE, in a Nubian tomb. The wooden and stone devices were designed to be portable. The seat was placed over a large jar, which was cleaned daily by workers of the state.

Additional reading: Williams, T.(1987). *The history of invention.* New York: Facts on File.

Fig 27
Early Toliet

Token (Clay)   Economics
Origin: Mesopotamia   Date: 8000 BCE

As far back as 8,000 BCE, the Mesopotamians (inhabiting what is modern Iraq) used clay tokens to tally shipments of grain and animals. This token system was the basis for the first system of numeration and writing. The system spread eastward as merchants and explorers traveled throughout Asia and later Europe.

Additional Reading: Hobson, B., (1970). *Illustrated encyclopedia of world coins,* Robert Hale.

Tongue (Artificial)   Medical
Origin: China   Date: Antiquity

The Chinese invented a container of thirty human tongues that had been dyed different colors and were used by herbal doctors to help diagnose various sicknesses. Medical personnel matched a preserved or artificial tongue with that of the patient under observation. A medical textbook was developed and consulted by the medical personnel before making a diagnosis.

Additional reading: Bliquez, L. (1983). Classical Prosthetics. *Archaeology 36.*

Tool   Manufacturing
Origin: Tanzania   Date: Prehistoric

The earliest known tools date between three and one

million years ago. They were found along the edges of former lakes and marshes close to the Rift Valley in northern Tanzania, Kenya, and Ethiopia. Very small quartz tool fragments that showed signs of cutting wear were also found.

Additional reading: Ki-Zerbo, J. (1990). *General history of Africa: Methodology and African prehistory.* Berkeley: University of California Press.

Tower   Military
Origin: Palestine   Date: 7000 BCE

A tower discovered near the Dead Sea in Palestine is the oldest known to researchers. The tower was solidly built from stone and enclosed a central spiral stairway. The massive fortifications surrounding it made it an impressive structure.

Additional reading: Derry, T. and Williams, T. (1960). *A short history of technology.* Oxford: Clarendon Press.

Toy   Device
Origin: Africa   Date: Antiquity

A team of archeologists in southern Africa found a set of what appeared to be toys which included a doll, ball figures and other unidentified objects. These artifacts date back to prehistoric times and are the earliest known objects of pleasure.

Additional reading: O'Connor, D. (1991). *Early state along the Nubian Nile. In Egypt and Africa: Nubia from prehistory to Islam.* London: British Museum Press.

Fig 28
Toys

Tranquilizer   Medicine
Origin: India   Date: 3000 BCE

The Indians were the first to process tranquilizers.

Rauwolfia Serpentina was used for centuries in Indian medicine and known to contain a potent tranquilizer. Many naturally-occurring forms of numbing substances existed, but were not known to be produced for this specific use. This process spread throughout the central India region. Some local areas used this tranquilizing in religious ceremonies.

Additional reading: Kulke, John, (1998). *A history of India.* New York: Routledge.

Trap   Mechanical
Origin: Africa   Date: Antiquity

An archaeological dig in Tanzania turned up the bones of a wild hog, caught in a wooden trap device that was anchored by rocks. The trap was almost certain death for the animal. When it stepped into the trap, its leg was wedged and prevented the animal from escaping.

Additional reading: Africanus, L. (1896). *The history and description of Africa.* 3 Vols. ed. London: Brown, Kakluyt Society.

Fig 29
Animal Trap

Trapezi   see   Triangle.

Treaty   Science
Origin: Mesopotamia   Date: 2900 BCE

The Mesopotamian, as far back as 2900 BCE, was the first to use treaties during their presentation of "scientific materials." Treatises took the form of long lists of analytics and varied descriptions of the studied objects. The Sumerians around 2400 BCE, referred to the treatises as manuals.

Additional reading: Bottero, J. (1992). *Mesopotamia: Writing, reasoning, and the gods.* Chicago: University of Chicago Press.

Trepanning
Origin: China   **Date:** 6500 BCE   Medicine

The medical practice of trepanning has been a long-standing procedure. Trepanning, the drilling of a hole in the skull as a treatment for head injuries, was a practice in China as far back as 6500 BCE. Trepanation also may have been done sometimes as a religious ritual, but in many cases it appears to have been a medical treatment for a blow to the cranium and the resulting hematoma or swelling filled with blood. This medical procedure later spread to other parts of Asia and Europe. In some regions, it continued through the Middle Ages and even into the beginning of the twentieth century.

Additional Reading: Bettman, O. (1956). *A pictorial history of medicine.* London: Thomas Pub.

Triangle
Origin: Africa   **Date:** Prehistoric   Mathematics

Triangle-shaped arrows were found in a crystallized cave dating back to over 20,000 years ago. Such an arrow was also found to produce more shock and less bleeding than pointed arrows. The triangle shape was further developed by the Egyptians who used to build triangle structures around 5000 BCE. The militaries of Mesolithic Natufians of Palestine and the Helwanians of Egypt created triangular and trapezi–form shapes.

Additional reading: Sarton, G. (1936). *The study of the history of mathematics.* Cambridge: University Press.

Trigonometry
Origin: Egypt   **Date:** 3500 BCE   Mathematics

A study of the pyramids in Egypt shows that trigonometry functions were used in their design. Trigonometry, the study of triangles, began around 3500 BCE, with the work of Egyptian scholars.

Additional reading: Dugas, R. (1955). *A history of mechanics.* New York: Central Books Co.

Trigonometric Table
Origin: Egypt   **Date:** 140 BCE   Mathematics

Hipparchus, a mathematician, was the first to compile and use the trigonometric table. His table of chords helped to introduce the systematic use of the 360-degree circle. The trigonometric table was used as late as the modern period of mathematics.

Additional reading: Venn J. (1965). *The treasury of mathematics symbolic logic.* London.

Trumpet
Origin: Nubia   **Date:** 2000 BCE   Music

The earliest known trumpet, which is a wind instrument, was discovered in northern Nubia around 2000 BCE. The trumpet was straight in form for much of its history but in the fifteenth century, with improvements in metal making, it was redesigned and became curved into an S-shape.

Additional reading: Goldron, R. (1968). *Ancient and Oriental music.* Baltimore: Black Classic Press.

Try Square
Origin: Egypt   **Date:** 2600 BCE   Mechanical

Ancient Egyptian architects understood that they could make a perfect right angle by employing a try square instrument. The triangle had sides in the proportion 3:4:5. With this knowledge, they were able to set the walls of buildings in a very precise manner. Engineers of the period measured corners to ensure that surfaces were level.

Additional reading: Barber, F. (1900). *The mechanical triumphs of ancient Egyptians.* London: Trubner and Co.

Tubular Appliance
Origin: India   **Date:** 1000 BCE   Medical

The ancient Hindus excelled in the development of surgical instruments such as the tubular appliance. This device was spread throughout the region by traders and traveling merchants. Several modifications were made over time and the instrument soon became a useful medical tool.

Additional reading: Bennion, E. (1979). *Antique medical instruments.* London: Sotheby Parke Bernet Press.

Tunnel
Origin: Babylon   **Date:** 2170 BCE   Civil

Over the centuries, tunnels have been used for roads,

TWO HANDED PLANE

railroads, and water supplies. One of the oldest tunnels was built for Queen Semiramits of Babylon. Constructed around 2170 BCE, it was located under the Euphrates River and was 600 feet long. Eighteen hundred years later, portions of the tunnel were still intact.

Additional reading: Beaver, P., (1972). *A history of tunnels,* Secaucus, N.J., Citadel Press.

Two Handed Plane   see   **Plane.**

Tyrian Purple Ink   see   **Dye.**

U

Ultrasound   Physics
Origin: Egypt   Date: Antiquity

The ankh of Egypt produced high-pitched ultrasounds inaudible to the human ear but effective in frightening wild animals such as jackals and hyenas. This was particularly useful in the wilderness at night, protecting travelers from unseen dangers. Ultrasound was used to frighten insects, rodents, and maggots that sought to devour the bodies of the deceased.

Additional reading: Nur Ankh Amen, N. (1999). *The ankh: African origin of electromagnetism.* New York: A&B Publishers Group..

Umbrella   Domestic
Origin: Iraq   Date: 2400 BCE

A victory monument of Sargon, dating back to around 2400 BCE, included a replica of an umbrella. Sargon, king of Akkad, was shown striding ahead of his troops. Behind him stood an attendant carrying a sunshade. From Iraq, the idea of the parasol spread west to Egypt. Sunshades became popular all around the Mediterranean region.

Additional reading: Binford, L., (1981). *Bones: Ancient man and modern myths.* New York: Academic Press.

Unit Fraction   Mathematics
Origin: Egypt   Date: 4500 BCE

Men of the Stone Age probably had no use for

fractions, but with the advent of more advanced cultures during the Bronze Age the need for the fraction concept and for fractional notations seems to have arisen. Egyptian hieroglyphic inscriptions have a special notation for unit fractions – that is, fractions with unit numerators. The reciprocal of any integer was indicated simply by placing over the notation for the integer an elongated oval sign.

Additional reading: Boyer, C. (1968). *A history of mathematics.* New York: John Wiley and Son.

Universal Joint   Mechanical
Origin: China   Date: 140 BCE

The universal joint, developed in China about 140 BCE, enabled the relative angular displacement of two shafts where the geometrical axes converged at the same point. This made movement in all directions possible. It became the basis of the modern gyroscope.

Additional reading: Neugebauer, O. (1945). "*The History of Ancient Astronomy.*" J. Near Eastern Studies, Vol. 4.

University   System
Origin: Egypt   Date: 300 BCE

In 300 BCE, Ptolemy I during the Ptolemic Period built the first comprehensive university in Alexandria. Called the Museum University, it had a library that housed the largest collection of original manuscripts known outside of the ancient university of Ethiopia. The university taught subjects in the areas of literature, mathematics, philosophy, and science.

Additional reading: Stewart, J. (1960). *An archaeological guide and glossary.* London: Phoenix House.

Urban Planning   Civil
Origin: Babylonia   Date: 2200 BCE

According to ancient records, the Babylonians were the first to undertake urban planning for their cities. Rough engravings of city layouts were discovered dating back to 2200 BCE. Babylonians around this time period experienced a surge in population growth. The problems of food transport, water and waste management were the major challenges confronting the urban planners.

Additional reading: Chandler, T. and Fox, G. (1974). *3000 years of urban growth*. New York: Academic Press.

Uru see **Oxen.**

Utensil Domestic
Origin: Nubia Date: 300 BCE

The first uniform set of eating utensils originated in Nubia around 300 BCE. The excavation of tombs and sites uncovered a large number of knives and forks used for eating as well as serving food.

Additional reading: James, P. and Thorpe, N. (1994). *Ancient inventions*. New York: Ballantine Books.

V

Vaccination Medical
Origin: China Date: 1000 BCE

Evidence suggests that the anti-smallpox vaccination was originally developed in China by a Taoist monk. The anti-smallpox vaccination was rediscovered in the West during the eighteenth century in the form of 'variolation.' Vaccination was probably created following the attenuation of the germ's multiple transmission. The early vaccination process was achieved by the implantation of a pad that carried some attenuated germs in one nostril.

Additional reading: Dorland, N. (1994). *Dorland's illustrated medical dictionary*. Philadelphia: Saunders.

Vallum Mechanical
Origin: Syria Date: 2200 BCE

The Syrians were noted for their military campaigns. They were the earliest to develop a vallum for the purpose of fortifying against the advancing armies. A rampart or wall, usually constructed of earth, served as a defense obstacle around a fort.

Additional reading: Schreiber, H. (1961). *The history of roads*. London: Barrie and Rockcliff Pub.

Varnish Material
Origin: Egypt Date: 1000 BCE

By 1000 BCE, the Egyptians had prepared a varnish that contained the gum of the acacia tree. Natural resins were in use until they were replaced by the development of modern synthetic resins. Varnish was made of a solution of a hard resin, drying oil, and solvent.

Additional reading: Parker, S. (1984). *McGraw-Hill concise encyclopedia of science and technology*. New York: McGraw-Hill.

Vault Security
Origin: Assyria Date: 4000 BCE

Excavations conducted by the University of Chicago revealed that the construction of vaults was known to the Assyrians and Babylonians as early as 4000 BCE. It still remains unclear to many modern scholars who study antiquity as to what was contained in these vaults. The large sizes of these vaults cause some to speculate that they were an artifact to store food, animals, and other necessities for the afterlife.

Additional reading: Neuburger, O. (1930). *The technical arts and sciences of the ancients*. New York: The Macmillan Co.

Vending Machine Mechanical
Origin: Egypt Date: 215 BCE

As early as 215 BCE, the Egyptian developed and used a crude type of vending machine. At many of the open market religious ceremonies these machines accepted clay coins and individuals were able to purchase holy water.

Additional reading: Daumas, M. (1969). *A history of technology and invention: Progress through the ages*. New York: Crown Press.

Veneer Materials
Origin: Egypt Date: Antiquity

The earliest evidence of using veneer was seen in the Egyptian *Book of the Dead*. The more elaborate designed boxes were covered in veneer. Veneer was a very thin layer of wood, usually comprised of different species of rare woods, affixed to the surface of an object to give a decorative finish.

Additional reading: Hoffmam, M. (1980). *Egypt before*

the pharaohs, the prehistoric foundation of Egyptian civilization. New York: Knopf, A.

Vertical Water Wheel — Hydraulic
Origin: Egypt   Date: 2500 BCE

The rudimentary water wheel sweep first appeared in Egypt during 2500 BCE. It was the oldest known apparatus for raising water. A form of this ancient chadouf, referred to as a water wheel, is still in use today. The vertical wheel was used for elevating water. It was seen in the Middle East between the fifth and third centuries B.C.

Additional reading: Butzer, K., (1976). *Early hydraulic civilization in Egypt: A study in cultural ecology.* Chicago: University of Chicago Press.

Vessel   see   Jubbe.

Viticulture (Wine) — Agriculture
Origin: Egypt   Date: 3900 BCE

The Egyptian preference for wine led to the cultivation of the grapevine, and particular attention was given to the preparation of the beverage. The development of the technical apparatus used for the manufacture of wine was perfected, and from 3900 to 3000 BCE, as many as six kinds of wine were produced in the region.

Additional reading: Moorey, P. (1992). *Ancient Egypt.* Oxford: University of Oxford.

Vinegar — Chemical
Origin: Africa   Date: Antiquity

The fermentation of grapes was a process used to develop wine. However, to prevent converting the wine into vinegar, the process had to be stopped at the proper moment. Different strengths of vinegars were produced by allowing date or grape wine to sour. In the later periods of Mesopotamia, medicine-based vinegar was produced by fermenting an infusion of the root of Cyperus Papyrus. Vinegar was also used to remove poisons from the body.

Additional reading: Johnson, H., (1989). *The story of wine.* New York: Simon and Schuster.

Vise — Mechanical
Origin: Africa   Date: Antiquity

The use of animal jaw bones as a vise can be traced to the Paleolithic age. Manmade vises were created from wood. Around 1200 BCE, the development of the screw led to improvements in the construction of the vise. A screw-like device was used to connect the jaws so that the clamp would more effectively hold an object as it was being worked upon.

Additional reading: Mason, O. (1966). *The origin of invention.* Cambridge Mass: MIT Press.

Volcano   see   Lava.

Volume — Mathematics
Origin: Sumer   Date: 2500 BCE

Multiplication tables were drawn up by the Sumerians around 2500 BCE. These tables were used for determining the areas of fields (by multiplying length times breadth) and to estimate the volumes of such things as bricks and stacks (by multiplying length times breadth times height). The value of pi was taken as three and used to calculate the area of a circle and the volume of a cylinder. Measurements of volume revealed how much space was occupied by a solid, a liquid, or a gas.

Additional reading: Parker, S. (1989). *McGraw-Hill concise encyclopedia of science and technology.* New York: McGraw-Hill Pub.

W

Wahsdyke   see   Vallum.

Wallpaper — Construction
Origin: Egypt   Date: 3200 BCE

The earliest known form of wallpaper, recorded in Egypt around 3200 BCE, was primarily used for decoration. The use of mortar between stones was not a common practice during this era, hence wallpaper also served as insulation against cold weather. Decorative papers and variety in print designs came much later.

Additional reading: DeBono, E. (1974). *Eureka!: How and when the greatest inventions were made: An illustrated history of inventions from the wheel to the computer.* London: Thames & Hudson.

Waste Disposal — Tool
Origin: Assyrians   Date: 3000 BCE

As far back as 3000 BCE, the Assyrians developed a sewer system used to move waste from the cities. A large sewer was built around 500 BCE, in Rome, and it is still partially in use. These two systems became the model for most of the world's sewage systems.

Additional reading: (1979). *Ancient records of Assyria and Babylon, vol I. historical records of Assyria from the earliest times to Sargon.* Chicago: University of Chicago Press.

Water Clock   see   Clepsydra.

Water Craft   see   Boat.

Watermelon — Agriculture
Origin: Mesopotamia   Date: 6200 BCE

Farmers of the Fertile Crescent were the earliest known to domestically grow and cultivate watermelon. Eaten as food, it was primarily grown in the warmer climate of Mesopotamia. The watermelon was also used as a buoyancy device for some fishing craft.

Additional reading: Hickey, M. and King, C. (1981). *100 families of flowering plants,* Cambridge: University Press.

Water Mill — Agriculture
Origin: Israel   Date: 100 BCE

During the first century BCE, water mills appeared in the Mediterranean region. The Israelis are credited with being the first to construct and use water mills. They were primitive and somewhat inefficient mills that were powered by water and used by workers to grind and process grain.

Additional reading: Reynolds, T. (1983). *Stronger than a hundred men.* Baltimore: John Hopkins University Press.

Water Proofing — Construction
Origin: Syria   Date: 850 BCE

Between 900-850 BCE, Syria sustained heavy and long lasting rainfalls. During that time, homebuilders of Syria developed processes of waterproofing their buildings to safeguard the structures and their contents. The process involved coating the interior and exterior walls as well as the floor.

Additional reading: Heidel A. (1942). *The Babylonian genesis.* Chicago: University of Chicago Press.

Water Wheel — Mechanical
Origin: Turkey   Date: 100 BCE

As early as 100 BCE, water power was used to turn millstones. An unknown designer while working for the royal family designed a water wheel device that didn't required the use of humans or beasts of burden. The designs used horizontal axles as a part of the wheel receiving the flow of water. Beginning in the eighteenth century, steam engines gradually replaced water mills.

Additional reading: Landels, J. (1978). *Engineering in the ancient world.* Berkeley: University of California.

Water Weapon — Military
Origin: Zaire   Date: 16,000 BCE

The earliest examples of bone harpoons were left in what is now known as Zaire. Many archeologists believe that this crude form of fishing gear was developed in this region because of the geological landscape and its confluence of streams, rivers, and lakes.

Additional reading: Williams, T. (1987). *The history of invention.* New York: Facts on File.

Weapon — Tool
Origin: Africa   Date: 10,000 BCE

Spears were used by hunters to kill mammoth, mastodon, giant bison, camel, and wild horse. From about 10,000 BCE, a number of distinctive spear and dart points were developed or reinvented. Each was named after the site where it was first found (e.g., Sandia, Clovis, Folsom, Plain View, Scotts Bluff). Some of these were excellent examples of chipping and flaking craftsmanship.

Additional reading: Laithwaite, E. (1994). *An inventor in the garden of Eden*. Cambridge, Eng.: Cambridge University Press.

Weaving   Domestic
Origin: Africa   Date: Prehistoric

The process of weaving dates back to African prehistoric times. Plant cultivation led to weaving, first using crop fibers such as flax and cotton. Weaving from sheep's wool and silk used in other cultures came later. The loom was one of the great inventions of the Neolithic Age, when weaving emerged as an important occupation. The original looms, dating before 4000 BCE, in Egypt, were horizontal. The first textiles were fabricated in plain weave; a series of wefts passing over and under a series of warps.

Additional reading: Davision, P., (1980). Cotton weaving in South-East Africa: Its history and technology, *Textile*, Vol 2.

Fig 30
Weaving

Wedge   Mechanical
Origin: Central Africa   Date: 6000 BCE

As early as 6000 BCE, African warriors produced the hand axe and wedge. By attaching it to a handle, the wedge's advantage was coupled to that of the lever. About 3000 BCE, bronze was invented and humans honed this new metal into a blunt wedge and split into an extremely sharp sword that proved efficient for cutting.

Additional reading: Connah, G. (1981). *Three thousand years in Africa: Man and his environment in the Lake Chad region of Nigeria*. Cambridge: Cambridge University Press.

Weft   see   Cloth.

Weight   Mechanical
Origin: Egypt   Date: 4000 BCE

Many archeologists have recovered odd shape stones that were thought to be a weighting system. The earliest known uniform weights date from 7000 BCE, discovered in graves in Naqada I, Egypt; they were made of limestone and used in association with limestone balance-beams.

Additional reading: Barber, F. (1900). *The mechanical triumphs of ancient Egyptians*. London: Trubner and Co.

Weight System   Systems
Origin: Mesopotamia   Date: 2400 BCE

The oldest weight, dating to 2400 BCE, weighed about 477 grams (17 ounces). It was found in the Mesopotamian city of Lagash. Standard weights used in trade were developed by the Sumerians. The areas were based on the weight of the shekel (8.36 grams or 0.29 oz.) and the mina, which was sixty times as heavy.

Additional reading: (1979). *Ancient Mesopotamia: Portrait of a dead civilization*. Rev. ed. Chicago: University of Chicago Press.

Welding   Mechanical
Origin: Syria   Date: 1500 BCE

A headrest found in the tomb of King Tutankhamen offered the first example of welding. In order to weld two pieces of iron together, a metalworker heated them to a high temperature and hammered them together.

Additional reading: Hitti, P. (1943). *The Arabs*. Chicago: Gateway Edition, pp. 20-23.

Well   Agriculture
Origin: Egypt   Date: 3200 BCE

Some of the earliest wells were made of baked brick which lined the shafts of a courtyard. Wells used for a water source were installed in the houses of Egyptians during the Archaic Dynastic Period dating back to 3200 BCE. The depth of these wells varied from ten to two hundred and fifty feet deep.

Additional reading: Williams, T. (1987). *The history of invention*. New York: Fact on File.

Well (Drilled)   Mechanical
Origin: China   Date: 10 BCE

The Chinese are credited with the development of the first deep wells. About 10 BCE, the Chinese invented methods for drilling deep wells that reached 1460 meters (4800 feet) and were used to obtain salt, water, and natural gas.

Additional Reading: Fitzgerald, C. (1961). *China: A short cultural history*. New York: Praeger.

Wheat   Agriculture
Origin: Egypt   Date: 3400 BCE

Dating back to 3400 BCE, wild wheat and barley were grown by early Egyptian farmers. At the same time, wild wheat germinated naturally with grass. The new wheat strain had large seeds. Egyptians discovered that grinding the seeds produced a flour substance to make a new kind of food called bread.

Additional reading: Williams, T. (1987). *The history of invention*. New York: Facts on File.

Wheel   Mechanical
Origin: Sumer   Date: 4000 BCE

The wheel was first developed in the Near East in very early times and was used for transport and in the making of pots. Clay tablets from Erech, a city-state of Sumer, show a wheeled sledge in use between 4000 BCE and 30,000 BCE. The people of the Indus Valley Civilization were using the wheel by 2500 BCE. Metal-tired chariots and carts were in use in Elam, a country east of Sumer, before 2000 BCE.

Additional reading: De Camp, L. (1974). *The ancient engineers*. New York:. Ballantine Books.

Wheelbarrow   Tool
Origin: China   Date: 175 BCE

The wheelbarrow was invented in China around 175

BCE, by Ko Yu. The invention of the wheelbarrow was also attributed to Jugo Lyang around 200 BCE. The early wheelbarrow designs were often adapted to fit the various work needs of the region. Images of several different types of wheelbarrow have been identified during the same time periods.

Additional reading: Oakley, T., (1959). *Man the tool maker*. Chicago: University of Chicago.

Wheeled Vehicle   Transportation
Origin: Mesopotamia   Date: Antiquity

Historians have yet to pinpoint the exact date that the first wheeled vehicle machine materialized. The earliest recorded wheeled vehicles were used in Mesopotamia as evidenced by a pictograph from Urak. The models improved over a period of time, which evolved into the wheeled vehicle.

Additional reading: Lloyd, S. (1978). *The archaeology of Mesopotamia: From the old stone age to Persian conquest*. London: Thames & Hudson.:

Whitting Knife   see   **Knife.**

Whorl   Textile
Origin: Egypt   Date: 3200 BCE

Fiber that had been obtained from wool, flax, hemp, or cotton was spun into thread in order to produce the thread for weaving. The first ancient device designed to obtain this product was the spinning whorl, a disc equipped with a round hole and often ornamented, and made of bone, stone, glass, along with various metals. It was used by the ancient peoples of Asia and by the Egyptians around 3200 BCE.

Additional reading: Clark, G., and Piggott, S., (1965). *Prehistoric societies*. New York: Penguim.

Wig   Cosmetic
Origin: Egypt   Date: 3000 BCE

The first wig appeared in Egypt around 3000 BCE. Wigs consisted mainly of ornamental coiffure, made by using tapered and plaited reed instead of false hair pieces. Wigs were used by Assyrians, Phoenicians, and Romans. After the fall of the Roman Empire, they fell out of use and did not reappear until the sixteenth century in England.

Additional reading: Stevens, J., (1983). *The story of wigs, through the ages.* Toucan Press.

Winch   Mechanical
Origin: Egypt   Date: 1600 BCE

The only known remains of a winch were recovered in Egypt, which dated back to around 1600 BCE. Considered an essential component of the crane, its purpose was to give laborers more lifting power when hauling on a rope. Many historians believe that man employed a winch system much earlier than 1600 BCE, but the multi-part winch developed by the Egyptians used a series of ropes, gears and sleeves.

Additional reading: Gnudi, M. (Translator) (1979). The various and ingenious machines of Agostino Ramelli.

Windmill   Mechanical
Origin: Babylon   Date: 2700 BCE

The Babylonians are credited with the development of crude windmills. This windmill was used to aid in growing crops by enhancing the irrigation process which resulted in manifold increases in production. This process enabled communities to increase in size and expand outward to areas that were previously not considered habitable due to lack of arable land.

Additional reading::Kealey, E., (1987). *Harvesting the Air: Windmill pioneer in 12th century England.* Berkeley: University of California Press.

Wine (Pomegranate)   Chemistry
Origin: Egypt   Date: 3000 BCE

The earliest known reference to pomegranate wine is in Egypt. There is clear evidence that the Egyptians produced pomegranate wine as far back as 3000 BCE. This early wine was processed from a series of grapes, herbs and other unidentified substances.

Additional Reading: Johnson, H., (1989). *Vintage: The story of wine.* New York: Simon & Schuster.

Winnowing   Domestic
Origin: Nubia   Date: 700 BCE

Prior to the rule of Taharqa of Nubia, harvesting grain crops resulted in a considerable amount of waste because the ground was usually dry and dusty. The Nubians developed a winnowing tool used to blow away unwanted bits of grain-husk while leaving the grain. This significantly reduced the amount of lost grain.

Additional Reading: Grove, B., (1986). *Webster's third new international dictionary of the English language.* Springfield, Mass.: Merriam-Webster.

Wire   Chemistry
Origin: Egypt   Date: 3500 BCE

The Egyptians used wire, especially those made from precious metals, for many purposes. According to Saville, they formed wire into ornaments and also used it to fasten loose teeth. Discoveries dating from 3500 BCE included copper wire.

Additional reading: Hayes, W. (1965). *Most ancient Egypt.* Chicago: University of Chicago Press.

Wolf   see   Dog.

Wood Drill   Mechanical
Origin: Egypt   Date: 1000 BCE

Wooden drills were first used in 1000 BCE, and were shaped like a nail with an edge. Drilling produced drilled dust, which was expelled by reversing the direction of the drill. The screw auger evolved from this drilling device as depicted through illustrations in old manuscript copies of the poems of Hesoiod, 900 BCE.

Additional reading: Scarre, C., (1988). Past worlds. *The times atlas of archaeology.* London: Koonalda.

Fig 31
Early Drill

Wool   Textile
Origin: Babylonia   Date: Prehistoric

One of the earliest examples of wool production was a shroud found in an oaken coffin dating from the Early Bronze Age. Herodotus mentioned that the Babylonians wore woolen tunics. Their knowledge of the manufacture of woolen articles was spread by the Romans during the conquest and settlement of the Babylonian empire.

Additional reading: Heidel, A. (1942). *The Babylonian genesis:* Chicago: University of Chicago Press.

Wrench   Mechanical
Origin: America   Date: Antiquity

The earliest recovered wrench was constructed for straightening wood and bone. The wrench soon became valuable for a host of other uses. A modified device was constructed and used as an animal trap. This device was also deployed in open field battles.

Additional reading: Mason, O. (1966). *The origin of invention.* Cambridge Mass: MIT Press.

Writing (Ideographic)   Communication
Origin: Mesopotamia   Date: 6000 BCE

The earliest form of ideographic writing appeared in Mesopotamia about 6000 BCE. Scribes realized the need to arrange pictures in order to record the events.

In ideographic writing, formalized and commonly recognized pictures stand for concepts and ideas. For instance, a spear might also be understood to represent hunting while the moon represents nighttime.

Additional reading: Fisher, S., (2001). *A history of writing.* London: Reartion Books.

Writing Material   Communication
Origin: Mesopotamia   Date: 5000 BCE

Clay tablets were used as a writing medium by the Mesopotamians more than 5,000 years ago. However, around 2500 BCE, the pith or inner stem of papyrus reed growing along the Nile River was discovered to be a better writing material. Criss-crossed layers of reed were beaten then dried in the sun. About 200 BCE, skins of lambs and calves were found to make a fine writing material called parchment. By 100 CE, parchment was being produced in thin rolls rather than sheets. The manufacture of paper that used compacted plant fibers began in China around 100 CE.

Additional reading: Hart, G. (1990). *Ancient Egypt.* New York: Alfred Knopf Pub.

Wrought Iron   Chemistry
Origin: Egypt   Date: 3000 BCE

Wrought and cast iron were known in Egypt 3000 years ago. Objects made from these irons were found in Egyptian tombs dating from 1400 BCE. Iron was known very long ago to other peoples of the East on the cusp of Iron Age. The Egyptian kings brought back great quantities of iron spears and other weapons from campaigns. Iron was exported in great quantities to other countries.

Additional reading: Rice, M. (2003). Egypt's making: *The origin of ancient Egypt, 5000-2000 B.C.*, 2nd ed. New York: Roulledge

Y

Yam   Agricultural
Origin: Africa   Date: Antiquity

The yam was one of the earliest crops that originated in central Africa. The yam was first used to feed livestock and then became a popular food substance for the people of the area. The roots from the yam plant were widely used as medicine.

Additional reading: Coursey, D (1966). The cultivation and use of yams in West Africa., Ghana notes and queries, *legon no. 9*, November, pp. 45-54.

Yin and Yang   Medical
Origin: China   Date: 1027 BCE

During the Chou Dynasty two doctrines evolved to form the basis of Chinese medicine. One is the doctrine of Yin and Yang. The two principles of masculinity, light and heavy (yang) and femininity, darkness and earth (yin). The other is that of the five elements or phases: metal, wood, water, fire and earth. It is believed that humans require equilibrium among the two principles and five elements to remain in good health.

Additional reading: Singer, C., and Underwood E., (1962). *A story history of medicine.* Clarendon Press.

Yogurt   Agriculture
Origin: Asia Minor   Date: Antiquity

Yogurt appeared in Asia Minor as far back as 3000 BCE. Made from milk fermented by bacteria, yogurt guaranteed longevity, so it was believed that it held medical cures for some illnesses of the period. The early yogurt also was applied to the bodies of young children for religious activities.

Additional reading: Buck, J.(1937). *Land utilization in China.* Chicago: University of Chicago Press.

Yoke   Mechanical
Origin: Mesopotamia   Date: 3000 BCE

Ancient shepherds recognized that the broad backs of their herds could be used to carry heavy loads over long distances. They created a yoke-like wooden frame, which rested across the shoulders of a pair of oxen, enabling them to drag a heavily laden sled or to pull a plow more effectively.

Additional reading: Singer, C. (1954). *A history of technology.* Oxford: Clarendon Press.

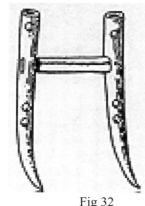

Fig 32
Early Yoke

Z

Zero   Mathematics
Origin: Babylon   Date: 400 BCE

The use of zero originated in Babylonia around 400 BCE. Mathematical tablets found in Uruk suggests that zero was used primarily to denote the absence of units with a number. The concept was used to express depletion, such as when a peasant reported that his grain supply was exhausted.

Additional reading: Van Sertima, I. (1983). *Blacks in science: Ancient and modern.* New Brunswick: Transaction Books.

Zinc   Chemistry
Origin: China   Date: 500 BCE

Zinc, atomic number 30 and chemical symbol Zn, was used as early as 500 BCE, as evidenced by ornaments containing zinc found by scientists. Early smelting and purification processes took place in China. Deposits of zinc were spread throughout the world, and found in conjunction with minerals containing lead and copper. Zinc was used in galvanizing metals, in particular iron and steel, to protect them against corrosion.

Additional reading: Schwartz, B. (1985). *The world of thought in ancient China.* Cambridge: Harvard University Press.

Zodiac   Astronomy
Origin: Babylon   Date: 2000 BCE

As early as the second millennium, the Babylonians

had developed a charting system that tracked the behavior of the stars. It wasn't until much later that the star rotation was associated with human behavior. The early use of this Babylonian chart enhanced ancient astronomers' ability to make astral predictions.

Additional Reading: Noel H. (1969). *Historical archaeology.* New York: Knopf Pub.

Zoo
Domestic

Origin: Egypt   Date: 276 BCE

Ptolemy II (284-245 BCE), a Hellenistic ruler of Egypt, was the originator of a zoological collection in the gardens that adjoined the Museum at Alexandria. The zoo housed lions, leopards, lynxes and other cats, Indian and African buffaloes, wild asses from Moab, a python that was forty-five feet long, a giraffe, a rhinoceros, parrots, peacocks, guinea fowl, pheasants, and a polar bear. Many of the animals in the collection had been previously entrapped in the course of elephant hunts. King Ptolemy's perception was that the purpose of his zoo was to satisfy the exotic attributes of a great king rather than the needs of an institution devoted to research. In the fifteenth century BCE, Pharaoh Thutmose III collected plants, birds, and animals during his military campaigns.

Additional reading: James, P. and Thorpe, N. (1994). *Ancient inventions.* New York: Ballantine Books.

INDEXES

Alphabet
Country
Subject
Date

Index by Alphabet

This is an attempt to develop a partial index list of inventions and discoveries contributed to the world by alphabet. This index will enable the reader to readily determine what events, subjects, inventions and discoveries offered to the world by people of color.

A

Abacus 1
Abrasive 1
Acacia Tree 1
Accordion 1
Accounting 1
Acupuncture 1
Addax 2
Adhesive 2
Adze 2
Aepyornis 2
Agriculture 2
Air Compressor 2
Air Transport 3
Alarm 3
Alcohol 3
Algebra 3
Algebra 2 3
Algorithm 3
Almond Tree 3
Alpaca 3
Alphabet 4
Alquerque 4
Amber 4
Amulet 4
Anchor 4
Anesthetic 4
Animal Domestication 4
Antibiotics 4
Anti-Hypertensive 5
Antimony 5
Anvil 5
Apricot Tree 5
Aqueduct 5
Arch 5

Architecture 5
Arithmetic 6
Armillary Ring 6
Army 6
Aromatic Plant 6
Arrow 6
Arsenic 6
Art 6
Arthritis Treatment 7
Artificial Spawning 7
Asphalt 7
Aspirin 7
Ass 7
Astro Survey 7
Astrolabe 7
Astronomy 8
Aulos 8
Auroch 8
Automation 8
Autopsy 8
Avocado 8
Awl 9
Ax 9

B

Bag Press 9
Bakery 9
Balance 9
Ball 9
Ball Bearing 10
Ballooning (Hot Air) 10
Bamboo 10
Banana 10
Bandage 10
Bank 10
Barley 10

Basalt 10
Basil 11
Basketry 11
Bathtub 11
Batter 11
Battering Ram 11
Battery 11
Bean 11
Bearing (Roller) 12
Bee Keeping 12
Beer (Alcohol) 12
Beeswax (Glue) 12
Beet 12
Bell 12
Bellow 12
Belt Drive 13
Benzoic Aldehyde 13
Bern 13
Birth Control 13
Bit 13
Bit 13
Bitumen 13
Blade 13
Blade Flake 13
Blast Furnaces 14
Blow Gun 14
Blow Pipe 14
Bludgeon 14
Boar 14
Boat 14
Body Armor 14
Bola 14
Bookkeeping 15
Boomerang 15
Borer 15
Boring Machine 15

Boron 15
Botany 15
Bottle (Glass) 15
Bow 15
Bow Drill 16
Bowl 16
Bowling 16
Bow-Ring 16
Boxing 16
Brahmi Numbers 16
Brain Surgery 16
Branding 16
Brass 17
Brazier 17
Bread 17
Brewing Beer 17
Brick 17
Bridge 17
Bridge (Floating) 18
Brocade 18
Bronze 18
Brush 18
Bubale 18
Bubble 19
Bucket 19
Buffalo 19
Burin 19
Burner 19

C

Cabbage 19
Cabinet 19
Calcite 19
Calculator 20
Calendar 20
Caliper Rule 20

Chronological Index by Countries

This is an attempt to develop a partial index list of inventions, discoveries, and innovations contributed to the world by country. This index will enable the reader to readily determine what events, subjects, inventions, Innovations, and discoveries offered to the world order.

Africa

Index by Subject

This is an attempt to develop an overall index of inventions and discoveries. The reader can readily determine what events, subject, inventions and discoveries were offered to the world by people of color.

Agricultural

Animal Domestication 4
Aromatic Plant 6
Artificial Spawning 7
Auroch 8
Barley 10
Beet 12
Boar 14
Bread 17
Brewing Beer 17
Cabbage 19
Cereal 23
Cheese 24
Citrus Fruit 25
Coconut 27
Coffee 28
Colter 28
Coriander 31
Corn 31
Cotton 31
Cow 32
Cream 32
Crop Rotation 32
Cucumber 33
Dairy 34
Date Palm 35
Drupe 39
Eohippus 42
Fantastic Tree 44
Farming 44
Farm (Seafood) 44
Fennel 44
Fermentation 44
Fertilizer 45
Fig tree 45
Flax 46
Flint Sickle 47

Food Preserving 47
Fruit 49
Fumigating 49
Garlic 50
Goose 53
Grape 53
Grass 54
Hemp 56
Herbarium 57
Horse 58
Insect (Domestic) 61
Karaka Tree 63
Kelp 64
Kneading 65
Leavened Bread 67
Leek 67
Legume 67
Lentil 67
Lettuce 67
Maize 71
Malt 71
Milk 76
Mill 76
Millett 76
Mint 77
Mustard 79
Numerical Record 81
Oat 81
Oil and Fat 82
Oil Seed 82
Olive 82
Onion 82
Ovine 83
Pea 85
Peanut 85
Peach 85
Pear 85

Pease 85
Pepper 86
Peppermint 86
Pig 87
Plough 89
Plum 89
Poppy 90
Potato 91
Quern 94
Radish 95
Raisin 95
Rattan 95
Rice 96
Rotary Mill 98
Rye 98
Saffron 98
Seaweed 101
Seed Drill 101
Sesame 101
Shaduf 102
Sheep 102
Sickle 103
Silo 104
Sow 107
Spawning 107
Spice 108
Squash 109
Sugar 111
Sugar Cane 111
Swine 112
Sycamore 112
Tea 113
Thyme 114
Viticulture (Wine) 119
Watermelon 121
Water Mill 121
Well 122

Wheat 123
Yam 125
Yogurt 126

Archaeology

Human 59

Architectural

Arch 5
Mastabah 73
Stone Building 110
Structures (Living) 110

Art

Art 6
Pictogram 87
Pottery 92

Astronomy

Armillary Ring 6
Astro Survey 7
Astrolabe 7
Astronomy 8
Calendar 20
Cartography 21
Catalog 22
Celestial Observation 22
Charting 23
Comet 29
Compass 29
Cycle 34
Eclipse (Solar) 40
Equinox 42
Horoscope 58
Meridian 75
Meteorite 76
Nova (Super) 80
Observatory 82
Saronic cycle 99
Solar Calendar 106
Solar Device 106

Medicine

Index by Date

This is an attempt to develop an overall index of inventions and discoveries. The reader can readily determine what events, subject, inventions and discoveries were offered to the world by people of color.

Barley 10
Beeswax 12
Burner 19
Coal 27
Hinge 57
Incense 60
Incense Burner 61
Lavatory 66
Marble 72
Unit Fraction 118
4300 BCE
Arithmetic 6
4228 BCE
Calendar 20
4200 BCE
Cheese 24
Duck 39
Goat 52
Leek 67
Len 67
Malt 71
Pea 85
Pease 85
Steel 110
4100 BCE
Glass Making 51
Toilet 115
4000 BCE
Abacus 1
Antimony 5
Bitumen 13
Boron 15
Boxing 16
Calculator 20
Cast 21
Cat 22
Catapult 22
Ceramic 23
Copper 30
Copper (Mining) 30
Counting Board 31
Crane 32
Enameling 42

Float 47
Glass 51
Granulation 53
Hoe 57
Insurance 62
Kiln 64
Loom 70
Lyre 70
Lyric 71
Mass Production 73
Metal 75
Metal Plating 75
Pancrace 84
Physiotherapy 87
Pi 87
Pin 88
Road 97
Saw 99
Ship 102
Shoe 102
Song (Written) 107
Sundial 111
Tanning 113
Tattoo 113
Vault 119
Weight 122
Wheel 123
3900 BCE
Viticulture (Wine) 120
3800 BCE
Anesthetic 4
Mandrake Plant 71
3700 BCE
Bronze 18
Charting 23
Drainage 38
Material (woven) 73
Pyramid (Structure) 93
3600 BCE
Accounting 1
Apricot Tree 5
Bookkeeping 15
Crop Rotation 32

Drab 38
Kelek 64
Plough 89
Sandal 99
Survey 112
Surveying 112
3500 BCE
Alcohol 3
Beer 12
Cabbage 19
Canopic Jar 21
Earthenware 40
Granite 53
Harp 55
Hieroglyphic Notation 57
Lead 66
Marble 72
Metal Leaf 75
Nail 79
Numeral 81
Oscillator 83
Seal (cylinder) 100
Spike 108
Tin 115
Trigonometry 117
Wire 124
3400 BCE
Batter 11
Paint (Tempura) 84
Wheat 123
3300 BCE
Adhesive 2
Cotton 31
False Teeth 44
Glue 52
Massonary 73
Teeth (false) 114
3200 BCE
Antibiotics 4
Bee Keeping 12
Bow Drill 16
Bowling 16
Camel 20

Cream 32
Dairy 34
Digit 37
Druper 39
Embalming 41
Emery Plaques 41
Food Preserving 47
Forcep 47
Gripper 54
Immunization 60
Karate 63
Knob 65
Martial Arts 72
Milk 76
Mummification 78
Nilomete 80
Paved Street 85
Peach 85
Quarry 94
Sexagesimal Fraction 101
Wallpaper 120
Well 122
Whorl 123
3110 BCE
Distillation 37
3100 BCE
Chimney 24
Limestone 68
Olive 82
Power (Numerical) 92
3000 BCE
Accordion 1
Almond Tree 3
Anchor 4
Arch 5
Benzoic Aldehyde 13
Boomerang 15
Burner 19
Calliper Rule 20
Cartography 21
Circumference (Math) 25
Cloak 26
Clock 26

Cited References

The publishers wish to point out that although every effort has been made to ensure that the details in this Reference are correct, some errors may occur as a result of the complexity and the international nature of this work.

Abell, G. (1975). *Exploration of the universe,* 3rd ed. New York: Holt, Rinehart & Winston.

Abungu, G.H.O. and Mutoro, H.W. (1993). *Coast-interior settlements and social relations in the Kenya coastal hinterland. In The archaeology of Africa: Food, metals and towns,* ed. T. Shaw, P. Sinclair, B. Andah and A. Okpoko, 694-704.

Adams, W. (1984). *The first colonial empire: Egypt in Nubia, 3200-1200 B.C.* Comparative Studies in Society and History 26(I), 36-71.

Adams, W. (1933). *The book of the master of the hidden places.* London: The Search Publishing Co.

Africanus, L. (1896). *The history and description of Africa,* 3rd ed. London: R. Brown. Hakluyt Society.

Aldred, C. (1980). *Egyptian art.* New York: Thames and Hudson.

Alexander, J. (1993). *Beyond the Nile: The influence of Egypt and Nubia in Sub-Saharan Africa.* Expedition 35(2), 51-61.

Allibert, C. and Vérin, P. (1996) *The early pre-Islamic history of the Comores Islands: Links with Madagascar and Africa. In The Indian Ocean in antiquity,* ed. J. Reade, 461-70.

Allison, P. (1962). Historical inferences to be drawn from the effect of human settlement on the vegetation of Africa. *Journal of African History* 3(2), 241-9.

Allman, W. (1994). *The stone age to present.* New York: Simon Schuster.

Amiet, P. (1980). *Art of the ancient Near East.* New York: Harry N. Abrams Pub.

Andrews, F. (1948). *The vegetation of the Tothill Sudan. Agriculture in the Sudan,* ed. J.D., Oxford University Press, 32-61.

Anquandah, J. (1993). *The Kintampo complex: A case study of early sedentism and food production in sub-Sahelian West Africa. The archaeology of Africa: Food, metals and towns* ed. 255-60.

Arkell, A. (1955). *A history of the Sudan: From the earliest times to 1821.* London: Athlone Press.

Asimov, I. (1982). *Asimov's biographical encyclopedia of science and technology.* 2nd ed. New York: Doubleday.

Asimov, I. (!989). *Asimov's chronology of science and discovery.* New York: Harper.

Asimov, I. (1988). *Asimov's new guide to science.* New York: Harper and Row.

Badawy, A. (1954). *A history of Egyptian architecture,* 3 Vol. Berkeley, Cal.: University of California Press.

Baldwin, T. (1986). *Inventors and Inventions of the ancient world.* New Jersey: Barnhart Books.

Bandi, H. and Breuil, H. (1970). *The art of the stone age: Forty thousand years of rock art.* 2nd ed., London: Methuen.

Barber, F. (1900). *The mechanical triumphs of the ancient Egyptians.* London: K. Paul, Trench, Trubner and Co.

Bart, J. (1964). *Pre-historic times,* New York: J.A. Hill Co.

Basalla, G. (1988), The evolution of technology. London: Cambridge Press.

Batta, C. (1936), *The history of India,* Calcutta: Calcutta Press.

Bennion, E. (1979). *Antique medical instruments.* Berkeley, Cal.: University of California Press.

Bettman, O. (1956). *A pictorial history of medicine.* Springfield, IL.: Charles C. Thomas.

Bikai, P. (1978). *The pottery of Tyre.* Oregon: Warminister and Forest Grove.

Birch, S. (1875). *Ancient Egypt from the monuments, Egypt from the earliest times to B.C. 300.* New York: Scribner and Armstrong

Bishop, W.W. and Posnansky, M. (1960). Pleistocene environments and early man in Uqanda." *The Uganda Journals,* vol. 24, no. 1

Bisson, M. (1976) . *The prehistoric coppermines of Zambia.* PhD thesis, University of California, Santa Barbara.

Bloon, P. (1954). *Grove's dictionary of music and musicians,* vol1, New York: St. Martin's Press.

Boyler, C. (1968). *A history of mathematics,* New York: Wiley.

Boyer, C. and Uta C. (1991). *A history of mathematics,* 2nd ed. New York: John Wiley & Sons.

Breasted, J. (1909). *A history of Egypt.* New York: Scribner & Sons.

Breasted, J. (1906). *Ancient records of Egypt; historical documents from the earliest times to the Persian conquest.* Vols. 1-5. Chicago: The University of Chicago Press.

Breunig, P. (1996). *The 8000-year-old dugout canoe from Dufuna* (NE Nigeria). G. Pwiti and R. Soper, 461-8. Harare: University of Zimbabwe.

Brooks, L. (1971). *Great civilization of ancient Africa,* New York: Four Winds Press.

Bunch, B. and Hellemans, A. (1993). *The timetables of technology: A chronology of the most important people and events in the history of technology.* New York: Simon & Schuster.

Buritt, M. C. (1928). *South Africa's past in stone and paint.* Cambridge, England: Cambridge University Press.

Burrow, T., (1975). *The early Aryans. In A cultural history of India.* New York: A.l. Basham, Oxford and New York

Burkitt, M.C.(1928). *South Africa's past in stone and paint.* Cambridge: University Press.

Burton, R. F. (1860). *The lake region of central Africa.* Vols. 1-2. London: Longman, Green Longman, and Roberts

Butzer, K. (1976). *Early hydraulic civilization in Egypt: A study in cultural ecology.* Chicago: University of Chicago Press.

Bynner, W. (1962). *The way of life according to Lao Tzu.* London and New York.

Cajori, F. (1929). *A history of physics.* New York: The Macmillan Company.

Carter, H. (1965). *The tomb of Tu-tankh-amen.* London: Excalibur Books.

Castiglioni, A. (1941). *A history of medicine.* New York: Alfred A. Knopf.

Caton, G. (1931). *The Zimbabwe culture.* Oxford, England: Clarendon Press.

Cerny, J. (1952). *Ancient Egyptian religion,* London and New York: Hutchinson Houe.

Chandler, T. and Fox, G. (1974). *3000 years of urban growth.* New York and London: Academic Press.

Chang, K. (1976). *Early Chinese civilization.* Cambridge: Harvard University Press.

Chi Ch'ao-Ting, (1970). *Key economic areas in Chinese history, as revealed in the development of public works for water-control,* New York: Kelly, A.M.

Childe, V.G.(1957). *Civilization, cities and towns.* Antiquity 31, 36-8.

Childe, V.G.,(1965). *Man makes himself.* London: Watts.

__ (1983). China: 7000 years of discovery, China's ancient technology. *China Reconstructs Magazine,* Beijing, China.

Chittick, N. (1975). *An early salt-working site on the Tanzanian coast.* Azania 10, 151-3, 185-90.

Clark, T. (1921). *The Nile and Jordan, the archeological and historical inter-relation between Egypt and Canaan.* London: James Clarke and Company.

Clark, D. (1981). *Pattern of the past.* Cambridge: Press, London.

Clark, J.D.(1950). The stone age cultures of Northern Rhodesia. Claremont: South Africa Archeological Society.

Clark, R. W. (1985). *Works of man.* New York: Viking.

Clegg, L. (1985). "Blacks rulers of the golden age," JAC: *Nile valley civilization,* ed. New York: Ivan Van Sertima.

Clymer, R. S.(1920). *The Philosophy of fire.* Quakertown, Pa.: The Philosophical Publishing Co.

Coe, M. D. (1994). *Breaking the Mayan Code.* New York: Thames & Hudson.

Colbert, E. H. (1984). *The great dinosaur hunters and their discoveries.* New York: Dover.

Cole, Sonia M. (1963). *The Prehistory of East Africa.* New York: Macmillan.

Colin, S. (1973). *Lost Discoveries.* New York: McGraw-Hill Co.

Collon, D. (1987). *First impressions: Cylinder seals in the ancient Near East.* Chicago: University of Chicago Press.

Connah, G. (1981). *Three thousand years in Africa: Man and his environment in the Lake Chad region of Nigeria.* Cambridge: Cambridge. University Press.

Cotterell, L. (1980). *Ancient civilization.* New York: Penguin.

Cotterell, L.(1980). *The Penguin encyclopedia of ancient civilizations,* New York: Penquin.

Cotterell, Y.Y. and A.B., (1975). *The early civilization of China,* London and New York: Penguin.

Coursey, D.G. (1980). *The origins and domestication of yams in Africa. In West African culture dynamics: Archaeological and historical perspectives,* ed. B.K. Swartz and R.E. Dumett, 67-90.

Craddock, P.T. (1991) Man and metal in ancient Nigeria. *British Museum Magazine.* 6,9.

Crawford, H. (1991). *Sumer and the Sumerians.* Cambridge University Press.

Cross W. (1982). *Enchanmant of the World-Egypt.* Chicago: Children's Press.

Curwen, E. C. and Hatt, G. (1953). *Plough and pasture: the early history of farming,* pt. 1: *Prehistoric farming of Europe and the Near East.* New York: H. Schuman Pub.

Daniel, G. (1968). *The first civilizations: the archaeology of their origins.* London: Thames and Hudson.

Daumas, M. (1960). *A history of technology and invention,* vol. II New York: Crown Pub.

Daumas, M, (1963). *History of Technology and invention,* vol. 3. New York: Crown Press.

Darwin, C.R. (1904). *The origin of species.* New York: Appleton.

Davidson, B. (1959). *The lost cities of Africa.* Little, Boston: Brown and Co.

Davison, P. and Harries, P.(1980). *Cotton weaving in South-East Africa: its history and technology.* Textile II.

Dawson, C. H. (1956). *The making of Europe,* New York: Meridian Books.

DeBono, E. (1974). *Eureka!: How and when the greatest inventions were made: An illustrated history of inventions from the wheel to the computer.* London: Thames & Hudson.

De Camp, L. S. (1993). *The ancient engineers.* New York. Barnes and Noble.

De Camp, L. S. (1974). *The ancient engineers.* New York:. Ballantine Books.

Degler, C.N.(1991). *In search of human nature.* New York: Oxford University Press.

De Maret, P. (1979). *Luba roots: The first complete Iron Age sequence in Zaire.* Current Anthropology 20(I), 233-5.

Denbow, J.R. (1986). A new look at the later prehistory of the Kalahari. *Journal of African History* 27, 3-28.

Derry, T. K. and Williams, T. I. (1960). *A short history of technology from the earliest times to A.D. 1900.* Oxford: Clarendon Press.

Didot, P. (1843). *Voyage in Egypt and Syria.* London: Oxford Press.

Diggs, I. (1983)., *Black Chronology: From 4000 B.C. to the Abolition of the Slave Trade,* Boston, Hal Pub.

Diop C. (1974). *The African origin of civilization myth or reality,* Westport: Lawrence Hill & Co.

Diop, C. (1981). "Orgin of the Ancient Egyptians," General History of Africa, Mokhtar, UNESCO.

Dolan, J. (1968). *History of nursing.* Philadelphia: W.B. Saunders.

Diringer, D. (1948). *The alphabet: A key to the history of mankind .* London: Hutchinson's Scientific and Technical Pub.

Driver, G.R.,(1944). *Semitic Writing from Pictograph to Alphabet,* Oxford, S.A. Hopkins.

Doresse, J. (1959). *Ethiopia.* New York: Putnam.

Dorsey, G. (1931). *The story of civilization; man's own show.* New York: Halcyon House.

Dow, S. (1995)., The Gale Encyclopedia of Science; New York: Gale Research.

Douze, S. (1993). *Inventions and discoveries.* New York: Facts on File.

Du Bois, W.E.B. (1947). *The world and Africa.* New York: International, Pub..

Edwards, I.E.S.(1970). *The pyramids of Egypt.* Harmondsworth and New York:.

Ehret, C. (1998). *An African classical age: Eastern and Southern Africa in world history, 1000 BC to AD 400.* Virginia: University Press of Virginia.

Erman, A. (1971). *Life in ancient Egypt,* New York: Dover Pub.

Eves. H.A. (1953). *Introduction to the history of mathematics.* New York: Holt, Rinehart and Winston.

Fagan, B.M. (1969). Early trade and raw materials in South Central Africa. *Journal of African History* 10(I), 1-13.

Faul, H., and Faul. C. *It began with a stone.* New York: John Wiley & Sons.

Finley, M.I. (1973). *The ancient economy.* London.

Forbes, R.J. (1967). *Man the maker, A history of technology and engineering,* London: Abelard-Schuman Limited.

Fossils Trace Man Back 600,000 Years in Gorge in Africa." *The New York Times,* August 24, 1959.

Frankfort, H.A.(1948). *The intellectual adventure of ancient man.* Chicago: University of Chicago Press.

Gascoigne, R. M.(1987). *A chronology of the history of science.* New York: Garland.

Gille, B. (1986). *The history of technique.* Vol. 2. New York: Research Science Pub.

Gjertsen, D. (1984). *The classics of science.* New York: Lillan Barber Press.

Golob, R., and Eric B. (1990). *The Almanac of the science and technology.* New York: Harcourt Brace Jovanovich.

Graves, M. (1942). *Africa: The wonder and the glory,* Baltimore: Black Classic Press.

Grayson, A.K. (1975). *Assyrian and Babylonian chronicles,* New York: Locust Press.

Griffith, S. (1976). *Egyptian grammar,* London: Oxford Press

Grun, B. (1982). *The timetable of history of technology.* London: Marshall's Editions.

Gwynne, M.D.(1975) . *The origin and spread of some domestic food plants of Eastern Africa.* ed. N. Chittick and R.I. Rotberg, 248-71.

Haaland, R. (1995). *Dakawa: An early Iron Age site in the Tanzanian hinterland.* Africa: Azania 29-30,238-47.

Hall, Richard N., (1903). *Prehistoric Rhodesia.* London: T.F. Unwin.

Hansberry, W. (1981). *Africa and the Africans,* vol. II, Washington D.C., Howard University Press.

Harris, J.R. (1971). *The legacy of Egypt,* Oxford and New York.

Hart, G. (1995). *Ancient Egypt.* New York: Time Life.

Hayes, W. (1965). *Most ancient Egypt,* London and Chicago.

Hays,T. (1964). *Most ancient Egypt,* Chicago: University of Chicago Press.

Hellicar, E. (1983). *But whose idea was It;* London: David and Charles Press.

Hellmans, A. and Bunch, B. *The Timetable of science,* New York: Simon & Schuster.

Hickey, S. (1981). *100 families of flowering plants,* Cambridge: Cambridge Press.

Hill, D. (1984). *A history of engineering;* London: Routledge.

Hitti, P. K. (1951). *History of the Arabs.* New York: Macmillan.

Hodges, H. (1970). *Technology in the ancient world.* New York: Knopf.

Hoffman M. (1980)., *Egypt before the pharaohs. The prehistoric foundation of Egyptian Civiliztion,* New York: Alfred A Knopf.

Holmyarp, A. (1954). *History of technology,* Vol. 3, New York: Oxford University Press.

Ho Peng-Yoke. (1966). *The astronomical chapters of the Chin Shu,* Paris. Dover Press.

House, H. (1934). *Wild flowers.* New York: MacMillan Co.

Houston, D. (1985)., *Wonderful Ethopians of the ancient Cushite empire.* Baltimore: Black Classic Press.

Huffman, T.N. (1971). *Cloth from the iron age in Rhodesia.* Arnoldia (Rhodesia) 5, 1-19.

Huetman, T.N.(1982). Archaeology and ethnohistory of the African iron age. *Annual Review of Anthropology II,* 133-50.

Hurry, J. (1926). *Imhotep.* London: Oxford University Press.

Ingils, Brain. (1965). *A history of medicine.* Cleveland: World Publishing Co.

Insoll, T. and Shaw, T. 1997. Gao and Igbo Ukwu: Beads, interregional trade, and beyond. *African archaeological Review* 14(I), 9-23.

James, G. (1954). Stolen legacy. New York: Philosophical Library.

James, P. (1993). *Centuries of darkness.* Rutgers: University Press.

Kane, J. N. (1981). *Famous first facts.* New York: H.W. Wilson Co.

Katz, F. (1972). *The ancient American civilizations,* London & New York:. K. Lois Simpson.

Kendall, T. (1997). *Kerma and the kingdom of Kush 2500-1500 BC: The archaeological discovery of an ancient Nubian empire.* Washington: Smithsonian Institution.

Kenrick, J. (1850). *Ancient Egypt under the pharaohs,* Vols. 1-2. London: B. Fellowes.

Kilind, L. (1985). African roots in martial arts. New York: *Journal of African Civilizations.*

Kosambi, D. D. (1965). *The culture and civilization of ancient India in historical outline,* London.

Kostof, S.A. (1985). *History of Architecture: Settings and Rituals.* New York: Oxford University Press.

Kramer, S.N. (1959). *History begins at Sumer,* New York; Doubleday & Co.

Lanning, E.C. (1953). Ancient earthworks in western Uganda. *Uganda Journal* 17(I), 51 62.

Low, R.K.(1980). *The horse in West African history.* Oxford: Oxford University Press, .

Larsen, A (1961). *History of invention,* New York: Phoenix House.

Leakey, L. (1931). *The stone age culture of Kenya colony.* Cambridge, England: The University Press.

Leakey, L.(1935). *The stone age races of Kenya.* London: Oxford University Press.

Leclant, J. (1978). Le monde egyptian. Les Pharaons Vol. I-Le temps des Pyramides. *De la Prehistorie aux Hyksos* (1560 B.C.), Paris, Gallimard.

Leo Africanus, J., (1896). *The history and description of Africa.* Vols. 1-3. London: Hakluyt Society.

Massey, G.(1881). *A Book of the beginnings.* Vols. 1-2. London: Williams and Norgate.

Levy, J. and Agnes G.(1983). *The concise Columbia encyclopedia.* New York: Avon.

Lucas, A. (1962). *Ancient Egyptian materials and industries,* rev. and enlarged ed. London: Edward & Arnold Pub.

Lucas, A. (1960). *Ancient Egyptian materials and industries,* London, Edward Arnold Pub.

Lumpkin, B. (1979)., *Young genius in old Egypt.* Chicago: University of Chicago.

MacDonald, K.C. and MacDonald, R.H. (1999). *The origins and development of domesticated animals in arid West Africa.* London: University College Press.

Macorini, E. (1988). The history of science and technology: A narrative Chronology. New York: Facts on Files,

Martell, H. (1995). *The Kingfisher book of the ancient world: From the ice age to the fall of Rome.* New York: Kingfisher Pub.

Mason, R. (1966). *The origins of invention,* Cambridge: The M.I.T. Press.

Maspero, Gaston C., *The dawn of civilization, Egypt and Chaldea.* London: Society for Promoting Christian Knowledge, 1901.

Massey, G. (1881). *Book of beginnings,* vols 1-2, University Books.

McGraw-Hill dictionary of science and technology. (1984). Edited by Sybil P. Parker. New York: McGraw-Hill.

McGraw-Hill encyclopedia of science and technology. 5th ed. (1982). New York: McGraw-Hill.

McGraw-Hill yearbook of science and technology. (1993). New York: McGraw-Hill.

McGrew, R. (1985). *Encyclopedia of medical history,* New York: McGraw-Hill.

Midonick, H; (1965). The Treasury of mathematics, New York: Philosophical Library.

Millard, A, (1971). *Egypt-The young archaeologist;* New York; Putnam's Sons.

Morley, J. (1992). *How would you survive as an ancient Egyptian.* New York: Grolier.

Mount, E. (1987). *Milestone in science and technology.* New York: Oryx Press.

Mueller, P. (1963). *How man creates in art and science.* New York: John Day Co.

Nenquin, J. (1961). Salt: A study in economic prehistory. Dissertationes Archaeologicae Gandenses 6.

Neuburger, O. (1930). *The technical arts and sciences of the ancients.* New York: The Macmillan Co.

Neugebauer, O. (1957). *The exact sciences in antiquity,* New York: Brown University Press.

Newberry, P. (1929). "The Shepherds Crook and the So-Called 'Flail' or 'Scourge' of Osiris," JEA, vol. XV, Egyptian Exploration Society.

Newsome, F. (1979), Black contributions to the history of Western medicine. New York: *Journal of the National Medical Association.* vol. 71,no. 2

Newton, F.G.,(1959). Excavation at El Amarnah, *Journal of Egyptian Archaeology.*

Oakley, K. (1956). *Man the tool maker.* London: British Museum.

Ochoa, G; (1995). *The timeline book of science.* New York: Stonesong Press.

Ochoa, G. (1997) *The Wilson chronology of science and technology,* New York: Wilson Co.

O'Connor, D. (1991). *Early states along the Nubian Nile. In Egypt and Africa: Nubia from prehistory to Islam,* ed. London: British Museum Press.

Ogilive, M. (1986). Women in science:

Antiquity through the nineteenth century.
Cambridge, Ma.: MIT Press.

Olby, R. C., et al., (1990). *Companion to the History of Modern Science.* London: Routledge.

Oliver, P. (ed.) 1971. *Shelter in Africa.* New York: Praeger,

Osburn, W. (1985). *The monumental history of Egypt,* London: Trubner & Co.

Pacey, A. (1990). *Technology in world civilization.* Cambridge, MA.: MIT Press.

Palmer, G. (1968). *Archeology a-z;* London: Frederick Warne.

Panati, C. (1984). *The browser's book of beginnings.* Boston: Houghton Mifflin.

Parker, S. (1989). *McGraw-Hill concise encyclopedia of science and technology.* New York: McGraw-Hill Pub.

Parker, S. (1992). *The dawn of man.* New York: Crescent Books.

Parlett, D. (1999). T*he Oxford history of board games;* Oxford: Oxford Press.

Parrot, A.(1961). *Sumer: The dawn of art.* New York: Golden Press.

Petterson R.T.(1968). *A field guide to wildflowers,* New York: Houghton Miffin.

Phillipson, D.W. (1993). *The antiquity of cultivation and herding in Ethiopia. In The archaeology of Africa: Food, metals and towns,* ed. T. Shaw, P. Sinclair, B, Andah and A. Okpoko Routledge, London:, pp. 344-57.

Phimister, I.R.(1974). 'Ancient' mining near Great Zimbabwe. *Journal of the South African Institute of Mining and Metallurgy* 74, 233-7.

Pine T. and Levine J.(1964). *The Egyptians knew;* New York: McGraw-Hill.

Piggott, S. (1950). *Prehistoric India to 1000 BC.* London: Harmondsworth.

Powell, T.G.E. (1966). *Prehistoric art. The world of art.* New York: Oxford University Press.

Randall-Maclver, David, (1906). "The Rhodesia Ruins: Their Probable Origin and Significance." *The Geographical Journal.* Vol. 27, No 4.

Rawlinson, T, (1887). *The story of ancient Egypt.* New York: Putnam.

Reade, J. (1991). Mesopotamia. London: British Museum.

Redman, C.L.(1978). *The rise of civilization: From early farmers to urban society in the ancient Near East.* San Francisco: Freeman.

Reid, A. and Meredith, J. (1993). Houses, pots, and more cows: The 1991 excavation season at Ntusi, Nyame Akuma 40, 58-61.

Rekhety, W. (1985). "Ancient and Modern Cattle Cultures of North and East Africa in Comparison," a paper presented at The Second Annual Egyptian Studies Conference, Northeastern Illinois University, Illinois.

Ries, E. (1930). *Mother wit.* New York: Century Co.

Robinson, C. (1984)., *Ancient Egypt, a first book.* New York: Franlin Watts.

Robinson, T.H. and Oesterley, W. (1932). *A history of Israel.* Vols. 1-2. Oxford: The Clarendon Press.

Royer, J.(1946). *World's great men of color.* vols. 1-2. New York: J.A. Rogers Pub.

Rogers, R.W., (1915). *A history of Babylonia and Assyria.* Vol 2, Cincinnati: Books for Libraries Press.

Rogers, B. (1946). *World's great men of color,* Vol. I, New York: Clarke.

Ronan, C. A.(1982). Science its history and development among the world's cultures. New York: Facts on File.

Ronan, C. (1975). *Lost discoveries.* New York: McGraw-Hill.

Rossi, N. and Rafferty, S. (1981). *Music through the centuries.* Washington D.C.: University Press.

Sanford, E. M. (1938). *The Mediterranean world in ancient times.* New York: The Ronald Press Co.

Sarton, G. (1959). *A history of science,* Cambridge: Harvard Press.

Saggs, H.W.F. (1965). *Everyday life in Babylonia and Assyria.* New York and London: B.T. Batsford

Sassoon, H.(1983). Kings, cattle and blacksmiths: Royal insignia and religious symbolism in the inter-lacustrine states. Azania I8, 93-106.

Schmidt, P.R. and Avery, D.H. (1996). Complex iron smelting and prehistoric culture in Tanzania. In T*he culture and technology of African iron production*, ed. P.R. Schmidt, 172-85.

Schmidt, P. and Avery, D. (1987). Science and anthropology, Washington D.C.: National Science Foundation.

Schoenbrun, D.L. (1993). Cattle herds and banana garden: The historical geography of the western Great Lakes region, ca AD 800-1500.

African Archaeological Review II, 39-72.

Schwartz, B. (1985). *The world of thought in ancient China*. Cambridge, Ma.:Harvard University Press.

Sedgwick, W. T. and Tyler, H. (1917). *A short history of science*. New York: Macmillan Co.

Semenov, S. A. (1964). *Prehistoric technology; an experimental study of the oldest tools and artifacts from traces of manufacture and wear*. New York: Barnes and Noble.

Sertima, I. V. (1985). *African civilizations*. New Brunwick: New York: *Journal of African Civilizations*.

Sertima, I. V. (1983). *Blacks in science ancient and modern,* New York: Transaction Books.

Sharks, M. (1992). *Experiencing the past.* London: Routledge Pub.

Shore, D. (1983). Steel-making in ancient Africa. *Journal of African civilizations.* [New Brunswick, N.J: Douglass College, Rutgers University] 5 (1-2).

Sigerist, H. (1967). *Primitive and archaic medicine:* New York: Oxford University Press.

Silverberg, O. (1967). *Before the sphinx-early Egypt.* London:

Smith, D. (1947)., *History of mathematics* vol. 1, New York: Viking .

Smith, H.S., & Hall, R.(1983). *Egyptain Centers of civilization,* Windsor Forest: The Kensal Press.

Snowden, F. M. (1970). *Blacks in antiquity: Ethiopians in the Greco-Roman experience.* Cambridge, Mass. Harvard University Press.

Sondergaard, A. (1964). *My first geography of the Suez Canal,* Boston: Little Brown.

Spears, N. (1960). *A treasury guide and glossary.* London: Phoenix House Ltd.

Steindorff, G & Seele, K. (1942). *When Egypt ruled the East.* Chicago: The University of Chicago Press.

Struik, D.J. (1987). *A concise history of mathematics.* 4th ed. New York: Dover.

Sutton, J.E.G. (1997). The African lords of the intercontinental gold trade before the black death: al-Hasa bin Sulaiman of Kilwa and Mansa Musan of Mali. *Antiquaries Journal.*77, 221-42.

Talbott, J. (1970). A *biographical history of medicine.* New York: Grune and Stratton.

Taylor, M.O.V.(1984). Southern Transvaal stone walled sites - a spatial consideration. In Frontiers: southern African archaeology today, ed. M. Hall, G. Avery, D.M. Avery, M.L. Wilson and A.J.B. Humphreys p. 248-51.

Taylor, J. (1979)., "The Black Image in Egyptain Art" *Journal of African Civilizations,* vol. I.

Thames, P. (1974). *An illustrated history of inventions from the wheel to the computer,* New York: Holt.

Theal, G.M. (1893). Records of southeastern Africa collected in various libraries archive departments in Europe. Vols. 1-9. London: The Government of the Cape Colony.

Thorp, C.R. (1995). Kings, commoners and cattle at Zimbabwe tradition sites. National Museums and Monuments of Zimbabwe, Harare.

Thurman, C.C.M. (1979). The textiles. In Ancient textiles from Nubia: Meroitic, X Group, and Christian fabrics from Ballana and Qustul, C.C.M. Thurman and B. Williams, 36-46.

Trager, J. (1992). *The people's chronology.* New York: Henry Holt.

Trauers, D. (1994). *World of inventions,* New York: Gale Research Inc.

Trefil, J. (1992). *1,001 things everyone should know about science.* New York: Doubleday.

Trench, P. (1902) A history of Egypt from the end of the neolithic period to the death of Cleopatra VII B.C. Vols. 1-8. London: Trubner and Co.

Unschuld, P. (1985). *Medicine in China: A history of ideas.* Berkeley: University of California Press.

Vail, C.H., (1909). *Ancient mysteries and modern masonry.* New York: Macoy Publishing

Van Doren, C. (1991). *A history of knowledge.* New York: Ballantine.

Van Nostrand's scientific encyclopedia. 6th ed. Edited by Douglas M. Consideine and Glenn D.

Van Sertima, I. (1983). *Blacks in science: Ancient and modern.* New Brunswick: Transaction Books.

Van Sertima, I.(1981). *The lost sciences of Africa: An overview. Blacks in science: Ancient and modern.* New Brunswick: Transaction Books.

Vercoutter, J. (1959). The gold of Kush: Two gold-washing stations at Faras East. Kush 7, 120-53.

Vogel, J.O. (ed.) (1997). *Encyclopedia of precolonial Africa: Archaeology, history, languages, cultures, and environments.* Walnut Creek, CA. AltaMira Press.

Waddell, L.A. (1926). *Egyptian civilization: Its Sumerian origin and real chronology.* Hawthrone, California: Christian Book Club.

Walton, J., and Beeson, P. (1986). *The Oxford companion to medicine.* Oxford: Oxford University Press.

Warren, R. (1968). *The Nile.* New York: McGraw-Hill.

Weber, M. (1925). *Ancient Judaism,* Glencoe Il. The Free Press.

Wells, H. G. (1922). *A short history of Africa,* New York: Macmillan Co.

Wetterau, B. (1990). *The New York Public Library Book of Chronologies.* New York: Prentice Hall Press.

Wiedner, D. L. (1962). *A history of Africa south of the Sahara.* New York: Random House.

Wilinson, R. (1992). *Reading Egyptian art: A hieroglyphic guide to ancient Egyptian painting and sculpture.* New York: Thames and Hudson.

Williams, T. (1982). The history of invention, New York: Facts on Files.

Williams, B. (1985). "The Lost Pharaohs of Nubia," *Nile Valley Civilizations,* ed., Ivan Van Sertima.

Windsor, R. (1969). *From Babylon to Timbuktu; a history of the ancient black races including the black Hebrews.* New York: Exposition Press.

Winter, I.J. (1976). Phoenician and North Syrian ivory carving in historical context etc., Iraq, 38. pp 1-22

Wisseman, S. (1994). *Ancient technologies and archeological materials.* Gordon. London: Breach Science Pub.

Wolf, E.R. (1976). The valley of Mexico: Studies in prehistoric ecology and society, Albuquerque, N. Mex.

Wolf, W. (1989). *The origin of Western art: Egypt, Mesopotamia, the Aegean.* New York: Universe Books.

"43,000 Year Old Mines Discovered in Swaziland." *The New York Times,* February 8, 1970. p. 6.

Bibliography

The publishers wish to point out that although every effort has been made to
ensure that the details in this Bibliography are correct, some errors may occur as
a result of the complexity and the international nature of this work.

Aaboe, A. (1964). *Episodes from the early history of mathematics.* New York: Singer Pub.

Abbot, C. (1944). *Great inventions.* New York: Smithsonian Institution Series, Inc.

Abbot, D. (1986). *The biographical dictionary of scientists. Engineers and inventors.* New York: Harper & Row.

Adams, W. (1977). *Nubia, corridor to Africa.* London: Allen Lane.

Albright, W. (1940). *From the stone age to Christianity.* Baltimore: John Hopkins Press.

Alexander, J. (1993). *Beyond the Nile: The influence of Egypt and Nubia in Sub-Saharan Africa.* New York: Expedition Vol. 2. 35, 51-61.

Al-Kashi, J. (1956). *The key to arithmetic, treatise on the circle.* Moscow, Russia: Noskva, Gos

Allen, H. (1961). *A history of wine; great vintage wines from the Homeric age to the present day.* New York: Horizon Press.

Allman, W. (1994). *The stone age present: How evolution has shaped modern life: from sex, violence, and language to emotions, morals, and communities.* New York: Simon & Schuster.

_____ (1979). *Ancient records of Assyria and Babylon, vol. I, historical records of Assyria from the earliest times to Sargon.* Chicago: University of Chicago Press.

Angier, B. (1974). *Field guide to edible wild medicinal plants.* Harrisburg, Pa.: Stackpole Books.

Anquandah, J.(1993). The Kintampo complex; a case study of early sedentism and food production in Sub-Sahelian West Africa. *In the archaeology of Africa: Food, metals and towns* ed., T. Shaw, P. Sinclair and A. Okpoko, pp. 255-260.

Ashurst, F. (1982). *Founders of modern mathematics.* London: Fredrick Muller.

Asimov, I. (1982). *Asimov's biographical encyclopedia of science and technology: The lives and achievements of 1510 great scientists from ancient times to the present chronologically arranged.* Garden City, N.Y: Doubleday Pub.

Asimov, I. (1982). *Exploring the earth and the cosmos; the growth and future of human knowledge.* New York: Crown Pub.

Asimov, I. (1989). *Asimov's chronology of science and discovery.* New York: Harper & Row.

Babcock G. (2002). *Webster's third new international dictionary of the English language.* New York: Merrian-Webster.

Bailey, L. (1950). *The standard encyclopedia of horticulture.* 3 vols. New York: Macmillan Co.

Baldwin, G. (1973). *Inventors and inventions of the ancient world.* New York: Four Winds Pub.

Balsam, M. and Sagarin, E. (1972). *Cosmetic science and technology.* New York: Wiley Interscience.

Barber, F. (1900). *The mechanical triumphs of ancient Egyptians,* London: Trubner and Co.

Barrow, I. (1916). *Geometrical lectures.* Chicago: (Trans. and edited by J.M. Child).

Basalla, G. (1988). *The evolution of technology.* Cambridge Eng. University Press.

Beal, G. (1975). *Playing-cards and their story.* New York: Arco Pub. Co.

Beaver, P. (1972). *A history of tunnels.* Secaucus, N.J.: Citadel Press.

Bell, E. (1945). *The development of mathematics.* 2nd ed., New York: McGraw Hill.

Bennion, E. (1979). *Antique medical instruments.* Berkeley, Calif. University of California Press.

Beston, H. (1935). *Herbs and the earth.* New York: Doubleday, Doran and Co.

Bettman, O. (1956). *A pictorial history of medicine.* London: Thomas Pub.

Binford, L. (1981). *Bones: Ancient man and modern myths.* New York: Academic Press.

Bishop, W. (1960). *The early history of surgery.* London: Robert Hale Pub.

Bisson, M. (1976). *The prehistoric coppermines of Zambia.* California: Univ. of California.

Bliquez, L. (1983). *Classical prosthetics.* London: Sergius Silus.

Blunt, W. (1979). *The illustrated herbal.* New York: Thames and Hudson.

Bonar, A. (1985). *The Macmillan treasury of herbs.* New York: Macmillan.

Bonola, R., (1955). *Non-Euclidean geometry.* New

York: Dover.

Bottero, J. (1987). *Mesopotamia: Writing, reasoning, and the gods.* Chicago: University of Chicago Press.

Bovill, E. (1933). *Caravans of the Old Sahara:* London: Oxford Press.

Boyer, C. (2000). *A history of mathematics.* New York: John Wiley.

Breasted, J. (1906). *Ancient records of Egypt,* vols. 1- 5; Chicago: University of Chicago Press.

Breunig, P. (1996). *The 8000-year-old dugout canoe from Dufuna* (NE Nigeria). Harare: Univ. of Zimbabwe.

Bricklin, M. (1983). *The practical encyclopedia of natural healing.* Emmaus: Rodale Press.

Brooks, L. (1971). *Great civilizations of ancient Africa.* New York: Four Winds Press.

Buck, J. (1937). *Land utilization in China.* Chicago: University of Chicago Press.

Budge, E. (1895). The book of the dead; the papyrus of Ani in the British Museum. London: Longmans & Co.

Bunch, B. and Hellemans, A. (1993). *The timetables of technology: A chronology of the most important people and events in the history of technology.* New York: Simon & Schuster.

Buritt, M. (1928). *South Africa's past in stone and paint.* Cambridge: Cambridge University Press.

Burlingame, R. (1938). *March of the iron men: A social history of union through invention.* New York: C. Scribner's Sons, Ltd.

Burke, J. (1978). *Connections.* Boston: Little Brown Pub.

Burton, D. (1985). *The history of mathematics.* Boston: Allyn and Bacon.

Butzer, K. (1976). *The early hydraulics civilization in Egypt: A study in cultural ecology.* Chicago: University of Chicago Press.

Cajori, F. (1894). *A history of mathematics.* London: Macmillan & Co.

Canfora, L. (1989). *The vanished library.* London: Hutchinson Radius Pub.

Carlson, J. (1975). Loadstone Compass: Chinese or Olmec Primacy. *Science* 189.

Carter, H. (1972). *The tomb of Tutankhamen: With 17 color plates and 65 monochrome illustrations and two appendices.* New York: Excalibur Books.

Castiglioni, A. (1941). *A history of medicine.* New York: A.A. Knopf.

Chandler, T. and Fox, G. (1974). *3000 years of urban growth.* New York: Academic Press.

Chandler, C. (1965). *Famous modern men of medicine.* New York: Dodd Mead.

Chang, Kwang-chih (1976). *Early Chinese civilization.* Cambridge: Harvard University Press.

Chi Chao-Ting, (1970). *Key economic areas in Chinese history, as revealed in the development of public works for water control.* New York, A M. Kelly.

Childe, V. (1950). The urban revolution, *Town Planning Review,* 21. no. 1, London.

Childe, V. (1957). *Civilization, cities and towns.* London.

Chittick, N. (1975). *An early salt-working site on the Tanzanian coast.* London: Azania 10, 151-153.

Clark, D. (1964). "Prehistoric Origins of African Culture," *Journal of African History,* vol. 1.

Clark, G. and Piggott, S. (1965). *Prehistoric societies.* New York: Penguin.

Clarke, D. and Glynn, I. (1981). (Ed.) *Patterns of the past: Studies in Honor of David Clarke.* London: University Press.

Clarke, D. (1994). *The new illustrated science and invention encyclopedia: How it works.* New York: Stuttman.

Clark, G., and Piggott, S. (1965). *Prehistoric societies.* New York: Knopf Pub.

Clark, J. (1950). The stone age cultures of northern Rhodesia. Claremont: South African Archaeological Society.

Clark, J. and Brandt, S. (1983). *From hunter to farmer.* Berkeley: University of California Press.

Clark, R. and Grace, I. (1971). *Nature's colors; dyes from plants.* New York: Dover Publisher.

Coe, M. (1994). *Breaking the Mayan code.* London: Penguin.

Cole, S. (1963). *The prehistory of East Africa.* New York: Macmillan.

Connah, G. (1987). *African civilizations.* Cambridge: Cambridge University Press.

Connash, G. (1981). *Three thousand years in Africa: Man and his environment in the lake Chad region of Nigeria.* Cambridge: Cambridge University Press.

Considine, D., and Considine, G. (1983). *Van Nostrand's scientific encyclopedia,* 6th ed., New York: Reinhold Publishing Corp.

Contenau, G. (1954). *Everyday life in Babylon and Assyria.* London: Edward Arnold Pub.

Coolidge, J. (1945). *History of the conic sections and quadric surfaces.* Oxford: Clarendon.

Cook, S. (1930). *The religion of ancient Palestine in the light of archaeology.* London: Oxford University Press.

Coolidge, J. (1963). *A history of geometrical methods.* New York: Dover.

Cornwell, P. (2007). *Book of the dead.* New York: G.P. Putnam's Sons.

Cotterell, A. (1988). *The encyclopedia of ancient civilization.* New York: Penguin Books.

Cotterell, Y. & Cotterell, A. (1975). *The early civilization of China.* New York: Putnam Pub.

Cotterell, A. (1975). *The encyclopedia of ancient civilizations.* London: Penguin Books.

Coursey, D. (1966). The cultivation and use of yams in West Africa., *Ghana notes and queries,* Legon no. 9, November, pp. 45-54.

Curwen, E. and Hatt, G. (1953). *Plough and pasture: The early history of farming, pt. 1: Prehistoric farming of Europe and the Near East.* New York: H. Schuman Pub.

Daumas, M. (1969). *A history of technology and inventions.* Vol. 1, New York: Crown Press.

Dauben, J., (1985). *The history of mathematics from antiquity to the present.* London: Garland.

Davis, S., (1987). *The archaeology of animals.* London: Batsford.

David, A. (1986). *The pyramid builders of ancient Egypt: A modern investigation of pharaoh's workforce.* New York: Routledge.

Davidson, B. (1959). *The lost cities of Africa.* Boston: Little, Brown and Company.

Davidson, B. (1966). *Africa: History of a continent.* New York: Macmillan Co.

Davidson, B. (1969). *The African genius.* Boston: Little, Brown.

Davison, C. (1973). 'Glass beads in African archaeology'. AATA, 10,2

Dayagi-Mendele, M. (1989). *Perfumes and cosmetics in the ancient world.* Jerusalem: Israel Museum.

DeBono, E. (1974). *Eureka!: How and when the greatest inventions were made: An illustrated history of inventions from the wheel to the computer.* London: Thames & Hudson.

De Brag, L. (1978). *The wild garden: An illustrated guide to weeds.* New York: Mayflower Books.

De Camp, L. (1993). *The ancient engineers.* New York. Barnes and Noble.

De Camp, L. (1974). *The ancient engineers.* New York. Ballantine Books.

Denbow, J. (1986). A new look at the later prehistory of the Kalahari. *Journal of African history*

Derry, T. and Williams, T., vol. 27, (1960). *A short history of technology from the earliest times to A.D. 1900.* Oxford: Clarendon Press.

Diamond, J. (1993). *The third chimpanzee: The evolution and future of human animals.* New York: Harper.

Dickson, L. (1966). *History of the theory of numbers.* New York: Chelsea.

Diop C. (1974). *The African origin of civilization myth or reality.* Westport: Lawrence Hill and Co.

Diringer, D. (1948). *The alphabet: A key to the history of mankind.* London: Hutchinson's Scientific and Technical Pub.

Dolan, M. (2002). *The American porch: An informal history of an informal place.* Guilford Conn.: Lyons Press.

Dorland, N., (1994). *Dorland's illustrated medical dictionary.* Philadelphia: Saunders Press.

Dorsey, G. (1931). *The story of civilization: Man's own show: Civilization.* New York: Halcyon House.

Douze, S. (1993). Inventions and discoveries. New York: Facts on File.

Downs, R. (1982). Landmarks in science: Hippocrates to Carson. Littleton Colo: Libraries Unlimited.

Duchesne, G. (1976). *Music in ancient Mesopotamia and Egypt.* World Archaeology.

Dugas, R. (1955). *A history of mechanics.* New York: Central Books Co.

Dyer T., (1889). *The folklore of plants.* New York: Appleton and Co.

Eco, U. and Zorzoli, G. (1963). *The picture history of inventions, from plough to Polaris.* New York: Macmillan Co.

Edwards, I. (1970). *The pyramids of Egypt.* New York: Harmondsworth Press.

Erman, A. (1971). *Life in ancient Egypt.* New York: Dover Pub.

Erskine, B. (1927). *Vanished cities of Northern Africa.* London: Hutchinson and Co.

Eves H. (1953). *An introduction to the history of mathematics.* New York: Holt, Rinehart and Winston.

Fagen, B. (1985). *New treasures of the past.* New York: Windward Press.

Faul, H. & Faul, C. (1983). *It began with a stone.* New York: John Wiley and Sons.

Fink, R. (1988). "The Oldest Song in the World." *Archaeologia Musicalis* 2.

Finley, M. (1973). *The ancient economy.* Berkeley, Calif.: University of California Press.

Fischer, S. (2001). *A history of writing.* London:

Reaktion Books.

Fitzgerald, C. (1961). *China: A short cultural history.* New York: Praeger.

Foley, R. (1991). *The origins of human behavior.* New York: Hyman Pub.

Forbes, R., (1967) *Man the maker: a history of technology and engineering,* New York: Forbes Publishing.

Forbes, R. (1958). *Man, the maker; a history of technology and engineering.* New York: Abelard-Schuman.

Fox, R. (1950). *Milestones of medicine.* New York: Random House.

Frank, S. (1982). *Glass and archaeology.* Academic Press.

Gardiner, A. (1957). *Egyptian grammar: being an introduction to the study of hieroglyphs.* London: Oxford University Press.

Gelis-Didot, P. (1843). *Voyage in Egypt and Syria.* London.

Genders, R. (1972). *A history of scent.* London: Hamilton.

Gibson, C. (1948). *The story of the ship.* New York: Henry Schuman Pub.

Gilfillan, S.(1935). *Inventing the ship.* Chicago: Follett Pub. Co.

Gjertsen, D. (1984). *The classics of science: A study of twelve enduring scientific works.* New York: Lillan Barber Press.

Gibson, C. (1948). *The story of the ship.* New York: Henry Schuman.

Gille, B. (1986). T*he history of technique.* Vol. 2. New York: Research Science Pub.

Gillispie, C. (1981). *Dictionary of scientific biography.* Vol.8., New York, Charles Scribner's & Sons

Giscard d'Estaing, V. (1985). *The world almanac book of inventions.* New York: World Almanac Pub.

Gleason, K. (1987). Garden excavations at the Herodian winter palace in Jericho; *Bulletin of the Anglo-Israel Society* 7.

Glanville, S. (1942). *The legacy of Egypt.* Oxford: Clarendon Press.

Gnudi, M. (Translator) (1979). The various and ingenious machines of Agostino Ramelli.

Goodwin, G. (1982). *A Dyer's manual.* London: Pelhem Books.

Gosse, A. (1923). *The civilization of the ancient Egyptians.* London: T.C. and E.C. Jack, Ltd.

Gordon, C. (1974). *Riddles in history.* New York: Crown Pub.

Gouzel, D. (1975). *Mother nature's herbs and teas.*

Willits, Cal: Oliver Press.

Gove, P. (2002). *Webster's third new international dictionary of the English language.* Springfield: Merriam-Webster.

Graham, C. (1987). *African civilizations.* Cambridge: Cambridge University Press.

Greggs, B. (1981). *Green pharmacy: A history of herbal medicine.* New York: Vicking Press.

Grove, G. & Sadie, S. (1980). *The new grove dictionary of music and musicians.* London: Macmillan Pub.

Gwynne, M. (1975). *The origin and spread of some domestic foods plants in Eastern Africa.* New York: African Publishing Company.

Gullberg, J. (1997). *Mathematics: From the birth of numbers.* New York: W.W. Norton.

Guillemin-Duchesne, M., (1981). "Music in ancient Mesopotamia and Egypt." *World Archaeology.*

Gulberg, J.(1997). *Mathematics: From the birth of numbers.* New York: W.W. Norton

Gunther, J. (1955). *Inside Africa.* New York: Harper Brothers.

Haaland, R.(1995). An early iron age site in the Tanzanian hinterland . *Tanzania:* Azania Pub. 29-30, 238-47.

Hague, D.(1975). *Lighthouse: Their architecture, history and archaeology.* New York: Gomer Press.

Hapgood, C. (1966). *Maps of the ancient sea kings: Evidence of advanced civilization in the ice age.* Philadelphia: Chilton Books.

Harley, J. and Woodward, D. (1987). *The history of cartography.* Chicago. University of Chicago.

Hart, G. (1990). *Ancient Egypt.* New York: Alfred Knopf Pub.

Hassall, W. (1962). *How they lived.* Oxford: Blackwell Pub..

Hart, C. (1967). Kites: *An historical survey.* London: Faber and Faber.

Hayes, W.(1965). *Most ancient Egypt.* Chicago: University of Chicago Press.

Hawkes, J. (1966). *Pharaohs of Egypt.* New York. American Heritage Publishing Co.

Heidel A. (1942). *The Babylonian genesis.* Chicago: University of Chicago Press.

Hellemans, A. and Bunch, B. (1988). *The timetables of science.* New York: Simon & Schuster.

Hemphill, J. (1976). *Herbs their cultivation and usage.* New York: Simon and Schuster.

Hewat, M. & Miller, T. (1970). *Bantu folklore.*

Westport: Negro Universities Press.

Hill, D. (1997). *A history of engineering.* London: Routledge Pub.

Hill, N. (1930). *The intimate life of the Queen of Sheba.* New York: Putnam.

Hill, L. Fodder (1976). *Food and remedy.* New York: Universe Books.

Hill, P. (1917). *Prehistoric times,* New York: Harper & Row.

Hickey, M. and King, C. (1981). *100 families of flowering plants.* Cambridge Eng.: Cambridge University Press.

Himes, N. (1936). *Medical history of contraception.* London: Allen and Unwin.

Hirth, F. (1908). *The ancient history of China.* New York: Columbia University Press.

Hitti, P. (1908). *The ancient history of China.* New York: Columbia University Press.

Hitti, P. (1943). *The Arabs.* Chicago: Gateway Press.

Hitching, F. (1978). *The atlas of world mysteries.* New York: HarperCollins.

_____(1923). History of bees in Egypt. *Journal of Egyptian Archaeology,* London.

Hodges, H. (1970). *Technology of the ancient world.* New York: Knopf Pub.

Hoffmam, M. (1980). *Egypt before the pharaohs, the prehistoric foundation of Egyptian civilization.* New York: Knopf, A.

Holmyarp, A. (1954). *History of technology and invention.* Vol. 3. London: Oxford University Press.

Holmes, P. and Coles, J. (1973). "Prehistoric Brass Instruments," *World Archaeology* 12, MacNamara.

Holmyarp, A. (1954). *History of technology and invention.* Vol. 3. London: Oxford University Press.

Hobson, B. Obojsk, R. (1984). *Illustrated encyclopedia of world coins.* Garden City, N.Y.: Doubleday.

Hodder, I. and Issac, G. 1981. *Patterns of the past studies in honor of Davis Clark.* Cambridge, Mass: University Press.

House, H. (1934). *Wild flowers.* New York: Macmillan Co,

Hsu, Cho-Yun. (1965). *Ancient China in transition,* 722-222 B.C. Stanford, Cal: Stanford University Press.

Huggins, W. (1937). *An introduction to African civilizations in current Ethiopian History.* New York: Avon House.

Huffman, T. (1971). *Cloth from the iron age in Rhodesia.* South Africa: Arnoldia Press.

Hyams, E. (1971). *A history of gardens and gardening.* London: Dent Press.

Ibn Abd al-Hakam (1922). *The history of the conquest of Egypt, North Africa and Spain.* New Haven Conn: Yale University Press.

Iliffe, J. (1995). *Africans: The history of a continent.* Cambridge: University Press

Imperato, P. (1977). *African folk medicine: Practices and beliefs of the Bambara and other peoples.* Baltimore: York Press.

Iyi Kilindi, L. (1985). African roots in Asian martial arts, *Journal of African civilizations,* New Brunswick, N.J. 7 (1).

James, G. (1954). Stolen legacy. New York: Philosophical Library.

James, P. and Thorpe, N. (1994). *Ancient inventions.* New York.: Ballantine Books.

James, P. and Thrope, I. (1993). *Centuries of darkness: A challenge to the conventional chronology of Old World archaeology.* New Brunswick, N.J.: Rutgers University Press.

Johnson, H. (1989). *The story of wine.* New York: Simon and Schuster.

Kane, J. (1981). *Famous first facts: A record of first happenings, discoveries, and inventions in American history.* New York: H.W. Wilson.

Kealey, E. (1987). *Harvesting the air: windmill pioneer in 12th century England.* Brekeley: University of California Press.

Keay, J. (2000). *India: A history.* New York: Atlantic Monthly Press.

Keller, M. (1978). *Mysterious herbs and roots: Ancient secrets for Beauite health, magic prevention and youth.* Culver City, Cal: Peace Press.

Kenrick, J. (1850). *Ancient Egypt under the pharaohs.* Vols. 1-2. London: B. Fellowes.

Key, J. (1976). Chinese herbs. Rutland, VT: Charles E. Tultle.

Kilmer, A. (1976). *Sounds from silence: Recent discoveries in ancient near eastern music.* Berkeley: Bit Enki Pub.

Ki-Zerbo, J. (1990). *General history of Africa methodology and African prehistory,* Berkeley Calif., University of California Press.

Kowalchik C. and Hylton W. (1998). *Rodale's illustrated encyclopedia of herbs.* Pennsylvania: Rodale Press.

Kramer, E. (1970). *The nature and growth of modern mathematics.* New York: Hawthorn.

Kramer, S.(1959). *History begins at Sumer.* Garden City, N.Y.: Doubleday Pub.

Kramer S. (1956) *From the table of Sumer, twenty five firsts in man's recorded history,* Indian Hills, Colo. Falcon's Wing Press.

Krzyzaniak, L. (1977). *Early farming cultures on the lower Nile: The Predynastic Period in Egypt.* Varsovie: Scientifiques de Pologne.

Kulke, J. (1998). *A history of India.* New York: Routledge.

Landels, J. (1978). *Engineering in the ancient world.* Berkeley: University of California.

Laithwaite, E. (1994). *An inventor in the garden of Eden.* Cambridge Eng.: Cambridge University Press.

Leo. A. (1896). *The history and description of Africa,* 3 vols. ed.. London: Brown, Kakluyt Society.

Lepsius, R. (1852). *Discoveries in Egypt,* Ethiopia and the peninsula of Sinai. London: Hakluyt Society.

LeStrange, R. (1977). *A history of herbal plants.* New York: Arco Pub. Co.

Lewis, J. (2003). *Ancient Egyptians.* New York: Carroll and Graf Pub.

Lewin, S. (1968). 'The conservation of limestone objects and structures.' Paris: ICOMOS.

Ling Wang & Needham, J. (1955). *Homer's methods in Chinese mathematics.* T'oung Pao Leidon, Vol. 43.

Lloyd, S. (1978). *The archaeology of Mesopotamia: From the old stone age to Persian conquest.* London, Thames & Hudson.

Lockyer, J. (1964). *The dawn of astronomy: A study of the temple worship and mythology of the ancient Egyptian.* Cambridge Mass.: M.I.T. Press.

Low, A. (1947). *Your world tomorrow.* London: Hutchinson.

Lucas, A. and Harris, J. (1962). *Ancient Egyptian materials and industries.* London: E. Arnold Pub.

Lucas, A. and Harris, J. (1999). *Ancient Egyptian materials and industries.* Mineola N.Y.: Dover Publications.

MacDonald, K., and MacDonald, R. (1999). *The origin and development of domesticated animals in arid West Africa.* London. University College Press..

MacGregor, S. (1926). *The Kabbalah unveiled, the lesser holy assembly.* London: Routledge and Kegan Paul.

Mahmoud, Z. (1959). *The land and people of Egypt.* New York: J.B. Lippincott Pub.

Marshack, A. (1972). *The roots of civilization.*

London: Weidenfield and Nicolson.

Martell, H. (1995). *The Kingfisher book of the ancient world: From the ice age to the fall of Rome.* New York: Kingfisher Pub.

Mason, O. (1966). *The origin of invention.* Cambridge: MIT Press.

Maspero, G. (1901). *The dawn of civilization: Egypt and Chaldea.* Society for Promoting Christian Knowledge.

McGrath, K. and Travers, B. (2001). *The Gale encyclopedia of science* Detroit: Gale Group.

McGrew, R. and McGrew, M. (1985). *Encyclopedia of medical history.* New York: McGraw-Hill Pub.

MacMichael H.(1922). *A history of the Arabs in the Sudan.* Vols. 1-2 Cambridge: Cambridge University Press.

Melzack, R. and Wall, P.(1982). *The challenge of pain.* New York: Basic Books.

Merritt, F. (1950). *Gray's manual of botany.* 8th ed. New York: D.Van Nostrand Co.

Montet, P. (1958). *Everyday life in Egypt.* New York. Edward Arnold Press.

Moore, F. (1931). *Ivory: Scourge of Africa.* London: Harpers & Bros.

Moorey, P. (1992). *Ancient Egypt:* Oxford: University of Oxford.

Morrison, T. (1987). *The mystery of the Naza lines.* Woodridge: Nonesuch Expeditions Ltd.

Moule, A. (1937) *Boats towed by a swimming buffalo in China.* T'oung Pao, 2nd ser., XXXIII, p. 94 .

Mount, E. and List, B. (1987). *Milestones in science and technology. The ready reference guide to discoveries, inventions, and facts.* Phoenix : Oryx Press.

Murray, D. (1983). *A history of Western psychology.* Englewood: Prentice-Hall.

Murray, M. (1963). *The splendor that was Egypt.* New York: Hawthorn Books, Inc.

Murry, S., Little, W., Fowler, H., Coulson, J.; and Onions, C., (1937). *Oxford universal English dictionary on historical principle* London: From the original English dictionary.

Needham, D. (1988). *Chinese state of medicine.* New York: Jackson Press.

Neuburger, O. (1930). *The technical arts and sciences of the ancients.* New York: The Macmillan Co.

Neugebauer, O. (1945). "The History of Ancient Astronomy." J. Near Eastern Studies, vol. 4.

Neugebauer, O. (1962). *The exact sciences in antiquity.* New York.: Dover Pub.

Newman, J. (1956). *The world of mathematics.* New York: Simon and Schuster.

Newsome, F. (1979); Black contributions to the history of Western medicine. New York: *Journal of the National Medical Association.*

Newton; F. (1923). Excavation at El Amarnah. London: *The Journal of Egyptian Archaeology.*

Nketia, J. (1975). History and the organization of music in West Africa. Legon: University of Ghana.

Noel H. (1969). *Historical archaeology.* New York: Knopf Pub.

Nur Ankh Amen, N. (1999). *The ankh: African origin of electromagnetism.* New York: A& B Publishers Group.

Oakley, K. (1956). *Man the tool maker.* London: British Museum.

Ochoa, G. (1995). *The timeline book of science.* New York: Stongsong Press.

O'Connor, D. (1991). *Early state along the Nubian Nile. In Egypt and Africa: Nubia from prehistory to Islam.* London: British Museum Press.

Ohrbach, B. (1986). *Scented room Chercbez's book of dried flowers.* New York: Clarkson N. Potter.

Oliver, R. (1961). *The dawn of African history.* London: Oxford University Press.

Oppenheim, L.A.(1979). *Ancient Mesopotamia: Portrait of a dead civilization.* Rev. ed. Chicago: University of Chicago Press.

Pacey, A. (1990). *Technology in world civilization: A thousand year history.* Cambridge, Mass.: M.I.T. Press

Palmer, G. (1968). Archaeology a-z, a simplified guide and dictionary. New York: Frederick Warne Pub.

Parker, S. (1989). *McGraw-Hill concise encyclopedia of science and technology.* New York: McGraw-Hill Pub.

Parkinson, C., (1985). *Breakthroughs: A chronology of great achievements in science and mathematics.* Boston: G.K. Hall.

Pannell, J. (1964). *An illustrated history of civil engineering.* London: Thomas and Hudson.

Pappademos, J. (1983). *An outline of Africa's role in the history of physics, in: Blacks in science;* New Brunswick NJ: Transaction Books.

Payne, E. (1964). *The pharaohs of ancient Egypt.* New York: Random House.

Payne, R. (1959). *The canal builders.* New York: Macmillan Co.

Peckham, S. (1960). A guide for highway salvage programs in archaeology, history and paleontology. Society for Archaeology.

Publication No. N.P.

Perlin, J. (1991). *Forrest journey: The role of wood in the development of civilization.* Cambridge Mass: Harvard Press.

Perlin, J. (1991). *The role of wood in the development of civilization.* New York: Norton Pub.

Perlman, I. & Isaro, F. (1969). 'Pottery analysis by neutron activation,' *Archaeometry.* II.

Petrie, W. (1924). *A history of Egypt.* Vols. 1-6. London: Bracken Pub.

Petrie, W. Sir, (1900). The royal tombs of the first dynasty, 1900-1901. London: Office of the Egypt exploration.

Phillipson, D. (1993). *The antiquity of civilization and herding in Ethiopia.* London: Routledge Pub.

Phillipson, D. (1985). *African archaeology:* Cambridge: Cambridge University Press.

Phimister, I. (1974). Ancient mining near great Zimbabwe. *Journal of the South African Institute of Mining and Metallurgy* 74, 233-37.

Phimister, I. (1975). History of mining in Southern Rhodesia to 1953, Dissertation Thesis (D. Phil)—University of Rhodesia.

Piggott, S. (1950). *Prehistoric India to 1000 B.C.* Harmondsworth: Middlesex.

Pritchard, J., (1969). *Ancient Near Eastern text relating to the old testament.* Princeton: Princeton University Press.

Redman, C. (1978). *The rise of civilization: From early farmers to urban society in the ancient Near East.* San Francisco: W.H. Freeman.

Reid, A. and Meredith, J. (1993). *Houses, pots and more cows.* New York: Nyame Akuma Press

Reiner, E. (1989). *Babylonian birth prognosis.* Zeitschrift: Assyriologie.

Rene D. (1968). *The treasury of mathematics.* London.

Reynolds, T. (1983). *Stronger than a hundred men.* Baltimore: John Hopkins University Press.

Rice, M. (2003). *Egypt's making: the origin of ancient Egypt, 5000-2000 B.C.* 2nd ed.. New York: Roulledge Pub.

Rice, M. (2003). *Egypt's making: The origin of ancient Egypt, 5000-2000 B.C.* 2nd ed. New York: Roulledge Pub.

Ries, E. (1930). *Mother wit.* New York: The Century Co.

Robinson, T. and Oesterley W. (1932). *The history of Israel.* Vols. 1-2, Oxford: The Clarendon Press.

Robinson, C. (1984). *Ancient Egypt, a first book.*

New York: Franklin Watts Press.

Roberts, J. (2003). *The complete history of China.* London: Sutton Pub.

Roberts, V. and Trent, I. (1991). *Bibliotheca Mechanica.* New York: Hill J.A.

Rogers, R. (1915). *A history of Babylonia and Assyria.* vol. 2, Cincinnati: Books for Libraries Press.

Ronan, C. (1975). *Lost Discoveries.* New York: McGraw-Hill Pub.

Ronan, C. (1982). Science: Its history and development among the world's cultures. New York: Facts on File.

Rosengarten F. (1973). *The book of spices.* New York: Jove, Publisher.

Ross D. (1967). *Alexander and the faithless lady.* New York: Birkbeck Press.

Rossi, N. and Rafferty, S. (1981). *Music through the centuries.* Washington D.C.: University Press.

Roux, G. (1966). *Ancient Iraq.* New York: Penguin.

Rowling, J. (1989). The rise and decline of surgery in dynastic Egypt. *Antiquity* 63, Saggs.

Saggs, H. (1965). *Everyday life in Babylonia and Assyria.* London: B.T. Batsford

Sanford, E. (1938). *The Mediterranean world in ancient times.* New York: Ronald Press Co.

Sarton, G. (1936). *The study of the history of mathematics.* Cambridge: Harvard University Press.

Scarre, C. (1988). *Past worlds. The Times atlas of archaeology.* London: Koonalda.

Schauble, J. (1991). "Worrying New from China: It May Have Invented Golf." London: Independent Press.

Scheele, C.. (1970). *A short history of the mail service.* Washington D.C.: Smithsonian Institution Press.

Schmandt, B. (1992). *Before writing,* Texas: University of Texas Press.

Schoenburn, D. (1993). Cattle herds and banana garden: The historical geography of the Western Great Lakes regions. *African Archaeological Review* II, p 39-72.

Schreiber, H. (1961). *The history of roads.* London: Barrie and Rockcliff Pub.

Schwarty, D. (2001). *The great wall of China.* London: Thames and Hudson.

Schwartz, B. (1985). *The world of thought in ancient China.* Cambridge: Harvard University Press

Scott, J. (1969). *A history of mathematics,* London, Taylor and Francies.

Sedgwick, W. and Tler, H. (1917). *A short history of*

science. New York: The Macmillan Co.

Semenov, S. (1964). *Prehistoric technology; an experimental study of the oldest tools and artifacts from traces of manufacture and wear.* New York: Barnes and Noble.

Shepherd, R. (1980). *Prehistoric mining and allied industries.* New York: Academic Press.

Shore, D. (1983). Steel-making in ancient Africa. *Journal of African civilizations.* [New Brunswick, N.J: Douglass College, Rutgers University] 5 (1-2).

Sigerist, H. (1967). *Primitive and archaic medicine.* London: Oxford University Press.

Silver, G. and Sparer, M., (2004). "Health care systems," New York: *Grolier Multimedia Encyclopedia.*

Singer, C. (1978). *A history of technology.* Oxford: Clarendon Press.

Singer, C. (1956). *A history of technology.* Oxford: University Press.

Singer, C. and Underwood, E. (1962). *A short history of medicine.* New York: Oxford University Press.

Smith, D. and Karpinski, L., (1911). *The Hindu-Arabic numerals.* Boston: Ginn & Co.

Smith, N. (1971). *A history of dams.* London: Davies Pub..

Smith, D. (1923). *History of mathematics.* Boston: Dover.

Smith, D. (1987). *A concise history of mathematics.* 4th ed. Boston: Dover.

Smith, S. (1953). *The world's greatest bridges.* London: Phoenix.

Sonnedecker, G. (1976). *Kremer's and Urdang's history of pharmacy.* London: Lippincott.

Sonnedecker, G., Kremers, E. and Urdang, G. (1976). *Kremers and Urdang's history of pharmacy.* Philadelphia: Lippincott.

Spear, N. (1978). *A treasury of archaeological bells.* New York: Hasting House Pub..

Spencer, L. (1913). *The myths of Mexico and Peru.* London: George Harrap Pub.

Spindler, K. (1977). *The man in the ice: The discovery of a 5,000-year-old body reveals the secrets of the stone age.* New York: Harmony Books.

Spoerke, D. (1980). *Herbal medications.* Santa Barbara: Woodbridge Press.

Staikos, K. (2000). *The great libraries from antiquity to the renaissance 3000 B.C. to 1600 A.D.* New Castle, Del.: Oak Knoll Press.

Stanley, S. (1980). *New grove dictionary of music and musicians;* vol. 20, New York: Macmillan

Pub.

Stevens, J. (1983). *The story of wigs, through the ages.* Toucan Press.

Stewart, J. (1960). *An archaeological guide and Glossary.* London: Phoenix House.

Straub, H. (1952). *A history of civil engineering:* London: Leonard Hill Pub.

Strandh, S. (1979). *A history of the machine.* New York: A.& W. Publishers..

Struik, D. (1987). *A concise history of mathematics.* 4th ed., New York: Dover Publication.

Sutton, J. (1997). *The African lords of the intercontinental gold trade before the Black Death.* London: The Antiquaries Journal.

Swihart, T. (2004). "Supernova." Grolier Multimedia Encyclopedia.

_____(1935). *The stone age races of Kenya,* London: Oxford University Press.

Talbott, J. (1970). *A biographical history of medicine:* New York: Grvne & Stratton.

Thompson,W.(1983). *Medicine from the earth: A guide to healing plants.* San Francisico: Harper and Row.

Thomson, J., (1921). *Elements of mathematics theory of electricity and magnetism.* Cambridge: University Press

Thurman, C. (1979). *The textiles, In ancient textiles from Nubia.* Chicago: Art Institute of Chicago.

Tien, ch'ang-wu (1999). *History of chemistry in ancient China.* Shanghai: Jen-min Ch'u-pan she.

Todhunter, I. (1874). *A history of mathematical theories of attraction and the figure of the earth.* London.

Travers, B. (1996). *The Gale encyclopedia of science.* New York: Gale Group Pub.

Trefil, J. (1992). *1001 things everyone should know about science.* New York: Doubleday Pub.

Turnbull, H. (1969). *The great mathematicians.* New York: New York University Press.

Usher, A. (1954). *A history of mechanical inventions,* 2nd Ed. Cambridge: Harvard University Press.

Van Sertima, I. (1983). *Blacks in science: ancient and modern.* New Brunswick: Transaction Books.

Watson, B. (1969). *Records of the historian: Chapters from the Shih chi of Ssu-ma Ch'ien.* New York: Columbia University Press.

Webster, R. MacAlister, P.R. and Etting F.M. (1974). *The astrolabe: Some notes on its history, construction and use,* Lake Bluff, Illinois: Paul MacAlister & Associates.

Weigall, A. (1910). *A guide to the antiquities of upper Egypt, from Abydos to the Sudan frontier.* London: Methuen & Co.

Weil, A., (1984). *Number theory, an approach through history.* Boston: Birkhavoer.

Wells, H. (1922). *A short history of the world.* New York: Macmillan Co.

West, B. (1982). *The Prentice-Hall encyclopedia of mathematics.* New York: Prentice Hall Books.

Wheelwright, E. (1974). *Medicinal plants and their history.* New York: Dover Publisher.

Wilbert, J. (1987). *Tobacco and shamanism in South America.* Princeton: Yale University Press.

Williams, P. (1980). *A new history of the organ from the Greeks to the present day.* Bloomington: Indiana University Press.

Williams, T. (1987). The history of invention. New York: Facts on File.

Wilson, G. (1976). *The old telegraphs.* London: Phillimore.

Wilson, J. (1951). *The ancient culture of Egypt.* Chicago: University of Chicago Press.

Windsor, R. (1969). *From Babylon to Timbuktu: A history of the ancient black race including the black Hebrews.* New York: Exposition Press.

Winton, W. (1962). *Baghdad batteries B.C.* London.

Wisseman, S. (1994). *Ancient technologies and archaeological materials.,* Langhorne. Pa: Gordon and Breach Science Pub.

Woodforde, J. (1968). *The strange story of false teeth.* New York: Universe Books.

Wright, Q. (2004). "Peace Treaty" encyclopedia Americana Grolier Online.

Yang H. (1965). *The treasury of mathematics.* London: Yang Hui's Mathematical Work.

Yoke- Ho Peng, (1966). *The astronomical chapters of the Chin Shu.* Paris: Mouton.

Zaki, A. and Iskader, Z. (1942). *Ancient Egypt Cheese.* ASAE. XLI.

_____ "43,000 Year Old Mines; Discovered in Swaziland" (1970).*The New York Times,* February 8,1970, p. 6